D1538794

# A History of Scientific and Technical Periodicals

## The Origins and Development of the Scientific and Technological Press
## 1665 - 1790

by

David A. Kronick

# The Scarecrow Press, Inc.
# New York                    1962

To:

Berly Leah, who arrived with
the printer's proofs

My wife Marilyn

and

My parents, Barnett and Rose

# PREFACE

If scientific communication can be said to have any structure at all, it is in the sense that it can be considered as the sum of a large number of discrete and separate kinds of activities directed generally toward the goal of transmitting and storing scientific knowledge. The scientific periodical, as a device directed toward these goals, entered relatively late in the history of these processes, and constitutes perhaps only a small segment of all the activities involved. It is more amenable to study because it is a visible part of the total structure of scientific communications, and is represented by a large number of physical artifacts that can be examined and analyzed. It is possible to differentiate scientific communications from communications in society in general according to the subject matter with which it deals and according to the people to whom it is directed, but as a social phenomenon it must have a great deal in common with communications in general. What relationship, for instance, does the process of development and acceptance of a scientific theory have with the process of opinion formation in general? This study does not attempt to answer questions of this magnitude; rather it examines scientific journalism, in the hope that it may contribute something to our understanding of the nature of the process. There may be better methods of defining the requirements for a more efficient and effective communications system in the sciences, but the historical method has the advantage that it can provide us with some of the necessary background.

The beginnings of scientific journalism are generally placed in the year 1665, the year that saw the introduction of both the "Philosophical Transactions" and the "Journal des Sçavans," two publications which are unique, not only in having introduced a new medium of scientific communication, but also in having persisted to this very day.

The terminal date of the study has been placed at 1790 for a number of reasons, both expedient and logical. First, the number of publications to this point is small enough so that a single investigator can examine the titles involved. It would not be wise to claim that the period 1665-1790 has any historical unity, either politically or as far as the scientific

periodical is concerned.   The great proliferation of scientific
journals took place much later in the 19th century.   It is also
true that there were relatively few technological changes in
the printing trades in this period and that the influence of
this factor is therefore at a minimum, whereas it would have
to be considered as a significant element in the development
of the periodical in the 19th century.   There are a great
many precedents in studies of both political and literary history in terminating the study with the French Revolution.
For example, Paul Mellottee in his economic history of printing, (1) Robert Prutz in his history of German journalism,
(2) and Joachim Kirchner in his history of German periodicals, (3) all terminate their studies at this point.   Hatin in
his history of French journalism divides his study into two
periods, one preceding and one following the French Revolution. (4)   Kirchner's list was used as one of the basic
sources in compiling the list of periodicals for this study,
and it seemed wise to confine the selection from other
sources used to the same terminal date in order to try to
achieve comparable coverage for other countries.

The difficulties involved in this kind of study have been
pointed out by others who have worked in this field.  S. B.
Barnes in the preface to his dissertation calls attention to
some of them.  (5)   The great multitude of journals that must
be examined are widely scattered and impose severe physical
and financial burdens on the student.   Much of the relevant
material is hidden in letters, diaries and the unpublished
records of publishing houses.  He adds that:

> Only when all of the journals published from the seven-
> teenth to the twentieth century have been catalogued,
> studied and monographed from various points of view
> shall it be possible to pronounce significant generaliza-
> tions on the role of the learned journal in the history
> of culture. (6)

These necessary preliminaries have not yet been attained.
The fact that there are few comprehensive studies of the periodical may perhaps be belied by the length of the bibliography
appended to this paper, but it is true that there are few that
approach high standards of bibliographic description, and that
the lists available for study contain many inaccuracies and
discrepancies.   Thus Jaryc says:

> The historical investigations of non-political magazines
> lags in most countries far behind the study of news-
> papers.   If the contents and external history of periodi-
> cals like the "Journal des Sçavans" and the "Acta Erudi-

torum" have repeatedly been studied, almost nothing has been published in recent years about the editorial policies of other learned journals or the development of periodicals which specialized in the great branches of human knowledge. (7)

Some of the reasons for this comparative neglect have been advanced by other students of periodical journalism, e.g. Graham in his study of the early literary periodicals of England:

> Few things are more ephemeral than periodical publications. Of the many thousands of copies issued during the seventeenth century, a comparative few have been preserved. These have survived more by accident than design. (8)

There are numerous possible approaches to a history of the periodical press: (1) the bibliographic, involving the enumeration, and description of titles, and solving the bibliographic problems of issue, translation, etc.; (2) the sociological, delinating the place of the periodical in the intellectual history of its time and its connections with the progress of the Enlightenment; (3) historical, as a part of the description of the development of the apparatus for the communication of ideas; and (4) as a study in the economics and mechanics of the publication and distribution of literature. This study cannot hope to deal with all of these aspects of the subject, but may hope to contribute toward the construction of a part of the skeleton on which a series of such studies could be built. To leaf through these old journals is to follow one of the most exciting adventures of modern times, to watch the unfolding and flowering of the ideas that have contributed so much to our contemporary world. The history of ideas, however, will play only a very small part in the narrative that follows. It is devoted primarily to an exploration of the forms which serial publication took in the period covered. After a discussion of the historical background and the antecedents of the scientific periodical, the emphasis in this study will be solely on the formal aspects of the medium. Whatever original contribution this paper has to make lies in the discussion of the characteristic forms which the scientific serial assumed in the 17th and 18th centuries.

The study of the history of science is a relatively new discipline. The scientific periodical represents one of the more significant sources for the study of the development of scientific ideas. One of the functions of this study is to survey these resources and the available apparatus for their bibliographic control.

The structure of scientific communications is currently being examined critically by many people, and there are frequent appeals in the literature for rationalization of the scientific literature. A historical study of the scientific periodical suggests that it is an evolutionary growth in response to contemporary needs and that it is based on antecedent forms of publication. Our scientific journals of today are the direct descendants of the periodicals of the 17th and 18th centuries, and there is some feeling that they are no longer adequate for the complexity and volume of contemporary publication. If this study has a thesis, it is that the scientific periodical has undertaken to play two major roles in the processes of scientific communication, (1) that of serving as a vehicle for the communication of new discoveries and ideas, and (2) that of acting as a repository of knowledge. Further study may reveal that these functions are fundamentally incompatible and that they represent different kinds of problems in organization and management. It is also possible that this sort of an approach may bring into new perspective such problems as duplication and preservation of materials in libraries and a revaluation of our system of scientific communications.

Quotations are presented in translation, as much for the benefit of the author as for any potential reader. Translation forces one to make a firm commitment about the meaning of a text that may be more valuable than the fine style of the original. One can only hope that they make up in verisimilitude for what they lack in beauty.

This study is the result of work toward the Ph. D. degree done at the University of Chicago Graduate Library School. I wish to thank Mr. Herman Fussler at that Institution for his encouragement and for permitting me the freedom to follow my own bent. Most of the material was gathered in Washington D. C. while I was on the staff of the National Library of Medicine, and I owe a debt of gratitude to those far seeing collectors in the past who saw to it that many of the resources I needed were available in that rich collection. To my wife Marilyn I owe a debt of gratitude for many things among the least of which is the preparation of the index.

# Notes

(1) Paul Mellottee, "Histoire économique de l'Imprimerie" (Paris: Hachette, 1905), I, 4-5. "The date 1789 at which I have halted is not entirely an arbitrary one. The Revolution completely transformed printing by the proclamation of economic liberty which almost at once introduced improvements in the presses. It is a new period which begins, an era of immense production which is ushered in..."

(2) Robert E. Prutz, "Geschichte des deutschen Journalismus" (Hannover: C. F. Rius, 1845).

(3) Joachim Kirchner, "Die Grundlagen des deutschen Zeitschriftenwesens" (Leipzig: Verlag Karl W. Hiersemann, 1928-1931).

(4) Louis E. Hatin, "Bibliographie historique et critique de la Presse française" (Paris: Didot, 1866).

(5) Sherman B. Barnes, "The Beginnings of Learned Journalism, 1665-1730" (Unpublished Ph.D. dissertation, Graduate School, Cornell University, 1934).

(6) Ibid., p. ii.

(7) Marc Jaryc, "Studies of 1935-1942 on the History of the Periodical Press," "Journal of Modern History," XV (1943), 127.

(8) Walter Graham, "The Beginnings of English Literary Periodicals, a Study of Periodical Literature, 1665-1715" (London: Oxford University Press, 1926), p. i.

Table of Contents

## List of Tables

13

# Chapter I

## Introduction

A historical study perhaps requires no other exposition of its methods than to state that it hopes to follow the best tenets of historical scholarship and to indicate and evaluate the sources of the facts that make up its narrative and contribute to its analysis of events. However, this study besides being an approach to an examination of the origins and development of scientific journalism is also an attempt at a statistical analysis of the forms which the periodical literature assumed between the years 1665 and 1790. The attempt to generalize on the basis of a statistical enumeration introduces problems of validity. There is unfortunately no way of knowing how large or how representative a sample the list compiled for this study constitutes, since we have no way of knowing the size of the universe of publications that fit our criteria nor is there any method for determining its statistical characteristics.

The list used in this study was compiled from four basic sources. Each one of these is evaluated below. The basic list so compiled was augmented in the course of the study by the addition of titles encountered in other sources. The principal tool for locating the titles physically in this country was the "Union List of Serials" and its supplements. (1) The "Union List" is not a perfect instrument for our purposes. It does not include abridgements or translations of serials which are within the scope of this study since they provide important means of communicating scientific information.

The principal source of information about periodicals is the periodicals themselves. Editors expound their editorial policies, counsel with their readers, and comment on the success, and, less often, on the failure, of their enterprises. An attempt was made to examine as many of the periodicals as practical. Of the few more than one thousand titles in the final list, locations for less than half were found in the United States. Of these about three hundred were located in the District of Columbia where the study was made. This

15

number represents the maximum number of titles on the list which could have been personally examined by the author. A large number of additional titles were examined in the process of eliminating them from the final list. Those which the author was able to examine are indicated by an asterisk following the title. Other available sources of information were sufficient, in many cases, to establish whether the titles in question met the criteria for inclusion. Among these sources are the many specialized studies on groups of periodicals and on individual periodicals. (2) Callisen, (3) in his list, frequently provides annotations which enable the reader to get a fairly clear idea of the nature and contents of the periodicals in question. In addition many of the titles are encountered in reviewing journals of the period which frequently provide exhaustive analyses of the contents and critical comments; such reviews are to be found, for example, in the "Göttingsche Gelehrte Anzeigen,*" 1739-1801, and the "Allgemeine Literatur Zeitung,*" 1785-1803.

While the final list on which this study is based contains titles which do not appear in any of the other published lists, it probably contains as many lacunae and errors of commission and omission as many of the others. The only claim that can be made is that it probably represents the best available sample of the scientific and technological journals of the period in question and that the sample is a fairly large one.

It has been pointed out more than once that the basic difference between scientific literature, and aesthetic or humanistic literature, is that while the first type is cumulative, i.e. superseded by the literature that follows it, the belletristic literature and the literature of "inspiration" retains an interest over a much longer period. A writer on an early classic in the history of scholarship expresses this idea in the following terms:

> There is besides this difference between science and art or literature or politics that while in science there is a continual replacement of the old by the new, of the previous by the present, there is no superseding of a work of art, or of letters, or of philosophy, or of poetical work by anything that comes after. There are many literatures and many periods in them, but there is only one kind of mathematics or chemistry or physics, and the errors and defects and obscurities of older times are superseded actually and replaced by fuller and more accurate knowledge.

It is the permanence of periods in arts and literature
which make their history attractive to the ordinary
man--it is the superseding of one so-called fact, by a
more accurate statement of the phenomenon, which
does away with all interest in the previous phase in
science.  If a statement or description has been
proved wrong and is corrected, it had better be put
out of sight and forgotten.  It has served its purpose
and is now devoid of vitality.  It is an obstacle to
progress.  The theory of the composition of metals
from sulphur and mercury gave way to phlogiston,
phlogiston gave way to oxygen, what oxygen may have
to give way to has not yet been settled. (4)

If this is true of the monographic classics in the history of
science, it is even more true of the periodical literature in
which new ideas in science are in an even more tentative
state.  As a consequence there are many bibliographic gaps
in the history of the scientific periodical.

Two of the periodical lists on which this study is
based were compiled for study of the history of the periodical (Garrison and Kirchner), while the other two, while they
aim at comprehensiveness, are union lists emphasizing cur-
rency which were compiled largely for administrative reasons.  The first of these, the list issued by Scudder in 1879,
is a compilation of the "scientific serials of all countries including the transactions of learned societies in the natural,
physical and mathematic sciences, 1633-1876."  The list grew
out of a discussion about co-operative acquisition which was
held in the New England area in 1876 in which an agreement
seems to have been arrived at regarding the division of subject fields among the libraries concerned.  The list was intended to facilitate this co-operative enterprise and to include
all current titles.

It was intended to include the pure and exclude all the
applied sciences; but their more or less intimate union in many periodicals has compelled the admission
of many titles which should no doubt be properly
classed with the applied sciences.  Some of the minor
divisions of the latter were also so limited, both in
scope and in literature (e.g. apiculture, fish-culture,
etc.), that it was deemed best to admit them; but the
publications dealing exclusively with Medicine, Phar-
macy, Agriculture, Horticulture, Technology, Manufactures, Philology, and History have been omitted,
and such minor divisions of the applied sciences as
have been included may be readily determined by an

inspection of the last index in the volume. It should
be added, however, that Antiquities, as dealing with
historic periods, have been omitted; while Archeol-
ogy, as dealing with pre-historic times, and thus
allied to Geology, has been admitted. As is well-
known, a large number of historical and antiquarian
societies and magazines discuss archeological material relating to the pre-historic period; and where this
was known to be the case they are introduced; but
otherwise, or unless their titles indicate a broader
scope than history only, they have been excluded. It
is impossible that mistakes should not have arisen in
this part of the work, and in this particular it is
somewhat unequally treated, a greater latitude being
allowed in the latter than in the earlier part of the
volume. In attempting to separate the science and
their applications, or historic and pre-historic papers,
much must be left to the compiler's judgment, and
that of any two persons must necessarily conflict. (5)

Scudder used available published and unpublished bibliographies, and had access to the manuscript of Bolton's list. He
states that he also visited libraries of the Northeast Atlantic
area in the process of compiling the list and that he circulated advance copies to a number of selected libraries abroad
whose names are appended to his volume. Scudder calls his
publication a list of "serials" which permits the admission of
titles which are not periodicals in the common sense of the
term, e.g. Johann Beckman's "Beyträge zur Geschichte der
Erfindungen, *" which was published serially between 1780 and
1805.

A periodical is not always easily distinguished from an
eighteenth century book issued in parts because the differentiation between author and editor is not always clear, and because periodicals of this time frequently consisted of issues
written largely or entirely by the editor. Contemporary
sources frequently refer to the editor of a periodical as its
author. One example is the publication of J.C. Füssli, the
Swiss entomologist and bookseller, the "Archiv der Insectengeschichte," issued in Zurich in eight parts from 1781 to
1786. In describing the plan of his work, Füssli said that it
was his intention that the description and illustration of each
insect should constitute a unit, and that therefore neither the
pages nor plates would be numbered in consecutive order.
This would permit the purchaser to bind them in whatever
systematic order suited him best. However, to assist the
owners of the work he promised to issue a list of the contents
of each issue and that at the end of ten issues he would issue

a systematic general index.    Only eight issues appeared and Füssli was never able to keep his promise about the general index.    The issues appeared one each year with the exception of 1783 and 1786 in each of which two issues appeared. (6)    From the foregoing description it seems apparent that this title is not a periodical at all and yet it is included in each of the four bibliographies cited.

While books issues in parts complicate the problem of distinguishing between books and periodicals, periodicals were also issued as books, for example, Nicolas Blegny's "Nouvelles Découvertes sur Toutes les Parties de la Médecine" appeared in weekly issues, but Blegny also made them available bound in single volumes at the end of the year. (7) One title which is cited by Scudder, Bolton and Garrison as a scientific periodical is "Beiträge zur Naturkunde und den damit verwandten Wissenschaften*" by the German Botanist Friedrich Ehrhardt (1742-1795).    It was issued in seven parts in Hannover and Osnabrück from 1787 to 1792.    On the basis of the mixed character of its subject contents and its serial issue it may be possible to consider it a periodical. However, it contains a chronological arrangement of Ehrhardt's correspondence and short essays on a variety of topics, principally botanical, but also pharmaceutical, nutritional and medical.    Kirchner does not include it in his list although it is German both in language and in place of origin. Ehrhardt makes it quite clear in the preface to the first volume, moreover, that the publication is to be devoted to a collection of his own writings.

> Certain of my friends for whom it has been difficult to purchase such books in which heretofore my short essays have appeared, have besought me to collect them and to issue them separately, and also in the future not to permit them to be inserted in such large and expensive publications, but to consider my readers and their financial position. (8)

Scudder also includes some titles that are not serial in nature, e.g. Alexandre Marie Quesnay de Beaurepaire's "Mémoire et Prospectus concernant l'Académie des Sciences et beaux Arts des États-Unis de l'Amerique*" (Paris, Cailleau, 1788), (9) and a one volume edition of Perrault's "Mémoire pour servir a l'Histoire naturelle des Animaux et des Plantes" (Gravenhage, 1731).    Some of the titles he includes are not independent publications but part of larger works, e.g. the translations of the "Miscellanea Philosophicae-Mathematica" of the Societas Privata Taurinensia, which appeared as part of the "Collection Académique*" published in

Paris in 1779. (10)   In these cases as in others he undoubtedly follows a bibliographic principle which is frankly
stated in the preface to Bolton's list in which he quotes the
bibliographer Zuchold:

> Some of the journals included in this Catalogue are of
> doubtful scientific value, and the right of some to be
> classed as periodicals is questionable; in these and
> in other debatable cases titles have been admitted on
> the ground that in a bibliography it is much better
> that a book should be found which is not sought, than
> that one should be sought for and not found. (11)

Scudder shares this characteristic with the other compilers
of lists of scientific periodicals in interpreting his criteria
of selection rather broadly and in including many general
titles which have little or no scientific or technological interest.

Bolton's list, the second edition of which was published in 1897, approached the concept of a union list in that
he attempted to provide locations in this country for as many
of the titles as he could.   It is broader in scope than Scudder's list in that he admits periodicals of the applied sciences, but narrower in that, with a few exceptions, he ex-
cludes all the publications of societies.   The second edition
was published in two parts, the first containing 4954 titles,
and the second corrections and additions to the first series
as well as about 3600 additional titles.   Bolton circulated his
list to 200 libraries in this country and received usable re-
plies from 133 which were codified and inserted as an appendix to the second edition.   Of the 8600 some titles in the
list, locations were provided for about 3160.   As is the case
with other periodical bibliographies that attempt comprehensiveness, Bolton took many of his titles from printed sources,
and probably was able to examine very few of the titles personally.   In the statement on his method of compilation he
says:

> The material for this work has been gathered from
> all available bibliographies and by personal examina-
> tion of the shelves and of the printed and manuscript
> catalogues of many libraries in the United States,
> England, France, Belgium, Germany and Italy.   As a
> last resort circulars were sent out through the Smith-
> sonian Institution to publishers in several countries
> asking for specimen numbers of their journal; the
> titles were then transcribed from the numbers re-
> ceived. (12)

This method of compilation leads to such defects as Bolton
classifying an early journal devoted to public health, Johann
Daniel Metzger's "Bibliothek für Physiker" (Königsberg, 1787-
1789), as a journal in physics, although the error could have
been avoided without examining the title if Bolton had known
the meaning of the term in this period.   In addition to the
library checklist which provides locations for a number of
the journals, Bolton's list contains other useful features such
as a chronological table which correlates the volume of a
particular journal with the year in which it was published,
and a subject index.

Despite the brevity of Garrison's article it is a significant contribution to the history of the scientific periodical.
He isolates a number of the elements that entered into its
development.   His statement of the genealogy of the periodical, beside providing us with a reflection of one of Garrison's many interests, is a terse and perhaps somewhat glib
history-in-capsule of the scientific journal:

> The genesis of the medical and scientific periodical is
> out of the scientific society by the newspaper.   The
> scientific society, as a part of this pedigree, came
> out of the medieval guilds; the newspaper, derived,
> by way of the news-letter, from the so-called intelli-
> gence offices.   (13)

The principal value of Garrison's contribution for our study
is the catalog and checklist of the medical and scientific periodicals of the 17th and 18th centuries.   All the titles in this
list were considered for inclusion with the exception of those
which fall in the last decade of the 18th century.

Garrison's list is derived from one which he prepared
for the third edition of Stedman's "Reference Handbook of the
Medical Sciences" (14) but which was considerably enlarged
in 1934.   It seems to be based largely on Callisen's work
and one of the purposes of the compilation appears to be to
remedy the shortcomings of Callisen's arrangement.   Callisen's list ostensibly covers periodicals between 1780 and
1833, but he also includes a large number of earlier periodicals as the forerunners of the titles he cites.   Garrison has
accepted some of Callisen's entries uncritically with the result that he includes titles that do not fall within the scope
of his inquiry.   Garrison supplemented these titles by reference to a large number of other sources.   Garrison's comment on his method of compilation, that it was "...assembled,
bit by bit, from all manner of available sources" (15) could
be echoed by all other compilers of periodical lists.   Exclud-

ing the translations, abridgements and reprints (these entries are not numbered in the list) the list comprises 432
medical and 349 scientific titles.   The total number of items
including the translations, etc., is 1199 of which 107 fall in
the 17th century and 1092 in the 18th.   This total, however,
includes a number of encyclopedic works which were published serially, e.g. the "Encyclopedia Britannica" and the
French "Encyclopédie" as well as a large number of titles
under the heading "Serial collections of dissertations, cases
and observations" which Garrison has interpreted rather
liberally to include non-serial publications as well as the
serially issued works of individual writers.   Some of the society publications are definitely not scientific in character.
For example, the "Sammlung einiger ausgesuchten Stücke,"
issued by the Gesellschaft der freyen Künste (Leipzig, 1754-
1756), are the publications of a literary-historical society,
and the "Memorias de Literatura Portugueza,*" published by
the Academia das Ciencias de Lisboa from 1787 to 1792,
contain largely dissertations on Portugese history and jurisprudence.   Under the heading: "Scientific and belletristic
periodicals containing medical matter" Garrison includes
about fifty titles of general magazines which, although they
are of considerably more importance in the early history of
the scientific periodical than they are today, perhaps should
not be included in an enumeration of scientific periodicals.
For example, he includes the "Allgemeine Deutsche Bibliothek*" (Berlin, 1765-1796), (why not the "Allgemeine Litera-
tur-Zeitung,*" Jena, 1731-1833) and the "Gentleman's Magazine*" (London, 1731-1833) which are representative of a
host of similar publications that are not included.   There are
a number of lacunae in Garrison's list, as indeed there are
in all lists of this nature.   There are, for example, 28 medical journals containing original materials and thus falling
squarely within the scope of his list, which he does not include.   The majority of these additional titles were encountered in the Kirchner, with which Garrison does not seem to
have been familiar.   One example of the elusiveness of this
type of publication is an interesting medical news-weekly
which was encountered in the collections of the National Library of Medicine and which does not seem to be included in
any of the published lists consulted nor cited in any of the
studies on medical journalism.   This is the "Avvisi sopra la
Salute Umana" which was published in  Florence between 1776
and 1785.

      Kirchner calls his study "The Foundations of the Ger-
man Periodical with a Collective Bibliography of German
Periodicals to the Year 1790." It consists of two parts, the
first a discussion of the manner in which the periodical was

edited, printed and distributed in the 17th and 18th centuries, and the second a chronological list of German periodicals produced in this period. He covers the whole range of German periodical literature including the so-called moral and political weeklies, omitting only those titles which do not fit a set of elaborate criteria which he sets up as a basis for his selection. In an appendix to the second part he lists many titles which are sometimes indicated as periodicals and which he has rejected for one reason or another, usually on the grounds that they were actually books in parts rather than true periodicals. Nevertheless, he includes several titles that are open to question. Lang who, in his study of the periodical literature of Switzerland for the same period, (16) uses the same criteria that Kirchner proposes, is even more rigorous in applying them, and rejects many of the Swiss titles which are included in Kirchner's list. He states that many of the titles in Kirchner's list are actually books in parts, even though they bear such titles as "Archiv," "Beiträge," "Bibliothek," "Magazin," "Museum" and "Sammlung." Many of these, he says, are collections of papers issued at irregular intervals, without a view toward being continued indefinitely, which both he and Kirchner agree is one of the criteria of a periodical. However, Lang places too much emphasis on the necessity for regularity, especially in this early period when it was not always considered an important aspect of periodical publication. We shall consider later the concept of periodicity of issue and its effect on journal publication, but we can say here that insistence on regularity of issue would severely limit this class of publication in the period from 1665 to 1790, since the analysis of the titles in the final list prepared for this study reveals that a great number of them were issued irregularly. Among the titles rejected by Lang which have been included in this study are the following:

"Acta Helvetica, Physico-Mathematico-Botanico-Medica," 1751-1777.

"Beyträge zu der Naturgeschichte des Schweiz," 1773-1774.

"Repertorium der medicinischen Litteratur," 1790-1795.

The Swiss titles cited above fall within the scope of Kirchner's list since he includes all titles printed in German no matter what part of the continent they were printed, as well as all titles which appeared in Germany. Kirchner located a large proportion of his titles in the Preussischen Staatsbibliothek and in other libraries of Germany, but for many of his titles he is able to cite only bibliographic sources, some 34 of which he lists in an appendix to his book. The complete list includes a total of 3494 titles which he has classified under 28 different rubrics, of which the following are of primary interest to us:

| | |
|---|---:|
| Medical periodicals, medical book-review journals, and periodicals of medical and natural science contents | 149 |
| Mathematical periodicals | 4 |
| Natural science periodicals | 160 |
| Technical periodicals | 4 |
| Total | 317 |

Additional titles were selected from the following of Kirchner's categories: general scholarly periodicals, general scholarly and critical periodicals, periodicals of economic and agricultural content (the agricultural titles), and financial periodicals (includes journals with technological and agricultural content). Not enough titles in these categories were added, however, to make up the difference between the total in the first categories (317) and the total number of German titles (544) or the total number of titles published in Germany (570) which are included in the list compiled for this study. Apparently there are many German titles cited in other lists and other sources which do not appear in Kirchner's list despite the comprehensiveness of his survey.

The preliminary list for the study was compiled on keysort cards by extracting all the titles from the first three lists which had their origin in 1790 or before. From Kirchner's list all the titles falling in the scientific and technological subject categories as well as all the general titles were listed. Most of the titles in this last category were eliminated from the final list with the exception of such titles as the "Acta Eruditorum*" and the "Journal des Sçavans*" because of their importance in the history of scientific journalism. It is impossible to have a full picture of the dissemination of scientific information in the 17th and 18th centuries without taking full account of the general journals, but they were not included in the statistical analysis.

An attempt was made to analyze the title retained in the final list under the following categories:

1. Subject
2. Duration
3. Place of issue

Introduction

4. Frequency of issue
5. Language
6. Type of publication
7. Sponsoring agency
8. Translations, reprints and abridgements

Data could not be obtained for every title under each of these headings, but there were probably not enough omissions to distort the analysis of the general characteristics of the sample.

There can be many answers to the question of which topics are relevant to the study of the history of scientific journalism. Its history is inseparable from the history of the development of scientific thought and even more inextricably bound up with the social history of science, a subject that has to the present been very inadequately dealt with. It is closely allied to the history of the organizational development of the sciences and of scientists, and, similarly, there does not seem to exist any general and systematic treatment of the history of scientific societies. Ornstein's study (17) is one of the few major contributions to this subject. It does not aim at comprehensiveness, but was written to demonstrate that the independent scientific society was made necessary by the failure of the university to adapt itself to a changing outlook. The development of printing practices and the book-trade have direct relevance to our topic, and a great deal more has been written on these topics, but the economics of printing and the book-trade have not been nearly as adequately dealt with. The development of the postal services and other methods of distribution was a necessary precondition to the development of the scientific periodical. Censorship and the control of printing is another factor to consider in the history of the scientific periodical. This study is limited to a description of the various forms which the periodical assumed in this period. The discussion has been limited to the general scientific titles but occasionally a title in a special scientific subject has been cited for illustrative purposes. The development of specialization in scientific journalism had made significant progress by the end of the 18th century, but this subject will be treated only in statistical terms.

Notes

(1)    Winifred Gregory (ed.), "Union List of Serials in Libraries of the United States and Canada," (2d ed.; New York: H. W. Wilson Co., 1943) and Supplements,

January 1941-December, 1943.

(2)      See bibliography.

(3)      Adolph C. P. Callisen, "Medicinisches Schriftsteller-
         lexicon" (Copenhagen, 1836-1838), Vols. XXIII-XXVI.

(4)      John Ferguson, "Notes on the Work of Polydore Vergil
         'De Inventores Rerum' ", "Isis," XVII (1932), 73-74.

(5)      Samuel H. Scudder, "Catalogue of Scientific Serials
         of all Countries including the Transactions of Learned
         Societies in the Natural, Physical and Mathematical
         Sciences, 1633-1876" (Cambridge: Harvard U. Library,
         1879).

(6)      F. J. Griffin, "The 'Archiv der Insectengeschichte' of
         J. C. Fuessly, Heft 1-8, 1781-1786," "Journal of the
         Society for the Bibliography of Natural History," I
         (1937), 83-85.

(7)      Issued in Paris, 1679.   This has been called the first
         medical journal published in the vernacular.

(8)      This quotation from Ehrhardt is especially interesting
         in that it expresses a point of view antagonistic to the
         periodical as a means of scattering the work of a
         single author.

(9)      This is the plan printed and issued by a Frenchman,
         who fought in the American Revolution, to enlist the
         aid of the Académie des Sciences of Paris in estab-
         lishing a system of schools and universities in the
         newly formed United States.   The system was to cen-
         ter on an Academy of Arts and Sciences to be estab-
         lished at Richmond.   The plan never came to fruition.

(10)     See below for description of this series.

(11)     Henry C. Bolton, "A Catalogue of Scientific and Tech-
         nical Periodicals 1665-1895," 2d ed.; Smithsonian
         Miscellaneous Collections," XL (1898), v.

(12)     Ibid., p. vi.

(13)     Fielding H. Garrison, "The Medical and Scientific
         Periodicals of the 17th and 18th Centuries," "Bulletin
         of the Institute for the History of Medicine," II (1934),
         287.

(14)    Fielding H. Garrison, "Journalism, Medical," "A
        Reference Handbook of the Medical Sciences," ed. by
        Thomas L. Stedman (4th ed.; New York: William
        Wood and Co., 1923), V. 706-712.

(15)    Garrison, "Medical and Scientific Periodicals," op.
        cit., p. 297.

(16)    Carl L. Lang, "Die Zeitschriften des deutschen
        Schweiz bis zum Ausgang des 18. Jahrhunderts
        (1694-1798)" (Leipzig: Harrassowitz, 1939).

(17)    Martha Crnstein, "The Role of Scientific Societies in
        the Seventeenth Century" (Chicago: University of Chi-
        cago Press, 1938).

# Chapter II

## Definitions of the Periodical

The differentiation between periodical, serial and other forms of publication is usually made for administrative reasons rather than their contents. Serial publications pose problems which influence their acquisition, cataloging and servicing. However, the scientist or scholar does not make nearly as fine distinctions between the various forms of publication as do those responsible for organizing and analyzing research collections. The scholar is primarily concerned with the substance rather than the form of the communication and it probably does not matter a great deal to him in what form the information he uses is embodied, except in so far as it influences such aspects of the communications problem as his attitude toward its reliability and authority. These factors probably do not change a great deal with the different forms of publication. Nevertheless, the various forms of scientific communication have distinctive characteristics which we must consider, if only to indicate the boundaries of our inquiry. It is a decision which is necessary when one is concerned with compiling such lists as the "Union List of Serials," or the "World List of Scientific Periodicals." These decisions are also necessary in the everyday operations of the research library, for various classes of materials are usually separated in the library for different treatment. The library literature is therefore replete with discussions of what constitutes a periodical. (1) Like the results of other processes of organic growth, classes of publication have intermediate forms which may possess some of the characteristics of the class but not the others. In the early history of the periodical these distinctions are even more difficult to make since the forms and functions of this new class of publication had not yet become clearly defined. Lang in his study of the German periodical in Switzerland to the end of the 18th century (2) distinguishes three classes of publication: the book, the periodical, and the newspaper. In his classification the periodical assumes an intermediate position because it shares some of its characteristics of content with the book and some of its characteristics of format with the newspaper. It shares with the book the characteristic of not

28

being as firmly bound to the events of the day as the newspaper, and has in common with the newspaper that it is usually issued at regular intervals and generally with the view of
continuation into the indefinite future.

When we compare sets of criteria established for both
the newspaper and the periodical we find that they have other
characteristics in common as well.  Groth in his monumental
four volume study of journalism (3) sets up the following requirements for the newspaper:

1.      It must be periodic in its publication, that is, it must
        appear at regular intervals and for practical reasons
        at least weekly.

2.      It must be mechanical in its duplication, which, as
        Allen (4) comments, bars the handwritten newsletter
        but admits radio and screen newspapers.

3.      It must be available to all who wish to pay for it and
        not limited to an exclusive or esoteric audience.

4.      It should be general in its appeal.

5.      It should be timely.

6.      It should be provided with an effective organization to
        insure its continuity.

Periodicity had been established for a good half century before any publications which we can recognize as periodicals appeared.  The majority of these early publications
attempted to report the events of the day and resemble what
we would call newspapers today.  As forerunners of the periodical, they established certain precedents of form, as well
as methods of compilation and distribution.  Even today in
English we do not make the clear distinction in our termin-
ology that the Germans make in calling one class of publication "Zeitung" and the other "Zeitschrift."

Kirchner in his attempt to arrive at an understanding
of the meaning which the concept periodical had in the eighteenth century consulted many contemporary sources and arrived at the conclusion that the term was used first to designate only the publication of scholarly memoirs and the news
of the learned world.  With the introduction of the so-called
"moral-weeklies" of which the "Spectator" is an outstanding
example, and other journals of instruction and entertainment,
the concept was given a broader meaning.  He distinguished

the following characteristics which the periodical had acquired by the end of the 18th century:

1. Periodicity.   Although this is an important characteristic of the periodical, it cannot be insisted upon, he
says, as a distinguishing element, because we must remember that many books in the 18th century were also published
in parts at intervals.

2. Duration.   This characteristic distinguishes the
periodical from the book in parts.   The publisher of a periodical begins his publication with the firm intent of continuing it indefinitely.   The bibliographer of the 18th century
made no clear distinction between the two forms on this
basis, and many books which appeared in parts in this period
are included in periodical bibliographies.   Kirchner cites as
an example the "Sammlung medizinischer und chirurgischer
Anmerckungen" which was edited by Joachim Friederich Hen-
kel and which appeared in eight issues between 1747 and
1763.   The editor, says Kirchner, made it clear in the preface to the first number that he did not intend to continue
his publication indefinitely:

> I have decided to make the younger physicians ac-
> quainted with the useful observations made in the
> course of my practice of medicine and surgery, and
> to continue this work as often as there occurs some-
> thing, no matter how trifling to medicine and sur-
> gery. (5)

If it was indeed the editor's, or in this case probably the author's, intent not to continue the publication indefinitely, at
least within the limits of mortality, there is nothing in the
statement Kirchner quotes to make this clear to us.   We
would prefer to omit it from our list rather on the basis of
what Kirchner calls "collectivity of contents."

3. Collectivity.   Kirchner cites in the connection
Löbl who says:   "The heterogeneity and diversity of offerings
is however also the characteristic which distinguishes the
periodical (as well as the newspaper) from the book in parts.
(6)   This characteristic is reflected in the fact that the periodical is usually the work of many authors.

4. Availability.   A third characteristic which Kirchner
calls "Publizität" concerns the way in which the periodical is
distributed and is related to Groth's statement that it should
be available to all those who wish to pay for it.

5. Continuity.   Because it is issued at intervals, the periodical strives to attain a unified character through the consistency of its format and its editorial policy.   Some of this unity is achieved through the repetition of the title with each issue and in the methods of numbering each issue in some consecutive and systematic manner.

The characteristics enumerated thus far, says Kirchner, are not sufficient to distinguish the periodical from the newspaper, since they apply equally well to both.   Two further criteria are needed.   These are, however, negative criteria, in that they apply to the newspaper and not to the periodical.

6. Timeliness.   The newspaper is time-bound, i.e. closely associated with the events of the day.   Kirchner quotes an early study on the newspaper in this connection: "One reads newspapers not in order that one may become learned and skilled in judgment, but only in order to learn what is going on." (7)   Prutz captures this quality of the newspaper when it is projected into the future when he says:

> When we bury ourselves in the yellowed volumes of old newspapers, it is like entering a ghost town, another Pompei, in which, as if we were turning back the wheel of time, we suddenly surprise a people long disappeared, in the midst of their daily existence, in their most intimate domestic tasks. (8)

Timeliness is, of course, not without importance for the periodical as well.   Choulant in his discussion of medical journalism in the first volume of the "Allgemeine medicinische Annalen" which appeared in 1821 includes it as one of the most important characteristics of medical journalism, placing it first on his list of desiderata for the scientific periodical. (9)

7. Universality.   The newspaper is addressed to a much more general audience than the periodical.   Although they each have their "public," they are based on different factors.   The public for the newspaper has generally a geographic basis, while the public for the periodical is based more on a community of interests. (10)

> The public for the newspaper is the unknown circle of readers which is made of both sexes, of various ages and educational backgrounds, and who come from all circles of the population.   It is quite otherwise with the public of the special press.

The periodical has a more limited and a more differentiated
circle of readers.  He adds, however, that this characteristic is not nearly as important in the 17th and 18th centuries
in distinguishing the two forms of publication.  Kirchner ends
his discussion of the periodical form with definition in the
form of a marathon sentence which we shall attempt to translate literally:

> The periodical of the seventeenth and eighteenth cen-
> tury is a publication founded with a view toward in-
> definite duration, which appeared in more or less reg-
> ular issues, and for a generally circumscribed group
> of readers with similar interests, which was produced
> by means of mechanical duplication, and whose indi-
> vidual issues are recognizable as the (periodically) re-
> appearing parts of a unified whole, and which with its
> own particular specialty or field of knowledge strives
> for a diversity of contents. (11)

It is apparent from the foregoing discussions that no
clear distinctions can be made between the periodical and the
newspaper.  The term "Zeitschrift" did not appear until some-
time near the end of the 18th century (1) and this class of
publication was designated in Germany by a large variety of
descriptive names including: "Bibliothek," "Magazin," "Anzeiger," "Beyträge," and terms to indicate frequency of issue:
"Monatschrift," "Wochenschrift," etc.  The "Bibliothek der
besten deutschen Zeitschriften" (Pappenheim, 1788) and "Aes-
culap, eine medicinisch-chirurgische Zeitschrift" (Leipzig,
1790) are two early examples of the use of the term "Zeitschrift."  The term "Zeitung" was used for the learned journal all through the 18th century in Germany, the most celebrated example being the "Göttingische Anzeigen" which began
its existence in 1739 with the title "Göttingische Zeitungen von
gelehrten Sachen."

In France a similar pair of terms were used to describe the two classes of publication.  The term "Gazette,"
however, was usually reserved for the newspaper, and the
term "Journal" was applied very early to the publication of
learned news and information, the most celebrated example
being, of course, the "Journal des Sçavans."  Camusat, one
of the earliest of the French historians of the periodical
press, defined the term more narrowly than is usually the
case today:

> A journal is a periodical which, appearing regularly
> at indicated intervals, announces books which are new

or newly printed, provides some idea of their contents and which serves to conserve the discoveries
which are made in the sciences; in brief, a work in
which one reports everything which occurs daily in
the republic of letters. (13)

It is apparent that Camusat's definition is devised to fit neat-
ly the characteristics of the "Journal des Sçavans" to which
his incomplete history is almost exclusively devoted.   With
proper patriotic zeal he attributes the invention of this form
of journalism to France and to De Sallo, the first editor of
the "Journal." In pursuit of his goal he takes time to dis-
pose of the claims of priority sometimes made for the Greek
patriarch Photius, who died in Constantinople in 891.   Photius kept a sort of literary diary which he called a "Myriobiblion" and in which he recorded critical comments and extracts from his readings in the classics, and which he composed, says Camusat, for the education of a Frère Tariase
to whom the "Myriobiblion" was addressed.   The claim of
Photius for priority as  inventor  of the learned journal was
advanced by Constantin Wolf in a dissertation entitled:  "De
Photius Ephemeridum Eruditorum Inventore" (Wittenberg,
1689).   The claim can be considered irrelevant if we regard mechanical duplication and wide distribution as indis-
pensable characteristics of the periodical, and we can attribute it to the sort of scholarly zeal which attempts to find
origins as far back in antiquity as possible, even if it is not
as resourceful as Kaspar von Stieler, who in his "Zeitungs
Lust and Nutz" (Hamburg, 1695), Prutz says, attributes the
origins of the first newspaper to God and Solomon. (14)
Nevertheless, Photius' work even if it did have only an audience of one does reflect some of the important elements of
early learned journalism.   It is interesting to note that De
Sallo before he began to issue the "Journal" was also devoted
to the practice of annotating and extracting from his voluminous reading. (15)

Camusat's definition is repeated in the authoritative
compendium of the knowledge of the Enlightenment, the
"Encyclopédie:"

Journal, or periodical work, which contains extracts
of newly printed books, along with particulars of the
discoveries which are made every day in the arts and
sciences. (16)

The article goes on to say that the first publication of this
species which appeared in France is the "Journal des Sçavans," and that it was invented "for the comfort of those who

are too busy or too lazy to read entire books.  It is a
means of satisfying their curiosity and of becoming wise at
little expense."  The article distinguished as a separate class
of publication, the "Histoires" and "Mémoires" of the scientific
academies, which it says "are not journals in which an account is rendered of new publications, but the collections of
papers presented by the scholars who make up the various
learned societies."  This distinction between the independent
scientific journals and the proceedings of scientific societies
has never been an entirely valid one in the history of scientific journalism, because from its very origins, the proceedings of the learned societies were reported in the independent
journals, although in the 17th and 18th centuries the methods
and the infrequency of publication of the society publications
tend to set them apart as a class of publication.

Various other attempts at classification of the scientific periodical founder likewise on the difficulty that the scientific journal as we know it today is a composite of disparate elements:  original contributions, book reviews, abstracts from other journals and books, scientific news.
While these elements all contribute toward the same end of
keeping the scientist or scholar informed of the progress of
scholarship, they are all somewhat different in character and
function.   All these elements are represented in the journals
of the 17th and 18th century, and, as is true today, occupy
various portions of the different journals, and while most of
the journals are admixtures of these elements, in some of
the journals one of the elements may be the entire function
of the journal.   As we shall see later it is also true that in
the earlier period these elements are not as strictly differentiated from each other as they are today.   One early attempt to classify scientific periodicals, which recognized
these distinctions, is a review of medical journalism which
appeared in the first volume of the "Medicinische Argos."
The list included in the review contains many 18th century
titles, and the annotations which are appended make it a useful supplement to the lists consulted for this study.   The review divides medical journals into two major categories:
"eine gebende und eine nehmende" (17) which we can perhaps
best translate as:   "a contributory and a derivative" journalism.   In the first group fall all the journals with original
papers, although not necessarily in the form of original publication.   For example, there are included here many of the
German "Sammlungen" or collections which gathered together
papers from many different sources, but might also have included an occasional original publication.   Later in the review a classification according to the number of functions undertaken by the journal is offered:

1. The journals which follow one path:
   a. Those which are purely critical journals.
   b. Those that are purely compilations.

2. Those journals which follow two paths:
   a. These are principally compilations which contain also original papers.

3. Those which fulfil all three purposes:
   a. They contain critical reviews, compilations and original papers. (18)

The review also attributes the inception of medical journalism to the growth in the number of medical practitioners who were scientifically trained.

> Until the middle of the seventeenth century the number of physicians with scientific education and those who sought to improve themselves was in general so small that those who sought the same objectives were able to find one another easily in order to enter into personal communication and the exchange of knowledge and ideas. A lively correspondence which we can still thank today for much of importance, fulfilled the needs and desires of the majority of individuals. However other colleagues did not have part in this communication unless the correspondence was read to them. (19)

All the elements of scholarly journalism entered into learned correspondence, and we can, if we wish, consider a scientific journal as a kind of letter addressed to a group rather than to an individual recipient, except that unlike the learned letter it is not designed to specifically fit the needs and the background of the individual to whom it is addressed. In the beginnings, scientific journalism, has, as we shall see later, a great deal in common with the scholarly letter, and it is not until later that the different elements become standardized into the forms that we know today. The concept of original publication, for instance, is relatively late in arriving, and even as late as the 1770's we find frequently in Rozier's journal, one of the first scientific journals which begins to have a modern outlook, translations, extracts and reprints without designation of their origin.

The whole problem of original publication is tied up intimately with the problem that is central to the scientific journal and which provides the principal theme of this discussion. That is, it reflects the double role that the scien-

tific journal has had to play, that of being at the same time
a vehicle for and a repository of information, or, as the
medical editor cited above expressed it, falling into two
categories "eine gebende und eine nehmende." The earliest
statement of the problem which we have been able to find is
in an address made to the British Library Association in a
discussion of the necessity for periodical indexing which took
place at the turn of the century:

> Periodicals exist to disseminate information; but they
> also exist to record it; and when we find that the
> momentary dissemination of knowledge is obtained at
> the cost of permanent record of it, we may well pause
> and ask ourselves whether there is not a danger of
> a blessing being changed into a curse, unless we take
> measures to prevent it.

> To be brief, I may say, at once, that the develop-
> ment of Periodical literature has been such as to
> constitute a very considerable danger to the progress
> of knowledge; for while, on the one hand, it has en-
> couraged an excessive output of short and fragmentary
> articles, it has, on the other hand, equally attracted
> to itself a large number of very considerable works
> which should naturally have been issued as Separate
> 'Books;' and, having shorn them of their dignity as
> 'Books," has issued them to the world in the humble
> guise of 'Articles,' so buried amid other 'Collected
> Works' as to be comparatively useless for reference.
> (20)

If the scientific periodical serves principally as a vehicle for
the transmission of new information and if the new information is eventually to be embodied in some other medium, then
it is not important to distinguish whether its contents are
original contributions. In general, in the 18th century, orig
inal publication referred to the form of publication, i. e.
whether it is the author's original article or an extract, abstract or review of it, while in present day usage this generally refers to precedence of publication. For the purposes
of dissemination it probably does not matter a great deal
whether an original contribution is reprinted as often as, say
a United Press news story, but if the function of the literature is to serve largely as a repository, then the presence
of the same contribution in many different forms would need-
lessly complicate the problems of storage and retrieval of
information.

## Notes

(1)     For a summary and list of some of these definitions
        see David Grenfell, "Periodicals and Serials, Their
        Treatment in Special Libraries" (London: ASLIB,
        1953).

(2)     Lang, op. cit.

(3)     Otto Groth, "Die Zeitung, ein System der Zeitungs-
        kunde" (Mannheim: J. Bensheimer, 1928-1930).

(4)     Eric W. Allen, "International Origins of the News-
        paper: The Establishment of Periodicity in Print,"
        "Journalism Quarterly," VII (1930), 307-319.

(5)     Kirchner, op. cit., pp. 18-19.

(6)     Ibid., p. 21, citing Emil Löbl, "Kultur und Presse"
        (Leipzig: Kuncker and Humblot, 1903), p. 19.

(7)     Ibid., p. 24, citing Kaspar von Stieler, "Zeitung Lust
        und Nutz" (Hamburg: Benjamin Schiller, 1695).

(8)     Prutz, op. cit., p. 7.

(9)     L. Choulant, "Über medicinische Journalistik," "Allge-
        meine medicinische Annalen," 1821, pp. 11-30.

(10)    Kirchner, op. cit., pp. 29-30.

(11)    Ibid., pp. 32-33.

(12)    Ibid., p. 14.

(13)    D. F. Camusat, "Histoire Critique des Journaux"
        (Amsterdam: J. F. Bernard, 1734), I, 5-6.

(14)    Prutz, op. cit., p. 35.

(15)    Eugene B. Barnes, "The International Exchange of
        Knowledge in Western Europe, 1680-1689," (Unpub-
        lished Ph. D. Dissertation, Graduate Library School,
        University of Chicago, 1947).

(16)    "Encyclopédie, ou Dictionnaire raisonné des Sciences,
        des Arts et des Métiers" (Paris: Briasson, 1751-
        1765), VIII, 896-987.

(17)    "Medicinische Argos," I (1839), 61.

(18)    Ibid., p. 60.

(19)    Ibid., p. 74.

(20)    Frank Campbell, "The Bibliography of Periodical
        Literature," "The Library," VIII (1896), 49.   Em-
        phasis is the author's.

# Chapter III

## The Historical Background

It is no longer customary among historians of science to take a cataclysmic view of the introduction of modern science nor to regard the changes in thought and practice which were taking place in the 16th and 17th centuries as a "scientific revolution," although the term is still considered useful to characterize the profound and significant changes which took place in that period. The period of the introduction of modern science is now regarded as a logical extension of medieval activities and interests which came to fruition in the 17th century in what seemed like a new method of approaching nature and of applying knowledge to the improvement of the condition of man. These changes, social, economic and intellectual, were quantitative as well as qualitative. The isolated examples which historians find in the Middle Ages of individuals who took a critical view of Aristotle's ideas on physics tended to become the norm in the 17th century. There was, of course, a literate and a leisured class in the Middle Ages which could have provided a potential audience for the periodical, but with the economic expansion of the 15th and 16th centuries this class was considerably increased and what is more significant, its character changed. One of the important prerequisites for the existence of any medium of communication is an audience.

The beginnings of the modern era witnessed a growth in the number of individuals who had the means and the leisure to devote themselves to the cultivation of ideas. It is one of the paradoxes of the history of science that one of the important factors which contributed toward the creation of a larger class of people who were freed from having to devote themselves completely to the necessities of life was the improvements in technology which took place in the period preceding the development of modern science, and that these improvements in technology took place largely without the help of organized scholarship. That such important changes in technology as the improvement of mining and the development of new forms of power could take place and could be transmitted to other parts of the world without being committed to

print points up the fact that there was, and is, a great part
of the process of communication of scientific knowledge that
takes place outside the formal and organized channels.
Among the qualitative changes were those fundamental altera-
tions in attitudes toward individual responsibility, man's social role and relationship to authority which made up the
whole complex called the Reformation.   It may be useful to
examine some of these factors and their implications for the
development of scientific journalism.

If we define science in terms of the materials with
which it deals, as an area of knowledge which is concerned
with external reality and with the processes of nature and
with the manipulation of these processes, then science has
existed since pre-history.   The diletantes and amateurs of
science of the 17th century were presented with a prodigious
store of empirical data which had accumulated through the
centuries even though only a very small part of it had ever
been committed to paper.   They sought this knowledge wher-
ever they could and prided themselves on going to the crafts-
man and artisan to acquire it.   The significant change was
that the individuals who applied themselves to the type of
knowledge, which in the Middle Ages had been exclusively the
concern of the artisans, were in the 17th century a new
class with classical training and familiarity with scholastic
philosophy.   The change from scholastic philosophy to moder
science involved a change not so much in form as in the substance of discourse.   Zilsel points out that the elements necessary for the development of modern science existed in two
separate groups during the Middle Ages.   One group consisted of the humanists and university scholars who were
trained in rational thinking but who, on the whole, shunned
manual labor, experimentation and dissection.   The other
group was composed of the superior manual laborers, the
artist-engineers, instrument makers, surgeons and others wh
were able to solve a whole series of problems empirically
but who lacked methodical intellectual training.

> Thus the two components of the scientific method were
> separated by a social barrier:   logical training was
> reserved for upper-class scholars, experimentation,
> causal interest, and quantitative method were left to
> more or less plebian artisans.   Science was born,
> when, with the progress of technology, the experi-
> mental method eventually overcame the social prejudice
> against manual labor and was adopted by rationally
> trained scholars. (1)

It is inevitable that the university trained scholars brought

over with them to their new fields of interest many of their
habits and customs of thought and expression, although there
was, nevertheless, a conscious effort to create a new form
of expression as well as a new way of dealing with phenomena, which we find so well expressed in the early meetings
of the Royal Society at London.

The outstanding spokesman and the most influential
propagandist for these new methods of approaching phenomena and of accumulating and organizing knowledge was
Francis Bacon (1561-1626) who is acknowledged as the inspiration for the new movement.

The organization of the Royal Society was greatly influenced by the ideal research institute which Bacon outlined
in his "New Atlantis," and in the Society's early history we
see many attempts to put his ideas into effect.   The term
"fellows" which the Society adopted to designate its members
is said to have been adopted from this same work of Bacon.
(2)   Huyghens in his proposals to the newly organized Académie des Sciences in Paris advocated strongly that Bacon's
program be followed:

> The principal occupation of this assembly and the
> most useful would be, in my opinion, to work at natur-
> al history quite according to the design of Verulam...
> One should, in pursuing the various subjects of which
> I shall name a few, distinguish the chapters of this
> history and gather there all the comments and ex-
> periments concerning each particular one, not without
> taking the trouble of reporting therein those that are
> rare and difficult to perform, as well as those which
> appear essential to the discoveries which one seeks,
> and even those that are well known. (3)

When the "Journal Encyclopédique," one of the outstanding periodicals of the Enlightenment, was inaugurated
almost a century later, Bacon was still being celebrated as
the inspiration of the new science:

> It is a most favorable augury that we are permitted
> to make our debut before our associates and before
> the public with the philosophy of the Chancellor Bacon
> and with the fifth volume of the "Encyclopédie."
> These two works have so essential a connection that
> it is impossible to separate them without losing the
> rays of light that they send back one to the other,
> and which create for us the most fortunate reflections.
> One can not help comparing the first genius who dared

conceive the project of freeing all the sciences from
their chains, and of composing a table of human
knowledge, with the first society which had the power
and the courage of executing this grand plan which
touches in all parts on the boundaries of human understanding.  If this society owes everything to Chancellor Bacon, even to the glory of having surpassed
his plan, the philosoper does not owe less to the authors of the "Encyclopédie."  Without them this ad-
mirable project could not have been regarded but as
a brilliant chimera, and one of those vain efforts
which the arrogance of man makes from time to time
against the limits which circumscribe him...

The English Chancellor felt strongly the need of such
an aid which his century could not provide him.  His
genius projected itself into the future, there designated and chose his successors.   One believes oneself
to be reading a prophecy when one casts one's eyes
on this singular article of his testament:  'I leave,'
he said,  'and bequeath my name and my work to foreign countries, because it will be a long time before
my fellow citizens will acknowledge me.'  Who is it
that will dispute to the authors of the "Dictionnaire
Encyclopédique" such a glorious succession.  (4)

The society of which the editor speaks here was, of course,
the group organized under the direction of Diderot for the
purpose of compiling the great French encyclopedia which
represents not the first effort to bring together all knowledge
according to Bacon's program, but the culmination of a long
series of such efforts which began in the 17th century.

The most concrete expression of Bacon's ideas about
the organization of scientific research and its operational
methods is perhaps to be found in his "New Atlantis," an account of a visit to a utopian island, a work which he never
completed but which enjoyed wide circulation after his death.
Mish, in his study of best sellers in 17th-century fiction,
places it fifth on the list of English works.  It appeared in a
total of sixteen editions in the 17th century, although only in
one edition did it appear under its own title.  It was probably the most widespread English publication of scientific interest in 17th century England.  (5)  Bacon's description of
the research institute which is the state-controlled scientific
agency of this utopian society is described at the very end of
the book, in an interview which the party of stranded travellers has with its directors.  After detailing the program of
the institute and describing its facilities and plant, the direc-

tor goes on to an enumeration of its staff: (6)

> For the several employments and offices of our fel-
> lows, we have twelve that sail into foreign countries
> under the names of other nations (for our own we
> conceal), who bring us the books and abstracts, and
> patterns of experiments of all other parts. These we
> call Merchants of Light.
>
> We have three that collect the experiments which are
> in all books. These we call Depredators.
>
> We have three that collect the experiments of all me-
> chanical arts, and also of liberal sciences, and also
> of practices which are not brought into arts. These
> we call Mystery-men.
>
> We have three that try new experiments, such as
> themselves think good. These we call Pioneers or
> Miners.
>
> We have three that draw the experiments of the former
> four into titles and tables, to give the better light for
> the drawing of observations and axioms out of them.
> These we call Compilers.
>
> We have three that bend themselves, looking into the
> experiments of their fellows, and cast about how to
> draw out of them things of use and practice for man's
> life and knowledge, as well for works as for plain
> demonstration of causes, means of natural divinations,
> and the easy and clear discovery of the virtues and
> parts of bodies. These we call Dowry-men or Bene-
> factors.
>
> Then after divers meetings and consults of our whole
> number to consider of the former labors and collec-
> tions, we have three that take care out of them to di-
> rect new experiments, of a higher light, more pene-
> trating into nature than the former. These we call
> Lamps.
>
> We have three others that do execute the experiments
> so directed, and report them. These we call Inocula-
> tors.
>
> Lastly, we have three that raise the former discov-
> eries by experiments into greater observations, axioms,
> and aphorisms. These we call Interpreters of Nature.

We have also, as you must think, novices and ap-
prentices, that the succession of the former employed
men do not fail; beside a great number of servants
and attendants, men and women.  And this we do also:  We have consultations, which of the inventions
and experiences which we have discovered shall be
published, and which not; and take all an oath of se-
crecy for the concealing of those which we think fit
to keep secret, though some of those we do reveal
sometimes to the state, and some not.

It would be interesting to speculate which of these functions
correspond to those generally assigned to the librarian.
Nevertheless, of the thirty-six fellows whose duties the director outlines, half are engaged in the acquisition and recording of knowledge already in existence, or are occupied
with what we might call bibliographic functions.  The other
half of the group is concerned with research planning, the
execution of new experiments, and finally with the "interpre-
tation of Nature" or with synthesis, which Seyle calls the
most creative side of science.  (7)   The relative importance
which Bacon places on the compilation of "old" knowledge in
comparison with the pursuit of "new" knowledge is reflected
in the early activities of the Royal Society which set itself
to the compilation of some of the various "histories" which
Bacon outlined in his other works, and which consumed much
of the energies of the first members of the society.  As a
preliminary to the great plan he proposed for the reorganization of knowledge, Bacon advocated a thorough-going inven-
tory"... or an enumeration and view of inventions already discovered and in use, together with a note of the wants and
nature of the supplies." (8)   Some of these inventories
Bacon attempted himself, as a sample of the numerous "histories" which he proposed.  His "History of the Winds" was
published in 1622, the "History of Life and Death" in 1623.
His "Sylva Sylvarum" (A Forest of Materials) appeared one
year after his death in 1627.   Along with these subjects
which are also included in his "Catalogue of Particular Histories by Title" there are many more of a more pedestrian
interest, e.g. the history of cookery and the subservient arts
such as that of the butcher; the history of baking and the
making of bread; the history of the manufactures from flax,
etc.  Some of the early work of members of the Royal Society were carried out in this tradition and among the various histories which they compiled we find also histories of
the various trades.

In his "House of Solomon" Bacon describes what we
may call an intra-mural program which seems to have little

significance for the broader problems of the communication
of scientific ideas.  His emphasis on the compilation of
histories from existing sources seems to be more in the
scholastic tradition than in the spirit of the new inquiry
which he advocates.  This is, of course, another bit of evidence that even the most revolutionary thinkers carry over
a great deal from the periods and conditions with which they
are in revolt.  More significant for the history of the scientific periodical are Bacon's attitudes toward the old learning
and his emphasis on the experiment.  These are two factors which contributed a great deal to the form and the function of the scientific periodical.  Throughout his lifetime he
carried on a concerted campaign to break away from the ancient methods and to combat the reverence in which the
scholarship of the ancients was held.

> Bacon had talked of the need of 'minds washed clean
> of opinion,' but Descartes went further in his de-
> termination to unload himself of all the teachings which
> had been transmitted from the ancient world, his de-
> termination to doubt everything and start naked again.
> (9)

In his attacks on the learning of the past Bacon helped
to precipitate the great argument between the advocates of
the ancient learning and modern learning which became known
in the history of scholarship as the "Battle of the Books."
The Scholastics, he said, spent their time pouring over the
works of the ancients and spinning out tenous and laborious
threads of learning that were without substance.  As the posterity of the ancients we are actually wiser than they because
we have the benefit of the knowledge which has accumulated
since their time, so that in a sense it is we and not they who
are the ancients.  These arguments, though not exactly in
Bacon's words, are reiterated constantly throughout the century following his death.  The importance of this attitude for
scientific literature in general and for the periodical in particular is that this rejection of an established literature made
necessary the creation of a new literature.  The form which
this literature took was influenced greatly by the second contribution which Bacon made, his emphasis on observation and
experiment.

The great defect of the scholastic philosophers in
Bacon's view was that they placed too much emphasis on existing texts, neglecting their own powers of observation.  The
characteristic work of the pre-scientific period was the compilation and the commentary.  In the era before printing this
may have grown to some extent out of the fact that a manu-

script is unique and that in the act of copying and transmitting a manuscript a scholar might not be able to resist yielding to the temptation of annotating and commenting on the omissions and deficiencies of the basic text. The scarcity of copies would lead to scholars compiling collections of notes from the sources they consulted much in the same way a scholar might today accumulate collections of notes. The availability of the original sources today would make the publication of such collections of little value, while in a period of scarcity they might have had an important function to perform. The change from manuscript to printing introduced new problems in the transmission of information but there was a considerable carry over from the manuscript, just as the printed character was an attempt to reproduce the hand-drawn character. The practice of lengthy citation from original sources that persists in scholarship even today may perhaps be regarded as another example of the persistence of tradition.

Bacon made very little direct contribution to the methodology of the scientific experiment except as a staunch advocate of direct observation of nature as the basis of building the new knowledge he demanded. However, observation has a great deal in common with experiment in that an isolated phenomenon or group of phenomena is singled out for consideration. The experiment introduces more of the element of purposive interference with nature and greater control and isolation of the variables involved. The observation and experiment in confining themselves to a limited area have certain characteristics which are of great significance to the development of scientific journalism.

The single observation or experiment has a unity in itself and the publications in which it results is likely to be short. Thus the increase in the use of experiment led to the formula: one experiment or observation equals one communication, essay or publication. The characteristic form of publication before the appearance of the scientific periodical was the book which is not efficient for presenting the results of experiments or observations, because the author has to wait until he has accumulated a sufficient number of them to justify the publication of a book. Many of these observations could be, and were, published in the form of pamphlets; for example Harvey's work on the circulation of the blood appeared in a book of seventy-two pages. (10) At a later date when the periodical appeared it might very well have appeared in one of the scientific journals. This idea is constantly reiterated in the prefaces of the new scientific journals and in the correspondence of contemporary scholars in which they enthusiastically welcomed the new medium of scientific communication.

## Notes

(1)     Edgar Zilsel, "The Sociological Roots of Science,"
        "American Journal of Sociology," XLVII (1942), 544.

(2)     H. Lyons, "The Royal Society, 1660-1940" (Cambridge: Cambridge University Press, 1944), p. 3.

(3)     Joseph L. F. Bertrand, "L'Académie des Sciences et
        les Académiciens de 1666 a 1793" (Paris: Hetzel,
        1869), pp. 8-10, citing a manuscript note of Huyghens.  The note is dated 1666, the year in which
        Colbert proposed the foundation of the new academy.

(4)     "Journal Encyclopédique," I (1756), 5.

(5)     Charles C. Mish, "Best Sellers in Seventeenth Century Fiction," "Papers of the Bibliographic Society of
        America," XLVII (1953), 356-373.

(6)     Francis Bacon, "Essays and New Atlantis" (New York:
        Walter J. Black, 1942), pp. 299-300.

(7)     Hans Seyle, "Stress" (Montreal: Acta, 1950), p. xi.
        "There are many ways of studying life:--There is the
        tabulation of simple facts, such as the registration of
        structural detail or of bio-chemical changes produced
        by an experimental intervention. --This work is safe;
        it is the "book-keeping of Nature." -- There is the descriptive characterization of complex facts, such as
        clinical syndromes or intricate tissue reactions. --
        This work is inspired; it is the "landscaping of Nature."--Finally, there is the correlation of facts into
        a unified system, a Science.  For the explorer of Nature this yields a practically useful (though not necessarily complete or even correct) map of navigation.
        It helps him to remember the points he saw and to
        discover new ones along the roads of abstraction
        which connect them. --This work is creative; it may
        lead far astray, but apart from procreation, this is
        the closest man can come to the "making of Nature."

(8)     Fulton H. Anderson, "The Philosophy of Francis
        Bacon" (Chicago: University of Chicago Press, 1948),
        p. 33.

(9)      Herbert Butterfield, "The Origins of Modern Science, 1300-1800" (New York: Macmillan, 1950), p. 83.

(10)     William Harvey, "Exercitatio Anatomica de Motu Cordis et Sanguinis in Animalibus" (Francofurti: G. Fitzeri, 1628).

# Chapter IV

## Antecedent and Contemporary Forms of Communication and Their Influence on the Scientific Periodical

Like other forms of invention the scientific periodical was a selection and adaptation of existing means to serve existing ends. It is clear from the enthusiasm with which it was received and the comments that were made by the contemporaries of the first scientific periodicals that it was regarded as an invention. Morgan in her study of the "Journal des Sçavans" regards it as something entirely new on the literary horizon:

> Thirty years after the publication of the Gazette, fifteen after the letters of Loret, Denis de Sallo, the first in Europe, invented the literary and scientific journal, 'the father of all the publications of this genre which today fill Europe,' said Voltaire. (1)

But only if we accept as inventions those devices which are a combination of already existing elements does the journal of de Sallo qualify for the title, for all the elements which entered into its makeup were already in existence when it first appeared on the scene.

Among the antecdent forms which influenced it directly or indirectly were the newspaper, correspondence, the "Messrelationen," the fair catalogs, and the calendars. Some of these literary forms came into existence at a much earlier date and have persisted until the present day, because their functions have not been completely replaced by the periodical. It is the nature of inventions that they do not entirely supplant existing tools and devices. Just as the automobile has not completely replaced the horse, correspondence still serve an important and valid role in contemporary scientific communication.

On the other hand, we also find that institutions and practices persist even though they no longer have a useful function to perform. In spite of the greatly improved technical means of communication available in the 20th century

it may appear that our basic pattern of communicating the
results of scientific research have not changed considerably
from the days in which the scientific societies were first
organized.

There were very few changes in the techniques of
communication up to the end of the 18th century.  Printing
was carried out at the end of the period very much in the
same fashion as it had been performed in the century of its
invention.  The improvements which were introduced that influenced communications were in the field of distribution, the
introduction of postal services and the improvements of roads
and transport.  Although courier systems had existed from
antiquity and there are even Biblical precdents cited, (2) organized postal services in Europe are usually dated from the
16th century.  There is considerable disagreement in the
literature about the exact date in which this took place.
Storz (3) places its origins in 1595 under Emperor Rudolph
II of the Holy Roman Empire who contracted with Leonhard
von Taxis to establish and operate a courier service, although history relates that the family of Thurn and Taxis had
been active in this field in Europe for over a century before
that.  Harlow, a historian of the postal service, places its
origins in 1505 when, he says, Phillip I contracted with
Francis von Taxis for 12,000 livres annually to maintain a
mounted courier service between Brussels and Paris.  The
date 1516 which Garrison cites as the origin of the postal
service in Europe probably relates to the first time a regular postal system was established in England under Henry
VIII. (4)  It is clear, however, that the official organization
of postal services is closely connected with the growth of the
national state and were organized as a means of consolida-
tion of power. (5)  At about the same time private and mu-
nicipal letter carrying services were being established, while,
of course, the ancient system of sending communications by
means of travellers continued to operate.  It is related that
Erasmus had his own system of communications in which he
would send out a number of his young protégées at certain
times of the year to carry his letters to various parts of
Europe. (6)

The improved postal services doubtlessly played a
role in the increase of scholarly correspondence which preceded the introduction of the learned journal and as we shall
see later was an important element in the distribution system
for journals.  From its very origins the post was closely
bound up with the distribution of news and in the early history of the newspaper the postmaster is as frequently the
printer as the purveyor of news.  In an early work on jour-

nalism by Kaspar Stieler (1632-1707) the term "Postmeister"
is used interchangeably with "Zeitungsschreiber" or journalist, which suggests that at the end of the 17th century the
publishing of newspapers was largely in the hands of the
postmasters. (7)   At this time there existed a curious form
of combined newspaper and letter paper which points up the
connection even more closely.   "The Flying Post," issued
about 1695, was advertised as being printed on a sheet of
fine paper half of which was left blank for personal communications.   Another similar publication was "Dawkes's
News Letter." (8)   This close union is apparent also in the
names of some of the 17th century newspapers:   "Post-
reuter," "Hinkende Bote," "Postzeitung," etc.

    A form of communication which is intermediate be-
tween the erudite letter and the newspaper and which has
much in common with both is the manuscript news-letter.
The erudite letter like the manuscript news-letter or "nouvelles à la main" was frequently addressed to an audience
of more than one and written in an impersonal style.   They
differ in that the erudite letter per se was not undertaken
as a commercial enterprise while the production of manuscript news-letters in the 16th century and later represented
a flourishing and sometimes lucrative occupation.   Although
Hatin in his history of the press places their origin at the
end of the 16th century, (9) other authorities say that they
were known in Italy as early as the 14th century. (10)   The
agencies responsible for issuing the manuscript news-letters
ranged from a single correspondent who might be engaged
by a nobleman to provide him with the political, social and
learned news from one of the European capitals to a highly
organized news-gathering agency which maintained a network
of correspondents and an editorial office.   One of the best
known of the manuscript news-letters was that issued with
the aid of the great banking and mercantile family of the
16th century, the Fuggers.   Their news-gathering activities
were originally organized through their widely scattered mercantile and financial holdings all over Europe for their own
intelligence purposes, but eventually they gave permission to
a firm of scriveners in Augsburg to make and sell copies.
They are the only manuscript news-letters which seem to
have been preserved in any quantity and collections are said
to exist at the National Library of Vienna covering the years
1588 to 1605, and at the Vatican Library covering the years
1554 to 1571. (11)

    In London contractors seem usually to have under-
taken to send weekly letters to subscribers in the provinces.
When Sir Roger L'Estrange was given the monopoly of is-

suing parliamentary reports after the Restoration in England, Henry Muddiman who had held the position until 1663, retained his privilege of distributing manuscript news-letters, a privilege which he preferred since it had the advantage of being free from licensing and was a much more profitable enterprise.   Muddiman charged his subscribers 5 ₺ a year for these services, which was a high price to pay for news services when we consider that it was the equivalent of about 40 to 50 ₺ today.  (12)   Communication of the same type as the manuscript news-letter persist even today in the news and advisory services which are issued for special groups of subscribers.

Some of the printed periodicals of the 17th and 18th centuries actually had their origins in manuscript news-letters.   One example is the newspaper issued by August Hermann Francke, one of the many German scholars who in the 18th century also published learned newspapers.   His 'Hallische Zeitung," which was one of the important news-papers of the 18th century, originated as a manuscript news-letter which was issued from 1704 to 1707 as the 'Hallische Christliche Correspondenz." (13)   Some of the early special periodicals such as Houghton's "Collection for the Improvement of Husbandry and Trade,*" which was probably the first agricultural periodical to be issued, resembled the manuscript news-letter in both form and in content.

As late as 1754 Pierre Rousseau who later became the editor of one of the most successful periodical publishing enterprises of the 18th century, earned part of his livelihood by acting as a correspondent for the Elector Palatinate from Paris at the same time that he was one of the editors of the Parisian newspaper, "Les Affiches de Paris."  This implies that the current scientific and literary periodicals were not keeping their publics adequately supplied with the sort of information they desired and that it was necessary to have recourse to other means to obtain it.

> It was the epoch in which the petty princes of Germany appeared zealous for Parisian literary news and rivaled each other in trying to see who could be the best and most quickly informed. (14)

This kind of correspondence however bears a closer relationship to the learned letter than it does to the manuscript news-letter.

The primary medium available to scholars for the communication of ideas before the appearance of the periodi-

cal was personal correspondence. This was not the sort of
correspondence that is contained in personal letters sent today, although many of the scholars as a result of their education outside of their own countries or their travels abroad
were personally acquainted with the recipients of their letters. The erudite letter was used more as a form of exchange for ideas and news of the learned world, as well as
a form of primary "publication." Leibniz, for example,
wrote a complete treatise on philosophy in one of a series of
letters to one of the young German princesses. The correspondence of the scholars of this period, says Sigerist,
served as a place where new ideas could be developed and
critically examined before they were committed to the record,
which in the days before the periodical was either the printed
book or pamphlet, and it continued to play this role throughout the 18th century. Sigerist continues:

> When a scientist made a discovery in the 18th cen-
> tury, he did not publish it immediately but described
> it in a letter written in Latin that was sent to some
> friends abroad. They in turn would discuss these
> letters with their students and colleagues, would re-
> peat the experiments described and report what their
> experience had been. After a discovery had been
> tested in such a way, it might then be published either
> in a monograph or in the transactions of an academy.
> (15)

While there does not seem to have been any commercial
traffic in the erudite letter except for that news of the learned
world which might have found their way into the manuscript
news-letters, they were sometimes based on a sort of barter
or trade in kind. One scholar would write to another offer-
ing to send him the news from his particular part of the
world in exchange for similar services. These letters were
sometimes circulated and read abroad in very much the same
manner as the manuscript news-letters.

Throughout the period preceding the introduction of
the periodical and even later in the history of the sciences
there appeared men who constituted themselves, or else appeared to be selected because of their wide acquaintance or
industry, as centers of information of groups of members
of the Republic of Letters in various parts of the world.
Among the outstanding men of this character in the 17th century was the French cleric Père Marin Mersenne (1588-
1648) whom Sergescu calls "the secretary general of learned
Europe" and the most important animator of the scientific
movement of his time. His correspondents included some

of the most important scientists of his day:   Gassendi, Des-
cartes, Fermat, Galileo, Torricelli and others. (16)  In
England his correspondents included Sir Kenelm Digby, the
Duke of Newcastle, William Petty and Theodore Haak, all
men who were instrumental in the foundation of the Royal
Society. (17)   The extent of Mersenne's activities in this
field is indicated in the three volumes of his published cor-
respondence the final volume of which appeared in 1946. (18)
Another figure who played a similar role in France was
Nicolas-Claude Peiresc (1580-1637) whom Brown called the
chief link between the early academies of Italy and those of
France. (19)  He numbered among his correspondents beside
Mersenne, Gassendi, Dupuys, Naudé and Camden.

Theodore Haak (1605-1690) who was one of Mersenne's chief correspondents in England exemplified the important role that the emigré has played throughout the history of science, and which they have continued to play to
this day.   Leaving the countries of their birth for reasons
of religious or political intolerance, or to seek more favorable professional opportunities, they have brought with them
a knowledge of foreign languages and of the developments in
sciences and arts, and thus have contributed greatly to the
transmission of ideas.   They became even more important
with the breakdown of the unity of the humanistic world and
the development of nationalistic states, although there grew
up in the sphere of the sciences a sort of internationalism
which replaced the unity which was brought to an end by the
Reformation.   This internationalism was embodied in the
figurative and extranational state which was designated the
Republic of Letters.

Haak was born in Worms of Calvinist parents and
came to England at the age of twenty.   He is known chiefly
for his translation of the Dutch bible into English and for his
association with the early activities which led eventually to
the formation of the Royal Society.   Harcourt Brown in his
study of the predecessors of the Académie des Sciences has
unearthed enough evidence to

> ...justify the assumption that Haak was a correspond-
> ing secretary of the group, that his knowledge of lan-
> guages and the continent served not only himself but
> his friends.   These exchanges were not so much the
> letters of personal friends discussing topics of mutual
> interest as the news-letters of unofficial secretaries
> of informal societies prosecuting similar designs.
> Here is clear evidence of a systematic exchange of
> scientific news between Paris and London twenty years

and more before the Royal Society set up its Committee for Foreign Correspondence. (20)

Another German emigré who was perhaps even more
important in the transmission of intelligence was Samuel
Hartlib (1600-1662). He was active in the contemporary
movements for the improvement of education and was a member of the group that was instrumental in bringing Comenius
to England to attempt to introduce his educational reforms.
He was a man of wide acquantanceship both in England and
on the continent. The Governor of Connecticut, John Win-
throp, who was one of the first of the American colonists
who became a member of the Royal Society called him "the
great Intelligencer of Europe." (21) It is interesting to note
that Hartlib was also involved in an unsuccessful attempt to
establish an information agency in London on the model of
that of Theophraste Renaudot in Paris. (22) Robert Boyle's
first published work appeared in a collection of Hartlib's
letters. This essay is first mentioned in a letter which
Boyle wrote to Hartlib and which is dated 8 May 1647. In
it Boyle thanks Hartlib for a "receipt for the stone" from
which both he and Hartlib's wife seem to have suffered, and
promises Hartlib "an epistle I have drawn up to persuade men
to communicate all those successful receipts, that relate
either to the preservation or recovery of our health."
Boyle's letter which is reprinted in full in the article by
Rowbottom who unearthed this work, is a plea against secre-
cy in medicine. The burden of the plea is largely on arguments of Christian virtue. It was not published by Hartlib,
however, until the appearance of his "Chymical, Medicinal,
and Chyrurgical Addresses Made to Samuel Hartlib Esquire,"
London, 1655. (23)

John Collins (1624-1683), an English civil servant,
who despite his humble origins became a friend and counsel-
lor of a number of his distinguished contemporaries, acted
as a clearing house for news in London. He numbered a-
mong his correspondents, Newton and Wallis. He received
and answered inquiries and undertook to purchase books especially from the continent for those of his friends who found
it necessary to be absent from London. One of the biogra-
phers of Newton calls him "...an amateur scholar so en-
thusiastic and eager in the cultivation of correspondence that
he became the scientific gazette of his time." (24) Some of
his correspondence is included in the Macclesfield collection
of the correspondence of scientific men which was published
in 1841 under the editorship of S. P. Rigaud, (25) but it was
also published during his lifetime under the auspices of the
Royal Society. One of the reasons that the Society under-

took to publish his letters, according to contemporary reviews of the correspondence, was to strengthen Newton's
claims of priority over Leibniz in the discovery of the cal-
culus.    A review of his "Commercium Epistolicum D. Joannis Collins" (26) appeared in 1714 in Le Clerc's "Bibliothèque ancienne et moderne.*"    In the review it is stated
that the correspondence was published by the Royal Society
in order to show that Newton was the first to discover the
method of fluxions.  (27)   This view is confirmed by another
article which appeared in the same year:   "Remarques in-
serées dans le Journal de Novembre-Décembre 1713 sur le
différend entre MM.    Leibniz and Newton sur l'invention du
Calcul différentiel."   The author of this article also states
that the "Commercium Epistolicum" was published at the order of the Royal Society in 1712 in order to prove con-
clusively that Newton was the originator of the method.  (28)
We learn from Collins' correspondence that he was concerned over the slowness of communication.   He mentioned
in one of his letters two books which had, he says, been in
existence over six years before either he or Dr. Wallis had
been able to learn of them.   He discussed the difficulty of
finding publishers for scientific treatises and proposed to
remedy the situation by undertaking to publish some of them
himself. (29)

        The role of correspondence in the history of this
period is eloquently expressed by Morgan in her study of the
"Journal des Sçavans:"

        In this period the news of the capitals was not cried
        out in the streets of the provinces by means of news-
        papers.   At a time when ideas were advancing with
        such rapidity the universal desire to march with them
        seemed to be hindered by barriers of time and space.
        The scholars of the 16th and 17th centuries, however,
        derived advantages from this difficulty.   Their let-
        ters became the lines which joined Paris and the prov-
        inces of France with Europe.  (30)

This voluminous correspondence provides us with one of the
major sources for the history of science in the period before
the scientific periodical became established as a medium for
the communication of new ideas.    That they were written
with an eye on posterity rather than solely for the information or entertainment of their recipients is shown by the number of them which were published during the lifetimes of their
writers, although many of them remained buried in official
archives and family papers until they were resurrected by
editors of the 19th and 20th centuries.    Thus the Danish

scholar and physician Thomas Bartholin, who was responsible for one of the earliest medical and scientific periodicals, published five volumes of his correspondence and would
have published three more except for the fact that his manuscripts were accidentally burned in 1670. (31)

    This "commerce in letters" was greatly stimulated by
the formation of the official scientific academies in which a
part of the administrative organization was devised to solicit,
receive and respond to the letters of correspondents.   Committees were formed in many instances for this very purpose, but the duties generally devolved upon an overburdened
secretary.   Henry Oldenbourg (1615-1677) who was one of
these secretaries was another one of the emigrés who contributed to communication between England the the continent.
He was born near Bremen and, after several periods of
residence in England from 1640 onward, finally established
himself in London permanently in 1654.   He traveled extensively on the continent as a tutor of the nephew of Robert
Boyle, visited the many informal groups in Paris and elsewhere which were assembling for discussions of the new philosophy, and stored up a list of acquaintances among the scientists which was later to stand him in good stead as a correspondent for the Royal Society.   He corresponded at length
with Robert Boyle and many of the details of his activities
as the secretary of the Royal Society and as an editor of the
"Philosophical Transactions" are to be found in Boyle's published correspondence.   Despite his lack of scientific training and Hooke's low opinion of his knowledge of "philosophic
matters" he joined the Royal Society in 1660 when it was still
in the process of formation and soon became responsible for
its correspondence.   In 1666 he became one of the first of
the three paid officials of the Society.   In the early years of
his secretaryship, he describes his duties as follows:

> The business of the Sec. of the R.S.   He attends con-
> stantly the Meetings both of the Society and Council,
> noteth the observables said, done there, digesteth
> them in private, takes care to have them entered in
> the Journal and register-books.   Reads over and cor-
> rects all entries, solicites performances of taskes
> recommended and undertaken, writes all letters a-
> broad, and answeres the returns made to them, enter-
> taining a correspondence with at least fifty persons,
> employs a great deal of time, and makes much pains
> in satisfying Forreign demands about philosophical
> matters, disperseth far and neare, store of direction
> and inquiries for the Society's purpose and sees them
> recommended.   Query: Whether such a person ought

to be left unassisted. (32)

A part of the official activities at the meetings of the scientific academies, and this practice continued throughout the 18th century, was the reading of letters received from the societies' correspondents.  In many of the societies there was a class of membership designated as correspondent which included individuals selected in various classes of the sciences from various parts of the world who were commissioned to pass on news of scientific activities in their areas. While the academy members attending the meetings were thus informed about the correspondence received, the secretary was also under an obligation to inform those who could not attend all the meetings.  Brown points out how this state of affairs could easily lead to the development of labor-saving devices.

> It quickly became apparent to anyone who undertook such work that he spent much time in needless copying off the same news and views for his widely scattered correspondents.  To this defect in the system by which he was forced to work, the answer was clear; the printing press had already rendered the making of books in quantity a simple matter; the printing press would save labor by multiplying his letters endlessly.

> Other devices to help the correspondent were talked of and used in this age of invention and discovery: Petty's system of double and multiple writing; a means of printing without a press in which Huyghens was later interested; perhaps most radical of all, the numerous systems of shorthand invented in England, which could be used not only to steal plays in the theatre and sermons in church, but to speed up the process of writing reports for friends abroad.  The century saw a notable purification of spelling and the printed forms of words; increasing communication by letter had the effect of simplifying the handwriting of the Renaissance, so that by the middle of the century most of the letter-writers were using a limited number of abbreviations and a still more drastically reduced number of alternative letters.

> But what the secretarial correspondent had been able to do in his own field of hand-writing was still not enough; he sought a wider public, a public that the hand-written letter could not reach.  The models he had were limited; in addition to the Gazette, already

a European institution, and his own letter, there was
the quarto pamphlet of opinion or erudition, such as
the recent "Lettres écrits a un Provincial par un de
ses amis," published at intervals, sometimes weekly,
by Blaise Pascal. (33)

The direct ancestry of the erudite letter to the learned
journal and the justice of Prutz' remark that the "Journal des
Sçavans" and the "Acta Eruditorum" were a "...public correspondence...in which the scholars of Europe exchanged their
experiences and discoveries with one another" (34) is made
clear by an examination of the contents of the early scholarly
periodicals. Many of the communications that appear there
are in the form of letters, either sent directly to the editor
or else conveyed to him by the recipient of the letter, who
is acknowledged in the publication as often as the letter-
writer himself. The form of the first medical journal issued in the vernacular is that of a series of letters addressed to a provincial physician much in the same style as
the "Lettres" of Pascal. (35) Guitard in his study of pharmaceutical journalism mentions as a possible predecessor to the
"Miscellanea Curiosa Medico-Physica," a publication issued
in Germany before 1670 which was entitled "Epistolae Medi-
cinales Diversorum Authorum" and which was composed entirely of medical letters. (36) Giovanni Battista Morgagni
(1682-1771), whose "De Sedibus et Causis Morborum per
Anatomen Indagatis" is considered the first modern work in
Pathology, published his book in 1761 in the form of a series
of letters to a friend. The letter continued to hold its prominence throughout the entire period of the Enlightenment, and
journals were issued throughout the 18th century with titles
that clearly indicate their origins. Camusat, one of the
earliest historians of the "Journal des Sçavans," was one of
the editors of the "Lettres Serieuses et Badines sur les
Ouvrages des Savants," which appeared at La Haye from 1729
to 1740. Between 1750 and 1751 there was published at Hamburg the "Gesammelter Briefwechsel der Gelehrten, die zum
Wachstum der Wissenschaften...in eine sogenante corre-
spondirende Gesellschaft zusammen getreten." (37) As late
as 1786 there was issued in Halle the "Medicinischer Briefwechsel,*" which, despite its title, did not differ considerably in content and format from contemporary medical periodicals.

Paralleling the increase in scholarly correspondence
as a stimulus to the development of the periodical, is the increase in the number of books which had been taking place
steadily since the introduction of printing. These two stimuli
resulted in two basic genre of publication, one represented

by the "Philosophical Transactions*" which from the beginning was devoted primarily to the reporting of scientific
news and observations, and the other by the "Journal des
Scavans*" which was primarily a book-reviewing medium.
The close relationship between the book trade and the new
periodical form of publication has been adequately demonstrated by S.B. Barnes in his study of the learned journal
between 1665 and 1730, (38) but a glance at some of the statistics on the magnitude of the increase in book production in
this period may give us a better understanding of just how
great the stimulus was.

Book production statistics even today are generally
cited with some reservations as to their accuracy, and esti-
mates provided in the literature about output in the past are
perhaps even more open to question.  However, Krieg in his
history of book-prices provides us with the following figures
for book production from 1450: (39)

| | |
|---|---|
| 1450-1500 | 40,000 |
| 1501-1600 | 57,000 |
| 1601-1700 | 250,000 |
| 1701-1800 | 2,000,000 |

To demonstrate the impact of the Reformation on the growth
of printing in Germany he shows that whereas the average
number of titles issued in Germany from 1480 to about 1490
was 40 a year, and while there was little change in these
figures until 1507, the years following 1518 show a striking
increase: (40)

| | |
|---|---|
| 1518 | 71 |
| 1519 | 111 |
| 1520 | 208 |
| 1523 | 498 |

The increase is even more strikingly demonstrated when we
translate into yearly averages the figures which Peignot (41)
gives for hundred year periods:

| | | | | |
|---|---|---|---|---|
| 1436-1536 | Average per year | | | 420 |
| 1536-1636 | " | " | " | 5,750 |
| 1636-1736 | " | " | " | 12,250 |
| 1736-1816 | " | " | " | 22,500 |

These figures enable us also to provide an answer to the
question about the effect on book production of the increase
in the number of periodicals in the 18th century.  The answer
is similar to that provided by contemporary studies of the

effects of the introduction of new communications media on those already in existence, where it has been indicated that the new media usually have the effect of increasing the audience for the older media.

In the first place, a study of the literature of the 17th century seems to indicate that the journal probably was not accepted as a definitive form of publication and that scholars frequently gathered together their scattered journal contributions into the form of a book. This parallels in a fashion the current lack of acceptance of the "unpublished report" which is also regarded in most scientific circles as a form of preliminary publication. One example of this attitude is the collection of papers on the comparative anatomy of the intestines which Nehemiah Grew (1641-1712) issued in London in 1676 and which consisted in large part of the papers which he had read before the Royal Society. Nor did the journal immediately supplant the book as a preferred place of publication of short articles. Throughout the 17th and 18th centuries the publication of short articles in the form of pamphlets continued. Some insight into the relative importance of the book and journal in this period might be gained by an analysis of the citations which appeared in some of the books and journals articles. However, the style of scientific writing was a good deal less standardized then than it is today, and a citation analysis would probably provide even less of a reflection of the sources used than it does today.

The increase in book production resulted in two parallel attempts to bring the new and larger mass of material under control. One was the attempt by the booksellers to provide greater publicity for the output of their presses, and the other was the attempt by scholars to organize these materials for their own use. (42) That commercial motivations are sometimes stronger than intellectual ones is demonstrated by the fact that the booksellers were the first to issue periodical reports of the new books being issued. The periodic nature of these reports grew out of the fact that they were issued to coincide with the great fairs held at Frankfort and Leipzig which throughout the 17th and 18th centuries dominated the European book market. These periodically issued lists of books, called "Messkataloge," appeared at Frankfort between 1564 and 1749 and at Leipzig, which later supplanted Frankfort as the principal book center, from 1594 to 1660. They appeared semi-annually to coincide with the Easter and the Christmas Fairs. The "Messkataloge" represent another one of the antecedent forms of publication which suggested the element of periodicity to the scientific journal.

Another early form of periodical publication associated with the commercial fairs that deserves mention here
because it is one of the antecedents of the newspaper as well
as of the periodical.   These are the "Messrelationen" which
first appeared in Cologne in 1583.   They were first issued
by Michael von Aitzing, an Austrian gentleman who married
into the Fugger family.   He printed two volumes a year to
be sold at the Frankfort fairs.   For the first few years he
confined himself largely to reporting the news of Cologne and
the surrounding area, but after 1588 he enlarged his news
coverage to include an account of the military and political
events that were taking place all over Europe.   Aitzing continued the publication until his death in 1598 but he had many
imitators in Europe who carried on the tradition.   In 1597
the Emperor Rudolph II charged certain printers selected by
him with the responsibility of publishing each month a report of the events of the previous thirty days, and shortly
thereafter weekly journals were started up.   Only two years
before this the Emperor had arranged with Leonhard von
Taxis to organize a courier system, and it was surely more
than just a coincidence that the weekly interval of publication
coincided with the departure of the postal courier from the
imperial cities.  (43)

Another antecedent form of publication which also contributed toward the element of periodicity is the class of
publications called calendars, almanacs or ephemerides.
These terms are all related etymologically to the concept of
journal or diary and the characteristic which they have in
common is that they were all issued annually.   In the 18th
century these terms were frequently used to designate annual
publications which were indistinguishable from periodicals,
although they came later to be used for  more distinctive
types of literature.   They usually contained three different
types of information, lists of days of the year, scraps and
fragments of advice on matters of health and husbandry, and
collections of astronomical and meteorological data.   In the
period preceding the introduction of the scientific periodical
some of these publications can be regarded as periodicals in
embryo since they contained collections of miscellaneous information.

The first printed calendars go back almost to the beginnings of printing.   Lombard (44) in his analysis of the
medical content of the Swiss folk calendar in the 18th and
19th centuries cites as the first Swiss calendar the "Compost
et Calendrier des Bergiers" issued in 1497.   This may be
either a variant or a predecessor of a French calendar with
a long history which was issued throughout the 17th and 18th

centuries, "Le Grand Calendrier et Compost des Bergers."
Grand-Carteret who lists it in his bibliography says that it
appeared in Paris from 1600 but adds that it is known to
have appeared in the 16th century as well. (45)   In the
words of its title it contained such matter as "...the anatomy of the entire human body, the art and science of phle-
botomy, the regimen and health of the body...regulations
for the shepherd, how he must cure his sheep of the diseases which prevent their survival..." It included also
brief aphorisms relating to health and hygiene interspersed
with quatrains in both French and Latin.

Lombard cites an earlier publication than the "Compost et Calendrier" which was called the "Kungsberger Kal-
ender" and which appeared in 1476 and for some thirty years
thereafter.   It sold for twelve "Goldgulder," a high price for
those days.   However, they could not all have been so
costly, because Goldfriedrich in his study of the early German booktrade cites an author writing at the turn of the
17th century who says that there is no farmer so poor that
he does not each year buy a calendar. (46)   Many of the
calendars were confined to listing the days of the year and
giving the feast days and civil holidays, but the farther back
we go in their history the more they appear to be compilations of medical rules and precepts.   Many of the editors
of the early calendars and almanacs were physicians who
were also followers of astrology, and others were mathematicians or teachers.   One of Kepler's early activities,
made necessary by his difficulties in gaining a livelihood,
involved the compilation of such calendars.   In 1599 he wrote
to the Bavarian Chancellor, Kerwart von Hohenburg:

> If I occasionally write horoscopes and calendars, it is
> to me, by God, a highly tedious form of slavery, but
> a necessary one, in order that I eventually may be
> free and not have to occupy myself with such dis-
> graceful drudgery.   But now in order to obtain an an-
> nual wage and to keep my title and my house, I must
> comply with such foolish impertienences. (47)

It must have been a fairly lucrative form of employment.   The physician and astronomer Rudolf Buchback is
known to have received thirty-five Thaler a year for his work
on the calendars which appeared in the first part of the 17th
century. (48)

Another indication of the relationship between the early
calendars and the scientific periodical of the 17th century was
the occurence of accounts of monstrosities in both these

forms.  As late as 1781 the "Schriebkalender Schaffhausen"
gave account of a bearded lady whose ears hung down to her
shoulders, and the "Hinkende Merkurius" of 1783 devoted
some space to the description of a woman allegedly born of
mixed parentage at Lisbon, who was literally half white and
half black, since she was divided vertically in this manner.
(49)  There was also considerable emphasis on common
sense health rules.  The slogan "health is the greatest trea-
sure" was constantly reiterated.  Such items as lists of di-
agnostic signs were included, for example the relationship
between the color of the blood and the state of health which
was listed in the "Schreibkalendar" published in Baden in
1673.  Many of the publications were wholly astrological in
character, for example, the large number of almanacs which
appeared in London in the period following 1660, (50) but
others can be considered valid and important astronomical
publications.  The "Ephemerides ad Meridianum Vindobonen-
sem" which appeared under the editorship of Maximillian
Hell (1720-1792) from 1757 to 1793 contained many original
astronomical articles as well as reprints of articles appearing in other journals. (51)  The term "ephemerides" was
frequently applied in the 18th century to the proceedings of
learned societies, just as the term almanac was applied to
scientific periodicals which were published independently,
but other publications continued to carry on the functions
earlier associated with these terms.

　　　All the preceding classes of publication and methods
of disseminating information, the manuscript, the printed
newsletter, learned correspondence, the fair catalog and the
almanac, contributed elements to the early scientific periodical, but the publication which contributed most significantly
to the forms and functions which the scientific periodical
developed and which it has retained to the present was the
newspaper.  The newspaper had a long prehistory much of
which was the same as that of the periodical, but it did not
appear in a form recognizable to us until the beginnings of
the 17th century.  Claims of priority are sometimes made
for the "Gazette" which was first issued by Theophraste
Renaudot in 1631. (52)  These claims seem to be based on
its quality and significance, however, rather than on the
allegation that it had no predecessors.  Without going back
to God or Solomon, as Prutz accuses Kaspar von Stieler of
doing, or even to the "Acta Diurna" of the Romans, we find
that soon after the introduction of printing there appeared
publications that resemble newspapers in that their function
was to disseminate news.  These "feuilles volantes," "Flug-
blätter," or "fly sheets" were separately printed brochures
each usually with its own title.  They each dealt usually

with a single event in politics or in nature, battles, monstrous births, volcanos, etc. In the 16th century they were called "relations," "nouvelles" and "lettres discours" in France. We find these terms recurring in the titles of the early periodicals. The regular dispensing of news in this period was still probably in the hands of the scriveners and correspondents who issued the manuscript newsletters. Because of the regularly scheduled departures of the postal couriers the manuscript newsletter did develop some regularity of issue. Thus we have existing in many of the countries of Europe, periodicity without print as represented by the manuscript newsletter, and print without periodicity in the form of the "fly sheet." (53) It was but a short step to the union of print and periodicity to form the early newspapers.

The first newspaper is said to have appeared at Anvers in 1605 but printed newspapers appeared in many of the other countries of Europe at about the same time, at Strasbourg and Augsburg in 1609, at Hamburg in 1616, Antwerp in 1619, Braunschweig and Vienna in 1623. The first English newspaper, which appeared in 1622, confined itself entirely to the copying of foreign news, and the first printed newspaper of domestic news did not appear until 1641. (54) The practice of copying freely from other periodical publications which was established early in the history of the newspaper was carried on throughout the 18th century in both the general and the learned press as we shall see later. Items of scientific interest may have appeared in some of these early newspapers, for instance, in the "Relation," a newspaper printed at Strasbourg in 1609, there is an item dated from Venice, September 4, which states that Professor Galileo of Padua has devised a telescope and that the Venetian authorities had raised his salary in consequence. (55) Priestly in his "Vision, Light and Colours" (London, 1772) describes the way in which Galileo first learned of the existence of this ingenious device:

> About April or May, in 1609, it was reported at Venice, where Galileo (who was a professor of Mathematics in the University of Padua) then happened to be, that a Dutchman had presented to Count Maurice of Nassau, a certain optical instrument, by means of which, distant objects appeared as if they were near; but no farther account of the discovery reached that place, though this was near twenty years after the first discovery. (56)

Without thoroughly investigating all the particulars it is im-

possible to pass judgment on the significance of these two
accounts.

Theophraste Renaudot (1586-1653) whose statue shares
with that of Charlemagne and Henry IV the honor of being on
the "Ile de la Cité" in the center of Paris, is one of the
most interesting figures of the first part of the 17th century.
Allen calls him "...a 20th century mind wrestling with the
problems of the 17th century." (57)  He was born in Loudon,
the same town which had been the birthplace of Richelieu
whose favor he enjoyed during his entire career in Paris.
The "Gazette" which Renaudot inaugurated in 1631 under
Richelieu's protection was the least original of his innovations.   He was an early social reformer, and among his
many proposals was the suggestion that the poor be employed by the city to keep the streets clean.  It may have
been in connection with his interest in finding employment
for the citizens of Paris that he began his "Bureau d'adresse,
which was a sort of information agency, or, as he himself
expressed it, a place where "everyone could give and receive information about all the commodities and necessities
of life and human society." (58)  He later added a "Bureau
de vent à grace" which was organized for the purpose of
dispensing charity and which are considered the origin of
what were later known in France as the "Monts-de-pieté."
He was active in medical reforms, being a physician in addition to his other activities.   He sought to organize a
school of medicine with a program at variance with the con-
ventional methods of training conducted by the Medical Faculty of Paris.  He began a series of conferences at his
"Bureau d'adresse" which are considered by some historians
as one of the first of the scientific academies.   These conferences, however, were all of a rather popular nature and
should be considered rather as one of the first forums organized for public education. (59)  He incurred the wrath of
the Parisian Faculty by establishing a public clinic in Paris
to provide free medical service.  With the death of Richelieu and the loss of his support at court, Renaudot was tried
on an action brought by the Faculty and forbidden to practice
medicine.  He was required to close his "Bureau" and his
free clinic, but he was permitted to continue to issue the
'Gazette," a monopoly which he passed down to his sons.
Richelieu's sponsorship of the "Gazette" is usually attributed
to his recognition of the political and social potentialities of
the press and his attempts by these means to keep the press
under state control.   That Renaudot himself had different
ideas about the nature of the press is shown by his statement
which is frequently quoted in support of press freedom: "The
newspaper partakes of the nature of a raging stream in that

it is increased by resistance." (60)

From the beginning the newspaper reported scientific news and this function of the newspaper has been carried over into our own day in which we find news of scientific developments sometimes reported in our dailies before it appears in the scientific journals.  This creates difficulties in scientific communication because newspapers are generally considered outside the usual channels and are not taken into account by the scientific bibliographic apparatus.  Although periodicity, as it will appear later, was not a strong characteristic of the early journals, they did attempt to model themselves on the newspaper by appearing at regular intervals.  The characteristic of periodicity adopted by the scientific periodical to a large extent determined the role it was to play.  It made the journal predominantly a vehicle for the communication of scientific information rather than a repository of scientific knowledge.  One of the problems of regularity of issue was that of finding an adequate pay-load for the vehicle.  Henry Fielding, who was himself for a time a practicing journalist, states the problem in his "Tom Jones" in a somewhat different context than ours, but still with relevance to our problem:

> Such histories as these do, in reality, much resemble
> a newspaper, which consists of just the same number
> of words, whether there be any news in it or not.
> They may likewise be compared to a stagecoach, which
> performs constantly the same course, empty as well
> as full. (6)

The primary purpose of the newspaper from its very origins was that of providing the news.  As we shall see in the analysis which follows this was also to a considerable extent the function of the scientific periodical in the 17th and 18th centuries.  Since the audiences for the newspaper and the scientific periodical did not differ then in the degree in which they differ today, the newspaper may have provided an adequate prototype for the development of scientific communication in that period.

## Notes

(1)     Betty T. Morgan, "Histoire du Journal Sçavans depuis
        1665 jusqu'en 1701" (Paris: Presses Universitaires,
        1929), p. 17.

(2)     A. F. Harlow, "Old Post Bags" (New York: Appleton

and Co., 1928), pp. 14-15.

(3)     Werner Storz, "Die Anfange der Zeitungskunde"
        (Halle: E. Klinz, 1931).

(4)     Garrison, op. cit., p. 293.

(5)     Weill, op. cit., p. 18.

(6)     Harlow, op. cit., pp. 67-68.

(7)     Storz, op. cit., p. 26.

(8)     Harlow, op. cit., p. 139.

(9)     Hatin, op. cit., p. 363.

(10)    Gerhardt Menz, "Die Zeitschrift, ihre Entwicklung
        und ihre Lebensbedingungen" (Stuttgart: Poeschel Ver-
        lag, 1928), p. 9.

(11)    A translation of part of these letters appeared in
        English under the title:  "The Fugger News Letters
        Being a Selection of Unpublished Letters from Corre-
        spondents of the House of Fugger during the Years
        1568-1605" (New York: G. P. Putnam's Sons, 1924).

(12)    Harold Herd, "The March of Journalism" (London:
        Allen and Unwin, 1952), p. 33.

(13)    Storz, op. cit., p. 47.

(14)    G. Charlier and R. Mortier, "Le Journal Encyclo-
        pédique" (Paris:  Libraire Nizet, 1952), p. 13.

(15)    Henry E. Sigerist, "Nationalism and Internationalism
        in Medicine," "Bulletin of the History of Medicine,"
        XXI (1747), 12.  He adds that the discontinuation of
        this practice has been detrimental to scientific com-
        munication.  "In the 19th century and in the 20th cen-
        tury still more, the ease with which a paper could be
        published made it very tempting to announce an obser-
        vation or the results of an experiment before they even
        had been tested."

(16)    P. Sergescu, "Mersenne l'Animateur," "Revue d'His-
        toire des Sciences," II (1948), 6.

(17)    Dorothy Stimson, "Hartlib, Haak and Oldenbourg:

Intelligencers," "Isis," XXXI (1939-1940), 309-326.

(18)   Mme Paul Tannery (ed.), "Correspondence du Père Marin Mersenne, Religieux Minimé" (Paris, Beauchesne, 1933-1946).

(19)   Harcourt Brown, "Scientific Organizations in Seventeenth Century France" (Baltimore: Williams and Wilkins, 1934), p. 44.

(20)   Brown, op. cit., p. 44.

(21)   Syfret, op. cit., p. 97.

(22)   M.E. Rowbottom, "The Earliest Published Writing of Robert Boyle," "Annals of Science," VI (1950), 376-389.

(23)   Lyons, op. cit., p. 14.

(24)   L.T. More, "Isaac Newton, a Biography" (New York: Scribner, 1934), pp. 68-69.

(25)   S.P. Rigaud, "Correspondence of Scientific Men of the 17th Century" (Oxford, 1841).

(26)   London, 1712.

(27)   Amsterdam, II (1714), 61.

(28)   "Journal Littéraire," La Haye, IV (1714), 319-358.

(29)   More, op. cit., p. 140.

(30)   Morgan, op. cit., p. 27

(31)   "Epistolarum medicinalum" (Hafniae, 1663-1667).

(32)   Lyons, op. cit., p. 46.

(33)   Brown, op. cit., p. 186.

(34)   E.H. Lehmann, "Einführung in die Zeitschriftenkunde" (Leipzig: Hiersemann, 1936), p. 180, citing R. Prutz, "Neue Schriften zur deutschen Litteratur-und Kulturgeschichte," I (1841), 13.

(35)   Blegny's "Nouvelles Déscouvertes en Médecine.

(36)    Eugene Guitard, "Deux Siècles de la Presse aux Ser-
        vice de la Pharmacie" (Paris: Parmacie Centrale,
        1913), p. 25.

(37)    Kirchner, op. cit., No. 693.    Not located in the
        U.S.

(38)    S.B. Barnes, op. cit.

(39)    W. Krieg, "Materialien zu einer Entwicklungsges-
        chichte der Bücher-preise" (Vienna: Stubenrauch,
        1953), p. 70.

(40)    Ibid., pp. 222-223.

(41)    Gabriel Peignot, "Manuel du Bibliophile" (Dijon: V.
        Legier, 1823).

(42)    Estelle Brodman, "The Development of Medical Bib-
        liography" (Baltimore: Medical Library Association,
        1954).    A study of these efforts in the field of medi-
        cal literature.

(43)    Weill, op. cit., p. 20.

(44)    E. Lombard, "Der Medizinische Inhalt der Schweizer-
        ischen Volkscalender in 18. und 19. Jahrhundert"
        (Zurich: Fussli, 1925).

(45)    John Grand-Carteret, "Les Almanachs Français"
        (Paris: J. Alisie, 1896).

(46)    J. Goldfriedrich, "Geschichte des deutschen Buch-
        handels" (Leipzig: Verlag der Börsenverein, 1908),
        p. 29.

(47)    Krieg, op. cit., p. 80.

(48)    Ibid., p. 83.

(49)    Lombard, op. cit., p. 13.

(50)    See "British Museum Catalogue," under Ephemerides.

(51)    George Sarton, "Vindication of Father Hell," "Isis,"
        XXXV (1944), 97-105.

(52)    L.E. Hatin, "Histoire politique et litteraire de la
        Presse en France" (Paris:   Poulet-Mallassis et de

Broise, 1858), I, x. "These first attempts [at jour-
nalism] appeared simultaneously in different parts of
Europe, but it is France that retains the honor of
having created the first newspaper which truly deserves the name."

(53)  Allen, op. cit., p. 317.

(54)  Ibid., p. 317.

(55)  Ibid., citing L. Salomon, "Geschichte des deutschen
      Zeitungswesens von ersten Anfangen" (Oldenburg,
      1900).

(56)  Cited in More, op. cit., pp. 60-61.

(57)  Allen, op. cit., p. 319.

(58)  L. Dekeyser, "Les Origines de la Presse Médicale,"
      "Bruxelles Médicale," XXIX (1949), 1753.

(59)  See infra.

(60)  Cited in M. Laboulbene, "Histoire du Journalisme
      Medical," "Lancette Français," LIII (1880), 1059.

(61)  Henry Fielding, "The History of Tom Jones" (New
      York: The Modern Library, 1940), p. 40.

Chapter V

Original Publication: The Substantive Journal


The four major components of the scientific serial made their appearance with the first periodicals. These components are: the original contribution, the extract or abstract from other published journals or books, the book review, and the news report. In the analysis that follows the journals are classified under the dominant one of these four elements.

The two major categories into which the journals fall are (1) substantive journals, and (2) society proceedings, which together make up over 80 per cent of the total. The term "substantive" is defined as meaning "not derivative or dependent" and in our classification is confined to those periodicals which included original contributions. Those societies which published their proceedings sometimes also included in their journals other of the components of scientific journalism: book reports, abstracts, and news, so that the two forms, substantive journal and society proceedings have considerable overlap. The distinction is nevertheless important because there were important differences in methods of publication and regularity of issue. There are few purely "substantive" journals on the list; the majority of those journals so classified are composites of all the elements of scientific journalism. The class is probably swelled entirely out of proportion by the fact that those periodicals on which little information could be obtained were placed in this category if their titles did not indicate that they were either reviews or abstract journals.

The early journals can hardly be said to contain scientific contributions in the form of original papers as we know them today. The characteristic form of the scientific paper did not appear until much later in the history of scientific journalism and derives much more influence from the prize essay and the academic dissertation and oration than from the early contributions to the scientific journal. The distinction between authorship and editorship of the early journal is not made very clearly, so that many of the early

Table 1

Types of Scientific Periodicals 1665-1790
Titles Issued Classified by Decade
In Which They Had Their Origin

| | 1665-1699 | 1700-1709 | 1710-1719 | 1720-1729 | 1730-1739 | 1740-1749 | 1750-1759 | 1760-1769 | 1770-1779 | 1780-1790 | Totals | Per cent |
|---|---|---|---|---|---|---|---|---|---|---|---|---|
| Substantive | 20 | 7 | 9 | 11 | 16 | 16 | 40 | 65 | 92 | 225 | 501 | 48 |
| Proceedings | 8 | 2 | 2 | 9 | 10 | 24 | 38 | 38 | 56 | 77 | 264 | 25 |
| Collections | - | - | 1 | - | 3 | 3 | 11 | 9 | 15 | 39 | 81 | 8 |
| Dissertation | - | - | 1 | - | 4 | 4 | 6 | 4 | 11 | 10 | 40 | 4 |
| Abstract | - | 1 | 2 | - | 1 | 2 | 10 | 6 | 4 | 16 | 42 | 4 |
| Review | 2 | 1 | - | - | 1 | - | 5 | 2 | 9 | 20 | 40 | 4 |
| Almanac | 2 | - | - | - | 1 | - | 3 | 3 | 17 | 21 | 47 | 4 |
| All Others[a] | 3 | 1 | 3 | 3 | - | 3 | 6 | 2 | 8 | 8 | 37 | 4 |
| Totals | 35 | 12 | 18 | 23 | 36 | 52 | 119 | 129 | 212 | 416 | 1052 | |

[a]Includes: Collections of prize essays, satires, monographic series, question journals, and unclassified titles.

editors are described in the contemporary literature as authors of their journals. The contributions are presented as extracts from letters, as the observations of a particular individual, or as having been presented at a particular meeting, and frequently without any indication of source at all.

The "Journal des Sçavans,*" and the "Acta Eruditorum*" can be included only because so few other media existed at the time. As shown by Ornstein (1) one fourth to one third of the contents of the "Acta Eruditorum" for 1682-1700 dealt with science.

Henry Justel complained of the lack of scientific content in the "Journal des Sçavans," in a letter dated 27 January 1666, in which he said,

Those who work at our "Journal" are rather Historians than Philosophers, that is why you see nothing in it concerning Physics. In time perhaps they will devote themselves to it. (2)

And again on 7 January 1667:

> You will see in the "Journal" how the ecclesiastics
> have their way, but we may say nothing to that. (3)

Like the "Acta" the "Journal" was primarily a book
reviewing medium.

The difference in the roles played by these early
journals is indicated by E. B. Barnes in his study: "The International Exchange of Knowledge in Western Europe, 1680-
89." 1,243 reviews appeared in the "Journal des Sçavans,"
1,332 in the "Acta Eruditorum," and only 92 in the "Philosophical Transactions" and the "Philosophical Collections."(4)
Philip George (5) found 1898 papers as against 600 accounts
of books in the "Philosophical Translations" for the period
1665 to 1700 and from 1701 to 1749 he found only 94 book reviews as against 2170 papers.  His analysis of the subject
content of the journal indicates the predominantly scientific
character of the "Transactions." (6)  It is interesting to note
that this tendency of the amount of original work reported in
a journal to increase as the reputation of a journal becomes
established has been recognized for later journals as well. (7)

In his dedication to the first volume of the "Transactions" to the Royal Society, Oldenbourg states:

> In these Rude Collections, which are onely the
> Gleanings of my private diversions in broken hours,
> it may appear, that many Minds and Hands are in
> many places industriously employed, under Your
> Countenance and by Your Example, in the pursuit of
> those Excellent Ends, which belong to Your Heroi-
> cal Undertakings.

> Some of these are but Intimations of Large Comple-
> ments.  And some Eminent Members of Your So-
> ciety, have obliged the Learned World with Incom-
> parable Volumes, which are not herein mention'd,
> because they were finisht, and in great Reputation
> abroad, before I entered upon this Taske.  And no
> small Number are at present engaged for those
> weighty Productions, which require both Time and
> Assistance, for their due Maturity.  So that no men
> can from these Glimpses of Light take any just
> Measure of your Performances, or of your Prosecu-
> tions; but every man may perhaps receive some
> benefit from these Parcels, which I guessed to be
> somewhat conformable to your Design.

> This is my solicitude, That, as I ought not to be
> unfaithful to those Counsels you have committed to
> my Trust, so also that I may not altogether waste
> any minutes of the leisure you afford me.  And thus
> have I made the best use of some of them, that I
> could devise; To spread abroad Encouragements,
> Inquiries, Directions, and Patterns, that may ani-
> mate, and draw Universal Assistance.

And again in his "...preface to the Third Year of these
Tracts" which appear in the twenty-third number dated 11
March 1666, he speaks of the contributions as "fragments:"

> Having by Gods Assistance, finish'd my solicitations
> for the Philosophical Transactions of the last years,
> I crave leave to reflect a little upon what hath past.
>
> I think, I may safely assume, that in these frag-
> ments, something hath been contributed to sowe
> such seeds, as may somewhat conduce to the illus-
> tration and improvement of Philosophy, and of all
> Laudable and Useful Arts and Practices.  I hope,
> our Ingenious Correspondents have examin'd all cir-
> cumstances of their communicated Relations, with
> all the care and diligence necessary to be used in
> Collections; not only taking up old Fame, or flying
> Reports, upon too easie Truth; not straining for
> other Kinds of Wonders, than the most Wise Author
> of Nature hath allowed, but attending closely to the
> strict measures of Natural Truth, and to the useful
> contrivances of Art. (8)

The brevity of some of the articles in the early issues of the "Transactions" makes it clear that they are just
news notes or reports which Oldenbourg had picked up from
various sources, e.g. the report of the "Ingenious Mr. Hook"
on "a spot in one of the Belts in Jupiter" who "some months
since" intimated this fact "to a friend of his," occupies some
eight lines. (9)  Some of the articles are clearly extracts
from Oldenbourg's correspondence which he renders in his
own words with his own comments added, e.g. "an Account of
the Improvement of Optick Glasses" which Oldenbourg states
he has through a "Relation" from Paris of a book printed in
Rome "but not transmitted in these parts." (10)  The longest
contribution in the first issue is an abstract of a "printed
paper" sent by the Astronomer Azout to the secretary of the
Royal Society. (11)  There is also "An Account of a Very Odd
Monstrous Calf" which is extracted from a letter sent to Boyle
which he had communicated to the Royal Society.  There are

two contributions from a correspondent who is identified only
as an "Inquisitive Physician" in Germany.   The fact that science was largely a matter for amateurs in the 17th century
and that all classes had entree to the new science is pointed
out by a contribution from "an understanding and hardy Sea-
man" which appears under the heading:   "Of the New American Whale-fishing about the Bermudas." (12)   The source of
the communication is given sometimes as an "Extract of a
letter, written from Rome" (13) and in one case is prefaced
merely with the remark:   "I have received an Account from
very good hands." (14)   The papers delivered before the
Royal Society and the experiments performed there are rendered in Oldenbourg's own words.   Leeuwenhoek's letters
which began to appear in the "Transactions" under Oldenbourg's
editorship were presented in abridged form, and the fact that
Leeuwenhoek himself did not consider this a form of final
publication is attested to by the fact that he had them printed
in book form in his own lifetime in both Dutch and Latin. (15)
In the preface to the tenth number issued 12 March 1666
Oldenbourg states what he thinks is the function of the "Transactions:"

> These Transactions being intended, not only to be
> (by parcels) brief Records of the Emergent Works
> and Productions in the Universe; Of the Mysteries
> of Nature of later discoveries; And of the growth of
> Useful Inventions and Arts; but also and chiefly, to
> sollicite in all parts mutual ayds and Collegiate en-
> deavours for the farther advancement thereof:   We
> shall begin this Second year of our Publication in
> this Kind (in which for 3 months the Printing-
> presses were interrupted by the Publick Calamity)
> with a few more particular Observations upon the
> Balance of the Air, as they are most happily in-
> vented and directed by Mr. Boyle; and deserve to
> be prosecuted with care and diligence in all places.
> (16)

Among the general journals in the 17th century which
fall into the same category as the "Philosophical Transactions"
are the "Miscellanea Curiosa,*" the "Acta Medica et Philosophica,*" and the "Recueil des Mémoires et Conferences sur les
Arts et Sciences.*"   Since they represent some of the earliest
forms of the medium, we shall describe them briefly before
taking up the discussion of the "substantive" journal as a whole.
Although all of the above titles had some association with organized bodies, they are substantially "independent" in that
they were not restricted to reporting the activities of a particular organization.   The last title cited, the "Recueil," rep-

resents a hybrid in which the character of the journal changed
drastically in the middle of its first year.  It demonstrates
some of the difficulties involved in attempting to classify some
of the journals on the list.

The first scientific periodical which appeared in
Germany, the "Miscellanea Curiosa Medico-Physica, Sive
Ephemeridum Medico-Physicarum Germanicarium Curiosarum,"
was issued for the first time in 1670.  Like the "Journal des
Sçavans" and the "Philosophical Transactions" it was associated with the activities of a scientific society.  There seems
to be no basis for the statement of one of the historians of
the society that its publications which he styles "Ephemerides
Germanicae" were the result of discussions held at regular
meetings, (17) and the statement of another that it is the
oldest natural scientific-medical periodical in the world (18)
can be accepted only if one ignores the existence of the
"Philosophical Transactions."

The society which issued the "Miscellanea" was
founded in 1652 as the Collegium Naturae Curiosorum by four
German physicians in Schweinfurt and is probably the oldest
scientific society with a continuous history which is still in
existence.  In 1687 it became the "Academia Caesarea-
Leopoldina Naturae Curiosorum" and finally, in 1922 became
the "K. deutsche Akademie der Naturforscher zu Halle."

At the reorganization of the society in 1670, the
new regulations proposed that a collection of scientific papers
should be published every year, and that each member should
be required to undertake to study some new problem in the
mineral, animal or plant realm and to submit it in writing
for publication in the annual volume.  The regulation stated
further that the publication should also include book reviews
and obituaries of departed members, and that it should be
open to non-members who wished to submit contributions as
well. (19)  In order to encourage contributions from non-
members, the President, Fehr, sent out a circular letter of
invitation to the most distinguished European physicians.
The "Miscellanea" appeared in three series or "Decades," the
first in seven volumes (20) from 1670-1680, the second in
ten volumes, from 1683-1692, and the third in seven volumes
from 1694-1706.  A German translation of the "Miscellanea"
appeared from 1755 to 1771 under the title "Der Römisch-
Kaiserlich Akademie der Naturforscher auserlesene medicini-
sich-chirurgisch-anatomisch-chymisch und botanische Abhandlungen." (21)

The "Miscellanea" was an open medium for contri-

butions from physicians all over Europe is shown by the fact
that of the authors whose contributions were published in the
first ten years 98 were members and 198 were not.

With the next series which began in 1712 under a
changed title, "Ephemerides sive Observationium Medico-Physi
carum," the mode of publication seems to have changed, for
each volume contains two hundred communications, arranged
by hundreds or centuriae. The contributions appear to be arranged in chronological order of receipt, since the first one
is dated 24 December 1705 and the last 12 December 1711.
The first volume therefore seems to fill the gap between the
cessation of the "Miscellanea" and the appearance of the new
series, but indicates also that there was a delay of some six
years before the contributions made in 1705 made their appearance. The entire series contains five volumes, each with two
hundred observations, the last volume appearing in 1722.

The next series, which began in 1727, contain con-
secutively, 250, 209, 182, 150...observations per volume.
They appeared under the title "Acta Physico-Medica Academiae
Caesarae Leopoldino-Carolinae Naturae Curiosorum" in ten
volumes from 1727 to 1754. From 1757 to 1791 they appeared under the title "Nova Acta." They were issued at irregular intervals, with a gap of five years between the first
and second volume, and nine years between the seventh and
eighth, and with intervals of between two and five years in
the other volumes. A selection of three hundred fourteen of
the medical and surgical observations from the "Acta," 1727-
1754, appeared in a German translation by Georg Albrecht
Weinrich in two volumes in 1789-1790 under the title "Auszüge
medicinisch-chirurgischer Beobachtungen aus den neueren
Schriften der K. Akademie der Naturforscher." (22)

One reason, perhaps, why the "Miscellanea and its
successors were content to act as an irregularly issued repository of scientific and medical observations, is the appearance of a publication in 1717 in the same area which undertook some of the other functions of scientific journalism.
The nature of the publication "Sammlung von Natur-und Medizin*" is perhaps best revealed by a translation of its com-
pendious title:

> Collection from nature and medicine, as well as the
> associated craft and literary history which pertain to
> Silesia and other lands; namely in the form of 1)
> daily and periodic changes in the weather, 2) epidem-
> ic and seasonal diseases from month to month ac-
> cording to the atmosphere and weather, 3) the in-

crease and failure of field, forest and garden crops,
and also all sorts of animal products, which are
annually reported in all European countries, as well
as 4) important natural occurences in water, in man
and beast, also 5) the new physical and medical discoveries made known in the above subjects, including
6) those changes which have occurred in the realm
of physical-medical literature. All this brought together in an orderly array with all kinds of reflec-
tions from abundant correspondence and other accounts, as well as in large part from personal experience, and published as an experiment by several
Breslau physicians.

The "Sammlung" was edited for the first six quarterly numbers by Johann Kanold (1679-1729) with the assistance
of two fellow Breslau physicians, and thereafter for the last
thirty-two numbers by Kanold himself. The quarterly issues,
each approximately four hundred pages in length, began with
a survey of weather conditions in the past months in various
parts of the Empire along with the seasonal changes in ill-
nesses and the conditions of the crops; it continued with a
report of unusual natural events in the world, gave an account
of recent discoveries in medicine and other sciences, and
ended with a literary review and news and announcements of
the various scientific societies. It appeared in Breslau,
Leipzig, and Erfurt, and the frequent change of printers indicates to some extent that publication was controlled by its
editors. Kanold attempted to maintain anonymity not only for
contributions to the periodical but even for the editor, until,
as he states in the preface to the third quarterly issue, external events caused him to reveal the names of the editors:

> It is true that we preferred not to present our names
> in the first issue, not because of modesty or fear but
> only to show the entire world that our intentions were
> based on public need rather than an empty desire for
> glory. However, despite all our efforts, our names
> have been made publicly known by other means.
> Therefore, in order that we may not be accused by
> anyone of being ashamed of our defects, or, of mak-
> ing our work appear like a bastard, the anomaly of
> whose birth is established by the concealment of its
> parents' name; and in part also that our learned and
> well-disposed friends may be more assured that it is
> truly the work of our hands, we do not scruple in an-
> nouncing here publicly that our names are indeed those
> which were given in the "Neuen Zeitung von gelehrten
> Sachen," 1717, No. 64, page 516, namely: Dr. Joh.

Kanold, Dr. Joh. George Brunschwitz and Dr. Joh.
Christian Kundmann. Of these the first named who
after having made the proposal for several years,
finally in the first part of 1717 informed the latter
two of it and solicited their cooperation in the project to which they finally agreed. Although the matter remained for some time in abeyance, finally with
the approval of the last two, there was inserted in
the "Miscellanea Lipsiensia," volume 5, page 250, a
prospectus, and then without losing any time set himself to work, although many thought the work imprac-
tical because of its great scope. (23)

Kanold goes on in this preface to state that he had the assistance of many correspondents whose aid he had solicited and
among whom were to be found several noblemen, clergymen,
and various of the "curious" both at home and abroad. All
these contributors merge into the anonymity which Kanold im-
posed on the first issue.

The close association of the "Sammlung" with the
Academia Naturae Curiosorum is borne out by the fact that
the editors of the first numbers cite themselves as "Collectors" which was the title which had been given to the early directors of the "Miscellanea." The last issue of the first volume contains an index for the year consisting of (1) a contents list, and (2) an alphabetical subject index to the contents, illustrating again that authorship was not considered a
primary or an important consideration. After Kanold's death
in 1729, the publication was continued at Erfurt as a monthly
under the editorship of Andreas Elias Büchner (1701-1769) who
issued the fourth and last volume in 1734 shortly before becoming President of the Academia in 1735. It appeared under
the title "Miscellanea Physico-Medico-Mathematica, oder ange-
nehme, curieuse und nutzliche Nachtrichten von physical und
medicinischen auch dahin gehorigen Kunst-und Literatur-Ge-
schichten.*" Although it was published from 1731 to 1754 it
covers the occurrences which took place during the years 1727
to 1730 which suggests again that it was more in the nature
of a compilation of meteorological data and morbidity statistics rather than a scientific periodical, although it also reported on the new literature and disseminated scientific news.
An abridgment of the "Sammlung" appeared in Leipzig in 1750
under the title "Vermischte öconomische Sammlung," and both
series were reprinted in 1736 under the title "Schatz-Kammer
der Natur-und Kunst."

Like the "Miscellanea" of the Collegium Naturae
Curiosorum the "Acta Medica et Philosophica Hafniensia,*"

published in Copenhagen from 1673 to 1680, leaned heavily
toward medicine. Barnes, (24) however, is probably correct
in disagreeing with Lion (25) who calls it the first medical
journal. The "Acta" which appear in translation in the fourth
volume of the "Collection Académique*" deal as much or more
with zoology and botany as they do with medicine. Just as
the "Miscellanea" were largely a vehicle for Sachs, its editor,
the "Acta" provided an outlet for Thomas Bartholin (1616-
1680). Bartholin was the most celebrated physician of his
period in Denmark and perhaps in all of Europe. He was
professor of anatomy at the University of Copenhagen and
later became Dean of its Medical Faculty. The publication
seems also to have associated with the activities of a scientific society, although there seems to be little evidence for
Neuberger's statement that the "Acta" were the proceedings of
this society. The preface to the translation of the "Acta"
which are included in the "Collection Académique" gives the
following account of its origins:

> The academy of Copenhagen was founded by Frederick
> III, who was aware how much glory it brought to him
> and to Denmark by encouraging the sciences and by
> attracting and holding scientists in his kingdom. One
> finds little to clarify the history of this academy,
> even in the five published volumes. The editing of
> the memoirs was principally under the care of Bar-
> tholin, the first Dane to publish medical observations.
> His aim was first to make a collection which em-
> braced all parts of science; but, deterred by the im-
> mensity of the task, he limited himself to the differ-
> ent parts of medicine and to those observations that
> were offered to him. His sponsor was Count Griffen-
> feld, the grand chancellor of Denmark, who obtained
> an edict enjoining all Danish physicians to render ex-
> act correspondence with the Dean of the Faculty of
> Copenhagen and to inform him of all singularities in
> medicine and natural history observed in different
> parts of the kingdom. Bartholin had great hopes for
> this collection and one can truly find in the five vol-
> umes which he published many discoveries which
> would have been lost or perhaps not have existed if
> this correspondence had not brought them to light and
> encouraged them. (26)

The "Acta consisted primarily of short original observations on medical and natural scientific subjects, although it
also contained a few abstracts of books. The first volume included a list of medical book published in 1671 and 1672.
Bartholin availed himself of a prerogative, which journal edi-

tors no longer seem to enjoy, of adding comments and annotations to the articles.   For example, in the case history reported of a young girl who had the strange faculty of produc-
ing grains of wheat, small peas, and other bizarre objects
out of her eyes, the editor speculates on the authenticity of
this account and produces much bibliographic evidence to support the possibility of its occurrence.   However at the end
of the volume the fraud is exposed with a statement that the
girl had been found to have introduced these objects under
her eyelids and later to have pretended that they occurred
there naturally.   Juncker lists forty-eight Danish physicians
and scientists whose articles are preserved in the "Acta" including Steno, Borrichius and the Bartholins, father and son,
although the contributions were not confined to Danes.   (27)
The manner in which a contribution of the English anatomist,
Edward Tyson (1650-1708), found its way into the "Acta" provides an interesting sidelight on the part played by travelling
scholars in scientific communications and also indicates that
it is one of the vagaries of scientific publication that it is
sometimes impossible to predict what outlet a scientist may
find for his publications.   Among the many Scandinavians who
were visitors to England in the last quarter of the 17th century was a Dr. Holger Jacobaeus, who after taking his degree in medicine at Copenhagen, made the usual grand tour,
including in his itinerary France, Germany, Hungary, the
Netherlands and England.   In England he spent much time at
the meetings of the Royal Society and also found time to carry
out some experiments with Robert Boyle.   He becam an intimate friend of Tyson's, probably through his brother, Jans
Jacobaeus, who was studying medicine at Oxford.   At one of
their meetings Tyson discussed some observations which he
had made on various pulmonary conditions in lower animals
and in men.   Jacobaeus suggested to Tyson that he write them
up for inclusion in Bartholin's "Acta."   Tyson obliged by writing up a series of five cases which eventually appeared in the
last volume of the "Acta," covering the years 1677-1679, which
appeared in 1680.  (28)

      A publication which perhaps deserves more than the
"Journal des Sçavans" to be called the first scientific periodical in France is one about which some confusion seems to exist in the literature.   In the course of compiling the basic
list for this study, two titles were encountered which were
attributed to Jean Baptiste Denis (c1620-1704).   The first,
cited in Garrison's List, is "Recueil des Mémoires et Conferences sur les Arts et les Sciences Presentées a M. le Dauphin pendant l'Année 1672-73 par J. B. Denis qui y Continué
le Journal des Sçavans.*" Garrison gives as a location the
British Museum and indicates that it was published in 1682

at Amsterdam, so that it is very likely a reprint. The
second title is cited in the list of periodicals published by the
Académie des Sciences of Paris (29) which indicates that it
was published in 1672 at Brussels in duodecimo under the
title "Mémoires Concernant les Arts et les Sciences Presentez
a Mgr. le Dauphin." All the sources which mention the publication indicate that there was only one series with the exception of Barnes who insists that the titles represent two
different series. (3)   Dekeyser cites it under the title "Mémoires" and states that it was a monthly issued during 1672.(31)
Morgan (32) mentions it also as a single title, but seems to
derive all her information from Camusat who devoted a short
article to Denis' publication in his history of the "Journal des
Sçavans." (33)   In this article Camusat states that the "Mémoires sur les Arts et les Sciences" should be regarded as a
supplement to the "Journal," and that it was designed to fill
the gaps in publication which occurred under the editorship of
Gallois, who assumed charge of the "Journal" after De Sallo's
falling out with the authorities.

        The following description is at variance with most of
the other published descriptions.   It is based on a volume in
the collections of the National Library of Medicine.   The
volume consists of twelve numbers with the issue title "Mémoires Concernant les Arts et les Sciences," beginning with 1
February 1672, and with two issues a month with the exception of April of that year in which three numbers appeared.
The last issue of the "Mémoires," dated 11 June 1672, concludes with the announcement of

        the public conferences which are held on Saturdays at
        the home of the author of these memoirs and which
        will henceforth be printed.

The "Mémoires" are followed by a series of eleven numbers
with the running title "Conferences sur les Sciences," issued
at irregular intervals, from 1 July 1672 to April 1673.   The
title page for the volume reads "Recueil des Mémoires et Conferences qui ont este Presentées a Monseigneur le Dauphin
Pendant l'Année 1672 par Jean Baptiste Denis Conseiller and
Medécin Ordinaire du Roy," and bears the imprint, Paris,
1672.   The table of contents, appended to the volume, however, covers only the series of "Mémoires" and the seven
"Conferences" to the end of 1672, so that it appears that this
volume was bound with four extraneous issues, but does not
contain the three additional "Conferences" numbered 12 to 14,
said to have been issued between May 1673 and February 1674
or the fifteenth "Conference" which appeared in 1683.   The
page numbering is continuous to the end of the eleventh con-

ference, so it is apparently either a continuous series or
else another reprint.

   The "Mémoires" do appear to be designed in the style
of and as a supplement to the "Journal des Sçavans." In the
"avertissement" in the first number Denis states:

> The ordinary memoirs will be distributed at the be-
> ginning of each month; the extraordinary can be ob-
> tained around the 15th, and above all we will take
> care never to repeat anything which has already ap-
> peared in the "Journal des Sçavans." Those who
> have made new discoveries and who wish to have
> published the progress which they have made in the
> arts and sciences, should send their memoirs to Mr.
> Denis. (34)

The "Mémoires" consist largely of reviews of books, not only
in the natural sciences, but also on history and the humanities, a few extracts from the "Philosophical Transactions"
and Nazari's "Giornale dei Letterati," as well as a few original contributions such as the letter on "the prodigious infant
who has a beard and other parts like a thirty year old man,"
(35) a description of the small telescope built by Newton, (36)
observations on the comet of 28 March 1672, (37) and a letter on a merman seen off the coast of Martinique on 23 May
1671. (38)

   We can only speculate on the reasons Denis had for
changing the style of the publication to that of reporting on
the proceedings of his conferences, but it is possible that
Gallois, the editor of the "Journal des Sçavans," intervened
with the authorities to protect his prerogatives, as De la
Roque did later in the case of Nicolas Blegny and the "Nouvelles Déscouvertes sur Toutes les Parties de la Médecine."
However, if this is true, Denis fails to mention it in his announcement of the new series at the end of the twelfth memoir:

> Our assemblies are composed of persons of diverse
> qualities and professions. There are those who are
> excellent in mathematics; others cultivate philosophy,
> others practice medicine, and finally there are those
> of a quality of not being of any of these professions.
> We examine all the questions of physics, of mathe-
> matics and medicine which are proposed to us, and
> which are sent to us from different parts of Europe.
> The custom is that I speak first in order to orient
> the others; I explain the state of the question with-

out taking sides. I place my support on those principles which seem to me the most verisimilitudinous.
Everyone has the liberty of interupting me and of
contradicting me if I advance any proposition which
shocks experience or reason. Difficulties are presented and objections are made to what I have said;
I attempt always to respond immediately and I contribute as much as I can in order that I may profit
myself from the conferences and in order to make
them useful to those who do me the honor of attending.

Since I have been holding these conferences for eight
years there can be no doubt that among all the questions which we have examined there are several
which merit being presented to the public. Several
persons who assisted there have often asked me in
writing if their memoir could not be retained. Several others who were not able to attend, and to whom
they were reported only imperfectly, have requested
that they be presented in greater detail. I finally decided to look again at the principal conferences of
which I had only the rough drafts, to make a fair
copy of them and to have them printed one after another as soon as they were in condition to be presented. And finally to have more time to work at
this, we interrupt these "Memoirs" so that we will be
able to present the first conference on the first day
of the following July.

The issues that follow present the summarized discussion on
a single topic, or sometimes on several topics. They resemble in style the "Centurie des Questions Traitées ès Conférences du Bureau d'Adresse" which had been issued some
thirty years previously, (39) or the published conferences of
the Abbé Bourdelot which appeared some years later. They
represent the product of what we might call a scientific salon
rather than the more formal organization of scientific society.

When we look at the group of substantive scientific
serials as a whole (Table 2) we are struck immediately by
the large proportion of titles which appeared in Germany.
There was, of course, no such political entity in this period
which we can designate with this name, so we have equated
publication in German with publication in the geographic area
in which German was traditionally spoken. The exceptions
are those titles in German which were published in such countries as Denmark, Switzerland, Russia and Sweden. In those
cases we have attributed the titles to those countries of pub-

Table 2

Substantive Serials by Country and Subject

| | General | Medicine, General | Medicine, Special | Biological Sciences | Physical Sciences | Technological | Agricultural | Total | Per cent |
|---|---|---|---|---|---|---|---|---|---|
| Germany | 102 | 61 | 31 | 14 | 34 | 24 | 38 | 304 | 62 |
| France | 26 | 12 | 4 | - | 2 | 2 | 7 | 53 | 1 |
| England | 11 | 6 | - | 2 | 7[a] | 1 | 7 | 34 | |
| Italy | 13 | 7 | 1 | - | 2 | - | - | 23 | |
| Holland | 12 | 9 | - | - | 2 | - | - | 23 | |
| Denmark | 5 | 10[b] | - | - | 1 | - | 2 | 18 | |
| Switzerland | 7 | 3 | - | 4 | - | - | 2 | 16 | |
| Russia | 2 | 1 | - | - | 1 | - | 2 | 6 | |
| Sweden | 3 | 1 | - | - | - | - | 1 | 5 | 1 |
| Spain | 2 | - | - | - | - | 1 | - | 3 | .05 |
| Portugal | 1 | 1 | - | - | - | - | - | 2 | .05 |
| Other | 2 | 3 | 1 | - | - | - | - | 6 | 1 |
| Totals | 186 | 114 | 37 | 20 | 49 | 28 | 59 | 49 | |
| Per cent | 38 | 23 | 7 | 4 | 10 | 6 | 12 | | |

[a] All mathematics.
[b] Principally the journals edited by Tode.

lication.

　　　　The preponderance of German titles on the list (sixty-two per cent), however, is more apparent than real.　　This is made clear when we tabulate the titles according to those which were live in any particular year.　　Statistics of the growth of periodicals are usually given in figures which represent the numbers of titles which had their origin in a particular year. These figures are usually deceptive since they do not take into consideration the duration of the individual periodicals. They are particularly misleading for periodicals in the 17th and 18th centuries, because of the brevity of duration of many of the periodicals in this period.　　To simplify the presentation the figures are shown as averages for the indicated decade, i.e. if one title or combination of titles were active for less than a total of five years, there is no entry for the decade; all totals five or over are shown as one title, and all totals

over fifteen or over are indicated as two, etc. (Table 3).
This is brought out even more clearly by comparing the duration of the German substantive periodicals with those published in other countries (Table 4). When this data is summarized (Table 5) we find that thirty-nine per cent of the
titles published outside of Germany had a duration over five
years as compared with twenty-six per cent in Germany.
Although these figures do not dislodge German language periodicals from their position of leadership they reduce the dis-
parity between Germany and the other countries.

Another striking fact about the analysis is the large
proportion of the substantive periodicals which fall into special subject categories. (40)   The chronology of the development of specialization is not completely revealed by the analysis of active serials, because the earlier and sporadic ap-
pearances of specialized journals do not appear in the table.
However, the progression in the direction of more and of
greater specialization is clearly indicated.   Since we are concerned in this study with the formal aspects of the scientific
journal rather than with its subject content, we shall not discuss the development of subject specialization.   It is interesting, nevertheless, to note two examples of what we might
call premature specialization in which the editors found it
necessary to revert to a more general form of subject coverage.   These are the "Lettres Périodiques," issued by Buc'-
hoz between 1768 and 1770 and the "Journal Polytype des
Sciences et des Arts."

Pierre Joseph Buc'hoz (1731-1807), whom Guitard
describes as "lawyer, doctor, botanist, journalist and indefatigable traveller, compiler and writer," (41) issued his publication first in three different series, "Lettres Périodiques
sur la Méthode de S'enricher Promptement et Conserver sa
Santé par la Culture des Végetaux" (1768-1770), "Lettres
Périodiques, Curieuses, Utiles et Intéressantes, sur les
Avantages que la Societé Economique peut Retirer de la Con-
naissance des Animaux" (1769-1770), and "Lettres Hebdoma-
daires sur L'Utilité des Mineraux dans la Société Civile"
(1770).   In 1771 he found it either necessary or desirable to
consolidate the three publications under the title "La Nature
Considérée sous ses Differents Aspects, ou Journal des
Trois Regnes de la Nature." (42)   The "Journal Polytype des
Sciences et des Arts" is of interest in the history of the scientific periodical primarily because it was the first journal
which was printed by a newly introduced stereotype process
and because it contains in one of its issues one of Lavoisier's
original papers on the composition of water.   It was edited
from 1786 to 1787 by François Ignace Joseph Hoffmann, who

Table 3
Active Substantive Journals, Averages For
Each Decade by Subject and Country

| | 1670 | 1680 | 1690 | 1700 | 1710 | 1720 | 1730 | 1740 | 1750 | 1760 | 1770 | 1780 | 1790 | Titles Represented |
|---|---|---|---|---|---|---|---|---|---|---|---|---|---|---|
| **General** | | | | | | | | | | | | | | |
| Germany | 1 | 2 | 2 | 2 | 3 | 4 | 6 | 5 | 8 | 8 | 10 | 13 | 14 | 102 |
| France | 1 | 1 | 1 | 2 | 2 | 2 | 2 | 2 | 4 | 4 | 6 | 5 | 4 | 26 |
| England | 1 | 1 | 1 | 1 | 1 | 1 | 1 | 2 | 2 | 2 | 2 | 2 | 3 | 11 |
| Italy | — | — | — | — | — | — | 1 | 3 | 2 | 1 | 3 | 4 | 5 | 13 |
| Holland | 1 | 2 | 1 | 2 | 1 | 3 | 1 | 1 | 1 | 3 | 3 | 3 | 3 | 12 |
| Other | — | 1 | 1 | — | — | — | — | — | — | 1 | 1 | 5 | 6 | 22 |
| **Medicine, General** | | | | | | | | | | | | | | |
| Germany | — | — | — | — | — | 2 | — | 1 | 2 | 4 | 4 | 7 | 12 | 61 |
| France | — | 1 | — | 1 | — | — | — | — | 1 | 3 | 3 | 4 | 4 | 12 |
| England | — | — | — | — | — | — | — | — | — | — | 1 | 3 | 3 | 6 |
| Italy | — | — | — | — | — | — | — | — | — | 1 | 1 | 2 | 2 | 2 |
| Holland | — | — | — | — | — | — | — | — | — | 1 | 1 | 1 | 1 | 1 |
| Denmark | — | — | — | — | — | — | — | — | — | — | 1 | 2 | — | 10 |
| Other | — | — | — | — | — | — | — | — | — | 1 | 1 | 2 | 3 | 3 |

| | 1790 | 1780 | 1770 | 1760 | 1750 | 1740 | 1730 | 1720 | 1710 | 1700 | 1690 | 1680 | 1670 | Titles Represented |
|---|---|---|---|---|---|---|---|---|---|---|---|---|---|---|
| **Medicine, Special** | | | | | | | | | | | | | | |
| Germany | 11 | 7 | 1 | — | — | — | — | — | — | — | — | — | — | 31 |
| Other | 1 | 1 | — | — | — | — | — | — | — | — | — | — | — | 6 |
| **Biological Sicences** | | | | | | | | | | | | | | |
| Germany | 8 | 3 | — | — | 1 | — | — | — | — | — | — | — | — | 14 |
| Other | 2 | 2 | — | — | — | — | — | — | — | — | — | — | — | 6 |
| **Physical Sciences** | | | | | | | | | | | | | | |
| Germany | 6 | 8 | 3 | — | — | — | 1 | — | — | — | — | — | — | 34 |
| Other | 4 | 1 | 3 | 3 | 3 | 2 | — | — | — | — | — | — | — | 15 |
| **Technological** | | | | | | | | | | | | | | |
| Germany | 10 | 9 | 1 | 1 | — | 1 | — | — | — | — | — | — | — | 25 |
| Other | 1 | 1 | 1 | 1 | — | — | — | — | — | — | — | — | — | 4 |
| **Agriculture** | | | | | | | | | | | | | | |
| Germany | 8 | 7 | 5 | 4 | 3 | — | — | — | — | — | — | — | — | 38 |
| France | 4 | 2 | 2 | 1 | — | — | — | — | — | — | — | — | — | 7 |
| England | 1 | 1 | 1 | 1 | — | — | — | — | — | — | — | — | — | 7 |
| Other | 2 | 2 | 1 | 1 | — | — | — | — | — | — | — | — | — | 7 |
| **Total** | 118 | 93 | 55 | 41 | 27 | 17 | 12 | 12 | 7 | 8 | 6 | 8 | 4 | 494 |

Table 4
Comparison of the Duration of the Substantive Periodical in Germany
With Those Published in Other Countries

| | General | | Medicine General | | Medicine Special | | Biology | | Physics | | Tech-nology | | Agri-culture | | Total |
|---|---|---|---|---|---|---|---|---|---|---|---|---|---|---|---|
| | G | O | G | O | G | O | G | O | G | O | G | O | G | O | |
| 1[a] | 29 | 18 | 17 | 17 | 9 | 4 | 2 | 1 | 9 | 4 | 8 | 1 | 8 | 6 | 133 |
| 2 | 19 | 12 | 13 | 8 | 5 | 1 | 1 | 1 | 6 | – | 4 | – | 8 | 1 | 79 |
| 3 | 10 | 8 | 8 | 3 | 4 | – | 4 | – | 5 | 3 | 3 | 1 | 2 | 1 | 52 |
| 4 | 10 | 7 | 8 | 4 | 3 | – | 2 | – | 2 | – | – | – | 2 | 2 | 40 |
| 5 | 6 | 4 | 4 | 4 | 3 | – | 2 | – | 3 | 2 | 2 | – | 4 | 1 | 35 |
| 6 | 3 | 1 | 1 | – | – | – | 1 | 2 | 3 | 1 | – | – | 4 | 2 | 18 |
| 7 | 1 | 2 | 2 | 5 | – | 1 | – | – | – | 1 | 1 | – | 1 | – | 13 |
| 8 | 1 | 2 | 1 | 1 | 1 | – | – | – | 2 | – | – | – | 1 | 1 | 10 |
| 9 | 1 | 5 | 2 | – | – | – | – | – | – | – | 1 | – | – | 3 | 9 |
| 10 | 1 | – | 1 | 3 | – | – | 1 | 1 | 1 | 2 | 1 | 1 | 2 | 2 | 14 |
| 11–15 | 9 | 8 | 1 | 3 | 6 | – | 1 | – | 2 | – | 3 | – | 5 | – | 43 |
| 16–20 | 5 | 4 | 1 | – | – | – | 1 | – | – | – | 1 | – | – | – | 12 |
| 21–25 | 1 | 4 | 1 | 1 | – | – | – | – | – | 1 | – | 1 | – | 2 | 9 |
| 26–30 | 1 | 2 | 1 | 1 | – | – | – | – | – | 1 | – | – | – | – | 6 |
| 31– | 5 | 7 | – | 3 | – | – | – | 1 | 1 | 1 | – | – | – | 2 | 19 |
| Totals | 102 | 84 | 61 | 53 | 31 | 6 | 14 | 6 | 34 | 15 | 25 | 4 | 38 | 21 | 492 |

[a] One year or less.          G– Germany          O– Other

Table 7

A Summary of the Comparison of the Duration
of German Substantive Serials With
Those in Other Countries

|  | Germany | | Other | | Total | |
|---|---|---|---|---|---|---|
|  | Number | Per cent | Number | Per cent | Number | Per cent |
| Five years or less | 225 | 74 | 115 | 61 | 340 | 69 |
| Over five yrs. | 79 | 26 | 74 | 39 | 153 | 31 |
| Total | 304 | 100 | 189 | 100 | 493 | 100 |
| Ten years or less | 258 | 85 | 146 | 77 | 404 | 82 |
| Over ten yrs. | 46 | 15 | 43 | 23 | 89 | 18 |
| Total | 304 | 100 | 189 | 100 | 493 | 100 |

claimed to have invented the process, and by Bailly de Ben-
field. It was issued weekly in three separate and distinct
parts each paged continuously, a "Partie des Sciences" issued on Monday, a "Partie des Arts Utiles" issued on
Wednesdays, and a "Partie des Arts Agreeable" which appeared every Friday. Beginning with the fifty-eighth issue
all three parts were combined into a single journal which
was issued three times a week. (43)

The class of general substantive periodicals is by no
means a homogenous one. It includes those periodicals which
could not be included under the various subject rubrics, and
represents a range from the most general to those covering
two or more subjects. For many of the titles, unfortunately,
we possess a bare minimum of bibliographic detail which is
enough in most cases to classify them, but not enough to
describe them adequately. This class includes translations,
reprints and abridgments of individual titles. Each journal
is, of course, more or less unique in format and editorial
policy, a creature of the editor or editors, and which therefore reflects their interests, predilections and/or judgments
of a particular audience. Taken as a whole they can be
characterized according to (1) type, i.e. whether they are
substantive, review, abstract or news journals, (2) audience,
i.e. whether their appeal is in general popular or scholarly,

and (3) by the range of their subject matter.  Very few of
the substantive journals in the general group represent any
of these classes in pure form; they are mainly hybrids.
It is possible, however, to consider them in three categories:   (1) those which contain a significant proportion of
original articles, (2) those made up basically of articles
borrowed from other journals, but which also contain some
original articles and the other appurtenances of scientific
journalism, news, book reviews, etc., and (3) journals
which fall into either of the two categories above, but which
are of popular appeal.  We shall consider some of the representative titles in each of these three categories.

In the early history of scientific journalism we find
several titles that are transitional in form between the book
and the periodical.   One example is the "Monatliche Erzehl-
ungen allerhand Künstlicher und natürlicher Curiositäten,
unter einer anmuthigen Romaine, aus den neuesten Büchern
herausgezogen und mit eigener Erfahrung bewähret" which
can be translated as "Monthly Relations of Various Curiosi-
ties of Art and Nature, in the Form of Pleasant Tales Selected from the Newest Books and Verified by Personal Experience."  It appeared from May to August of 1689 in three
issues, each one devoted to a particular subject, the first
dealing with barometers, and thermometers, and the second
and third with the subject of color. (44)   Barnes calls it
the first specialized scientific journal in Germany published
in the German language, (45) and Prutz goes further in
claiming for it the distinction of being the first learned journal printed in German. (46)   A similar publication, although
this time in Latin, was the "Observationes Chymico-Physico-
Medicae Curiosae, Mensibus Singulis Continuandae," which
appeared successively in Frankfurt, Leipzig, Halle and Mag-
deburg between July 1697 and May 1698.   It was edited by
the celebrated chemist and physician George Ernest Stahl
(1660-1734).   Each number was devoted to the discussion of
a particular subject, for example, the August issue dealt
with the industrial preparation of vitriol, the September with
the mining of iron, and the October issue with a subject of
perennial interest, the preparation of wines and other fer-
mentations.   It is difficult to say with the information at
hand how many of these early titles were written by one man
and how many were contributions of various authors.   Some
of these may have begun as collections of essays by an individual, hoping later to attract other contributions.   As an
example, in 1789 we find Johann Georg Albert Hopfner
(1759-1813) expressing pleasure in the preface to the third
volume of his "Magazin für die Naturkunde Helvetiens*"
that he need no longer include so many of his own papers.

In many cases the success and survival of a periodical depended on its ability to attract contributors, however, there
is an example of a periodical which resulted from the desire
of a savant to publish his own papers. It probably resulted
from the practice of the Académie des Sciences of printing
in full in its "Mémoires" only selected papers from among
those which had been delivered in its assemblies. Antoine
Parent (1666-1719), the French mathematician who had been
admitted to the Académie in 1699, began his journal "Re-
cherches de Physique et de Mathematiques" largely to publish
those of his papers which did not appear in the "Mémoires."
(47)

It is difficult to say how much of the content of the
18th century scientific periodical is original contributions or
first reports of observations, but even a cursory examination indicates that a large proportion was derived from other
printed sources. Borrowing articles from other journals
was a common practice throughout the 18th century. The
source was generally acknowledged, but frequently, although
it seems apparent that the article was borrowed, no indication of source is given. On this score we have the evidence of a contemporary medical editor who writes:

> ...it seems to be a peculiarity of the medical litera-
> ture of our time, that the appearance of a new prod-
> uct is always offset by the tenfold reprinting of an
> older one in ten various collections...I ask those who
> find this calculation an exaggeration to examine the
> literature of the last decade more closely in order to
> discover the huge disproportion between the substance
> of learned publications and its volume. (48)

Duplication is frequently defended in editorial comments, usually in the form of an apologia to the reader.
The comments of the editor of the "Mémoires" of the Academie Royale de Chirurgie of Paris relate rather to the
uniqueness of the observations rather than to their original-
ity, i.e. the work might have been original with the individual as a result of his own inspiration and industry and yet not
unique in the sense that similar or even idential work may
have been reported in the literature. These comments are
of interest in their expression of a typical 18th century editorial point of view:

> We do not pretend that all the observations that we
> will publish will be absolutely new. It would be nec-
> essary to have surveyed all those authors who have
> collected the facts of surgery and the large number

of journals which communicate unusual things in their
own particular field. Thus we will be neither sur-
prised nor shocked when we will be made aware that
certain observations are to be found in a particular
author. However, it is almost impossible that all
the circumstances will be the same, and, if they do
find there some differences the observors have lost
nothing. If they are found to be exactly the same,
we would not believe them less worthy of being published because they would appear to be either very
useful or very rare. If they are useful the duplication is not an inconvenience. If they are rare they
are upheld by added examples. (49)

This attitude might be expressed more succinctly by the
phrase "what care I how old they be as long as they be new
to me," an attitude which is echoed by the editor of the
Memoirs of the American Academy of Arts and Sciences,
Boston, 1785:

The medical papers may, probably, contain many observations not entirely new. However, this ought not
to be considered a sufficient objection to their being
inserted into this work, because many important discoveries in pathology, as well as in the animal oe-
conomy, have been in great measure useless to this
part of the world, in consequence of a situation so
remote from ancient seats of learning and improvement. And of such publications as have reached this
country, the smallness of the number has greatly
limited their usefulness, as but few have had an opportunity for pursuing them...The contents of some
of these papers, therefore, though they may afford
nothing new to the European, yet, to many American
readers may have the recommendation of novelty. (50)

The differences in attitudes toward duplication in this
period as compared with attitudes that may prevail today,
grow out of the differences in the economics of periodical
publication. In the earlier period when cost of material
such as paper, ink, etc., exceeded those of labor for composition, printing, etc., it was not nearly as uneconomic a
practice to duplicate articles as it is today. This also helps
to account for the continued existence of periodicals with editions as small as five hundred copies. These statements,
of course, require much fuller documentation than can be
attempted here.

To provide a more adequate picture of 18th century

scientific journalism we must add that portion of the substantive journals which is made up of extracts, and abstracts of articles appearing in other journals and to book reviews. It is difficult to estimate what proportion of the journals which have been classified as "substantive" in this study were devoted to derivative literature. Among the periodicals devoted largely to extracts from other journals is the "Physikalische Belustigungen*" which appeared in Berlin from 1751 to 1757. The editor Christian Mylius had been associated with an earlier popular scientific periodical called "Der Naturforscher" which had been issued in Leipzig from 1747 to 1748. He makes the popular nature of his present undertaking clear in the preface to the first volume.

> A few years ago when one wished to give some one an idea of a new monthly which was appearing one said, 'It is like the "Belustigungen.' Just as well-known and well-loved as the "Belustigungen" have been among the lovers of poetry and witty prose, so have the friends of nature and natural history found pleasure for two years in the "Hamburgischen Magazin." So now that I wish to inform my readers about a new scientific monthly, I can give them no shorter description than to say, 'It will be like the Hamburgischen Magazin.' This concerns only the superficial aspects; its inner qualities my readers will have the opportunity of judging in the future.
>
> I have called my monthly "Physikalische Belustigungen" although this may perhaps give many professional philosophers a contemptuous idea of my intentions. I declare, therefore, that the principal object of this monthly is utility. I believe that in the study of nature as well as in other matters, the useful is also the entertaining... (51)

He goes on to say that the journal will deal with commerce and domestic economy but will also include subjects of less evident utility such as microscopy and entomology. He states one negative policy forcefully:

> Since there are reviews in so many learned periodicals and day books, that they disgust and almost nauseate us, they will be entirely omitted from this monthly. It appears to me that when one has fifty reviews of a book, one can dispense with the fifty-first. (52)

A sampling of the first two issues gives us an idea of the

nature of the periodical. The first issue contains a proposal for the erection of a weather observatory; a translation of a French essay on the origin of language and the
significance of words; a translation of a Dutch work on the
natural history of cochineal, which is continued through the
first five numbers; and an unsigned report about an unusual
fire. The second issue includes a discussion on the ripen-
ing of dates; the description of a new South American metal,
translated from the English of William Watson; a letter to
the editor on silvered deer (elk's?) teeth, and two translations from the "Journal Britannique." The third volume was
issued with a preface signed by Abraham Gotthelf Kästner
(1718-1775) whose name occurs frequently in the history of
the scientific serial as a translator of the proceedings of
foreign scientific societies.

> The multitude of scientific papers which one now sees
> appearing in Germany indicates that at the present
> time the study of the natural sciences are well re-
> ceived among our fellow citizens. I will say, never-
> theless, that formerly there were lacking lovers and
> students of the natural sciences, but it now appears
> that the taste for such knowledge is much greater
> than it has been. I believe that I can with justice say
> that this can be ascribed principally to the use of the
> native tongue in these writings which has become cus-
> tomary...The former editor of this work finds him-
> self in another part of the world. Because of our
> friendship I could not deny him the courtesy of writ-
> ing a preface to this third volume. (53)

Mylius sent in several translations from English literary journals, principally the "Gentleman's Magazine," for inclusion
in the third volume, among them an article on the natural
history of tea from the "Universal Magazine," an original
piece on thermometric observations taken on and in the sea,
and a report of a battle among ants taken from the "Gentleman's Magazine."

Friedrich Heinrich Wilhelm Martini (1729-1778) is
only one example of a large number of practicing physicians
in Germany who became involved in the publication of natural science periodicals. One of his first ventures into the
field of literature had been the establishment of a circulating
library in Berlin for "medicine, agriculture and natural science" in 1764. (54) It may have been that the availability of
the materials provided for this club that led him to the establishment of the various journals which he edited. The
first of these was the "Berlinisches Magazin, oder gesam-

mlete Schriften und Nachrichten für die Liebhaber der Arzneywissenschaft, Naturgeschichte und der angenehmen Wissenschaften überhaupt," issued in Berlin between 1765 and 1769.
Martini provides us with a description of it himself in a list
of periodicals which he included in the first volume of his
second periodical, the "Berlinische Sammlung zur Beforderung der Arzneywissenschaft, der Naturgeschichte, der Haushaltungskunst, Cameralwissenschaft und der dahin einschlagen-
den Literatur.*"

> In so far as we ourselves have taken part in this work
> it is not seemly for us to comment on its merit. Its
> chief purpose is the dissemination of medical and
> natural scientific knowledge. In 1767 a second and
> revised edition of the first volume appeared, which
> would seem to indicate public approval.

The "Berlinische Sammlung" was issued in ten volumes between 1768 and 1779. It consists of original contributions, abstracts and extracts from the foreign literature,
book reviews and news, and covers the whole range of subjects in science and technology. In 1770 Martini added a
more general periodical to his list. It was the "Mannig-
faltigkeiten, eine gemeimnützige Wochenschrift," which continued with various changes of title until 1784. Neuberger
credits him also with being the founder of the Gesellschaft
für Naturforschender Freunde in Berlin in 1773. (55)

Jakob Samuel Wyttenbach (1748-1830), a Swiss clergy-
man, has an editorial history similar to Martini's, and like
Martini was also a founder of a natural history society. (56)
DeBeer calls him "one of the numerous amateurs whose un-
obtrusive labours did so much to further knowledge of the
natural history of Switzerland. (57) He published first the
"Beiträge zur Naturgeschichte des Schweizerlandes" of which
only three parts appeared in 1775. In the same year he followed it with a similar publication entitled "Bernisches Magazin der Natur, Kunst und Wissenschaften*" which continued
to appear until 1779. The word "Kunst" in the title has the
18th century meaning of technology, so the journal is devoted
largely to science and technology. It contains few original
papers; the contents consist largely of translations from
French journals such as the "Mémoires" of the Académie des
Science, Rozier's journal, and the "Gazette de la Litterature,
Sciences et Arts." There is a gap of two years between the
appearance of the first and second issue. The preface to the
second issue says that unavoidable hindrances prevented its
appearance and that since these were out of the way the journal could now proceed without interruption. It was only is-

sued three more times, and Wyttenbach had no better fortune with his last publication, the "Gelehrte Nachrichten aus
Welschland die Künste und Wissenschaften vorzüglich die
Physik und Naturhistorie betreffend," which he started in
1783 to make Italian natural science scholarship better known
in Switzerland. He planned it as a bi-monthly publication
but only one issue appeared when a call to a new post forced
him to relinquish it.

One of the first natural science periodicals to contain
a significant proportion of original contributions and to limit
itself to pure science is "Der Naturforscher.*" It was begun by Johann Ernst Immanuel Walch (1725-1778), professor
of philosophy at the University of Jens. It was issued at
Halle from the year 1774 and on the editor's death was taken
over by Johann Christian Daniel Edlen von Schreber (1739-
1810), professor of medicine and natural history at Erlangen,
who continued it until 1804. The preface to the first volume
states that it will be restricted to the natural sciences, and
its program is reiterated in the introduction to the tenth volume:

> The (natural science) enthusiast should not find it nec-
> essary to pay out ready money for essays which do
> not interest him. Moreover, the field of natural his-
> tory is already a sufficiently important field, that
> those, who wish to work in one or another area of
> natural history should not find it necessary to cross
> its boundaries and venture into foreign areas. This
> is the reason I have often found it necessary to turn
> down useful and learned papers when they do not defi-
> nitely belong to the subject of natural history. (58)

Of the seventeen papers in the first issue, ten are
original contributions, devoted to such subjects as the micro-
scopic examination of insects, the Linnean system of classifying birds, and descriptive papers in zoology and entomology.
It is interesting to note that of the eight contributors in the
first issue, three are designated as pastors, three as physicians, and two as professors at the University. The seven
remaining items in the first issue are devoted to short translations and abstracts from foreign literature. Journals of
this type did not appear with any regularity or in any great
numbers until the last quarter of the 18th century. Perhaps
the most outstanding of them was the "Observations sur la
Physique, sur l'Histoire Naturelle et sur les Arts" issued by
Abbé Rozier at Paris from 1773. It served as one of the
most valuable mediums for the exchange of ideas and a repository of the work of the amateurs and professionals of sci-

ence of the whole of Europe in the last quarter of the 18th
century. It is frequently referred to as Rozier's journal.

Jean Baptiste François Rozier (1734-1793) occupied
himself principally with agriculture and production of wine.
He is known as the editor of a dictionary of agriculture in
ten volumes, but his main claim to fame is the journal
which he inaugurated in 1771 under the title "Introduction aus
Observations sur la Physique" of which he published eighteen
octavo volumes in Paris by the end of 1772. The fact that
he did actually consider it a monthly supplement to that
great retrospective collection of the proceedings of earlier
societies, the "Collection Académique," (59) is borne out by
the alternative title to the series, "Tableau du Travail An-
nuel de Toutes les Académies de l'Europe; ou Observations
sur la Physique, sur l'Histoire Naturelle et sur les Arts et
Métiers." In 1773 he began a new series under a new title,
in quarto, to conform to the "Collection Académique." It's
title was "Observations et Mémoires sur la Physique, sur
l'Histoire Naturelle et sur les Arts Contenant l'Abregé de
l'Histoire & les Mémoires des Académies Étrangeres de Berlin, de Londres, de Bologne, de Suede, etc." It was issued
regularly every month until 1794, even during the visicitudes
of the French Revolution. Rozier edited the journal himself
until 1780 when he was joined by Jean André Mongez (1751-
1778) and Jean Claude de la Methrie (1743-1817), both well-
known scientific figures at the end of the 18th century. The
journal consisted largely of original contributions sent in by
members of provincial academies and Parisian scientists,
and by some of the leading scientists of the other European
countries. It numbered among its contributors, Priestly,
Macquer, Black, Lavoisier, Scheele and Morveau, and provides one of the most significant repositories of the scientific advances made in the last quarter of the 18th century.

In the preface to the first volume of the "Observations" we find Rozier reiterating some of the old arguments
about the necessity of establishing scientific periodicals,
which suggests that perhaps the medium still needed justifica-
tion even after a century of existence. We quote it here at
length because beside providing background on the history of
the periodical, it is an excellent reflection of the contemporary attitudes toward scientific journalism.

> This journal has no resemblance to the periodical pub-
> lications which are so widely distributed in France
> and in foreign countries. One can judge by the eigh-
> teen volumes published from the month of July 1771
> to the first of January 1773. The object of this pub-

lication is to announce the discoveries which are
made every day in the sciences. We will now reveal the motives which made us determine to undertake this literary enterprise, the plan of its execution, and the resources which we have in order to
achieve our goal successfully.

Scholars have always been aware of the infinite ad-
vantages which result for the advancement of science
from a lively and extensive commerce which joins
all the members of the Republic of Letters through
the regular communication of ideas, views, endeav-
ours and projects.

Hardly had the spirit of research and observation begun to spread in Europe, than there was established
between the scholars of France, Italy, England and
Germany, a correspondence by means of which discoveries soon acquired among them a celebrity which
redoubled their zeal and their emulation. It is known
that the Cabinet of Father Mersenne was established
to be a bureau of correspondence which occupied itself with physics. It was there that Pascal came to
bring the results of his experiments made on the Puy
de Dome, and there one also learned of the details
of the experiments of Torricelli and of Boyle.

This correspondence produced several periodical publications and soon afterwards the learned societies,
successively established by their sovereigns, made
known great numbers of discoveries by the publication
of the collections of their memoirs. However, the
majority of these academic collections are published
in their national language and printed several years
after the memoirs have been read. During this time
one remains ignorant of facts which could be of the
greatest utility for the sciences. In addition these
collections have become very numerous and thus very
expensive, often surpassing the resources of those
who are able to profit from them.

It seems that in the degree that the number of scholars has increased the correspondence among those of
different countries has decreased. Each one believed
doubtlessly that the national academies were sufficient
and that one received from them all the aid that was
necessary. The constitutions of these societies formed
by the sovereigns, having admitted foreign correspondents, seemed to prevent this illusion and thus to cor-

rect the inconvenience which resulted from it. However, this precaution, so sagely taken, has not been justified by success.

The result of this small amount of communication has been that the progress of the sciences is very slow, that scholars of two different nations work a long time on the same problem, and that they lose time which is precious for a fame which is at the end problematic. This inconvenience is less than that of working on a matter which has been clarified by work that has already been published but of which one has no knowledge. The author loses time which could be better employed for the good and the glory of his country, if in entering into the course he wishes to follow, he had under his very eyes the actual description of physical facts and the state they are in at the moment.

These motives led to the desire for a periodical supplied quickly and regularly which would announce the discoveries which are made each day in the different branches of science, either by short notices or by extended memoirs, which contain the development of all the proofs of the discoveries and which at the same time show the advance of the spirit of invention. It has been thought that the most prompt publication of new discoveries will at the same time accelerate the progress of the sciences, which are nothing more than the sum of these discoveries.

These then are the reasons which persuaded us to undertake this collection and we present it with as much confidence to the scholars abroad as if it were their own publication. It is written in a language which is today that of all those in Europe who have received any education. The Royal Academy of Sciences at Paris has long been aware of the importance of this collection. Many of its members proposed it last year almost according to the plan which we have chosen. Particular reasons have prevented the complete execution of this plan.

In spite of the favorable reception which this collection has received; in spite of the praise which scholars have given to it, we believe ourselves obliged to circumscribe its limits in order to make it still more worthy of them. We will in consequence reject everything which is nothing more than an undigested compi-

lation and which is lacking in new and useful views.
The importance of the material, and the manner in
which it is presented will guide our decision on the
choice of items to appear in this collection.   We will
not offer to idle amateurs works which are merely
agreeable, nor the pleasant illusion of believing oneself an initiate in those sciences of which one is ignorant.

We will occupy ourselves above all with the history
of those sciences which we are including in our plan
and it is with this in view that we will devote ourselves to reporting the pertinent facts and the different reasons which give them birth.   This manner of
viewing and of comparing facts presents an inex-
haustible foundation of knowledge which we will bring
together with the greatest care in order that one can
see at a glance the progression of facts which lead to
the establishment of important truths.

One cannot do too much to invite those who wish to
make progress in the sciences, to bring together the
knowledge transmitted by scholars of all the centuries
and all the countries.   It is a necessary preliminary
to arriving at new discoveries, and they should consider as the first steps they take, those which the
great men who preceded made in terminating their
last work.   The continuity of efforts of the former
and of the latter forms this union and this accord
must reign between the scholars of all countries in
order to extend the limits of knowledge.

It is from this union of work, this sum of knowledge
that we must take our departure in order to attain
new discoveries, and to give this collection the consistency which its goals seem to assure it.   The extent of this effort will be beyond our means, if a society formed by persons exclusively occupied with the
useful sciences do not vouchsafe to cooperate with us
to fulfill the objectives which we have proposed for
ourselves.

True scholars do not have a mania for keeping their
discoveries secret; as friends of humanity, their glory
is in being useful to humanity; thus, it is to those
whom we will offer our collection as a depository in
which they can record their discoveries.   We invite
them to consider our bureau like that of Father Mersenne.   We believe we are able to do it successfully,

since we are the proteges of an official who as much
fears praise as he has claim to merit it, and who
takes much care that our correspondence will be
solidly established with respectable men who are the
ornaments of their countries, and who were eager to
respond to our first invitations.  It would be fortunate
for the greater perfection of this collection if their
example, and the example which is provided by the
Royal Academy of Paris, were followed by all the
scholarly societies, and by all of those who devote
themselves to researches in physical knowledge.

Our promise to the public is to treat all branches of
general and experimental physics, the productions of
the three kingdoms of nature, and of their analysis;
of medicine which employs them to conserve our
days; of agriculture which knows how to draw from
it a part of our nourishment; of the arts and trades
which devise things for the needs and conveniences
of life, in a word, everything which is connected
with observation and experiment.

In the January 1778 issue of the "Observations," Rozier takes
up the subject of journalism again.

It is endlessly repeated that there has been too great
a multiplication of journals and some journalists add
that multiplicity leads to one periodical destroying
another.  Neither of these propositions are accurate
in themselves, and we will leave it to the special
pleaders to respond first:  M. Josse, your plea is a
selfish one.  The periodicals have two purposes, to
instruct and to entertain, to deal with the sciences or
the fine arts, and in either case to study the public
taste without which nothing succeeds in these enterprises.  The Public is composed of thousands and
thousands of minds which are differently organized
and which require special publications.  Each mind
has in its purlieu a circle of other minds more or
less of the same nature; from this arises the groups
of geometers, mathematicians, astronomers, physi-
cists, chemists, naturalists, agriculturalists, architects, sculptors, painters, musicians, poets, historians, orators, antiquarians, grammarians, etc.  Each
of these classes, or at least those who set themselves up as judges, thinks that it requires records
or martyrologies, and these martyrologies are the
periodicals.  The multiplicity of periodicals is therefore necessarily relative to the variations in intellect

and taste.   Thus the geometer who attended a presentation of one of the great tragedies at the Theatre
François answered him who asked him what he
thought of it:   'I believe the piece is very good, but
what does it prove?'   The Poet would surely not be
more content with reading a sublime Memoir on ge-
ometry or chemistry, and a pretty woman at her
toilette does not amuse herself with a commentary on
Barthole or Cujas.   The mere existence of periodicals presupposes their multiplicity and therefore it
is necessary.   It remains to prove that they are not
harmful to each other.   What harm can a medical
journal do the religious journal, that of physics to
one of music, a law journal to one of the theatre,
the "Post du Soir de Paris" to the "Journal des Savans," or to the "Mercure de France," or the Journal of Bouillon, the "Annee Littéraire," or the Journal des Beaux Arts," etc.?   The periodicals which
have a similar program, have, it is true, a form of
rivalry to fear, and so much the better for the Public.   It gives more energy to the rivals, the work is
done more carefully, the analyses are better made,
selections chosen better and since the taste of subscribers are so varied there is no fear that any will
fall, as long as the journal is well put together.
This last factor is the key to the enigma.   Indeed,
what a large number of readers would be idle, if
they had no journals to read.   The knowledge of the
multitude and its readers is periodic; it makes the
sovereign decisions about everything and without the
journals would perhaps not read a single volume a
year.   Thus it is on this mass of readers that the
foundations of journalism are built.   Happily one finds
among this large number many intelligent readers who
seek truly to know the best sources of instruction,
without partisan spirit and without pretensions; their
approbation encourages the author, who thus chances
the compensation of the judgment of the multitude.
Henri le Grand constantly reiterated:   'Faisons bien
et laissons dire.'   These words should be the motto
of the journalists.   Let therefore the multitude speak
and let good journals be issued.

Journals of Rozier's type are the exception rather
than the rule at this point in the history of scientific journalism.   A large proportion of the scientific journals of the
18th century must be regarded as media of education or of
the dissemination of established ideas rather than as repositories of contributions to science.   An established specialized

audience of scientists had not yet come into existence.
The term "scientist" itself did not appear until it was coined
by Whewell in the 19th century.  To quote a recent writer
on the sociology of science,

> The great scientists of the sixteenth, seventeenth and
> eighteenth century were typically 'amateurs,' or men
> for whom science was often an avocation, however,
> passionate their interest in it... If the 'amateurs'
> were particularly fortunate, they might find a patron
> who admired science and who would therefore give
> them funds for research.  Society as a whole laid
> out no clearly marked and generally approved careers
> for scientists.  Not until the late nineteenth century
> as we shall see later in some detail, is there a
> firmly established social basis for a large number of
> scientists in the universities and governments of
> Western society. (60)

The 18th century audience for the scientific periodical was
very limited and at the same time a great deal more homogenous in interest than the present-day audience.  May of the
substantive journals were issued for the instruction and entertainment of a lay readership, as often frankly revealed
by their titles, e.g. the "Journal Économique, ou Mémoires,
Notes et Avis sur les Arts, l'Agriculture, le Commerce, et
Tout ce qui peut avoir Rapport à la Santé, ainsi qu'à la
Conservation et à l'Augmentation des Biens des Famillies,"
which was issued in Paris between 1751 and 1772, the
"Physikalisch-Oekonomische Wochenschrift, welche als eine
Realzeitung das Nützlichste und Neuste aus der Natur-und
Haushaltungswissenschaft enthält," published in Stuttgart between 1753 and 1766, "Die Ehre Gottes aus der Betrachtung
des Himmels und der Erde, eine Wochenschrift," Nürnberg,
1766-1769, the "Magazin fürs Volk, medicinischen, ökono-
mischen und historischen Inhalts," Weimar, 1789.  These
journals and a great many others like them were instruments
of the Enlightenment and a reflection of a growing popular
interest in science.  They had their counterparts in the
many public series of lectures on scientific subjects which
began as long ago as the end of the 16th century in England
at Gresham College and which continued to be offered throughout the 18th century.  It is reflected in the comments in the
"Critical Review" on James Ferguson's "Astronomy Explained
upon Sir Isaac Newton's Principles, and Made Easy to Those
Who Have Not Studied Mathematics" published in London in
1756.  The book in expounding Newtonian physics provided
the reader with such homely examples as: "Let us imagine
a prodigious large room, of a round form, all hung with

pictures of men, women, birds, beasts, and fishes..."(61)
The reviewer comments: "The ladies may now rise above
the region of vapours, without running the risque of a ver-
tigo." (62)

Rozier in the preface to his new journal appears to
be presenting both a reform and a new departure in scientific journalism, and in avowing that he will reject mere
"undigested compilations" or publications "which are merely
agreeable" and offered to amuse "idle amateurs" he is doubtlessly characterizing many of the publications which have
been classed in this study as substantive scientific journals.
At this point in its history the periodical had by no means
dislodged the pamphlet or the book as a means of communicating new scientific discoveries.  This role was reserved
for a more dignified and a more austere form of publication
to which we turn next in our analysis, the proceedings of
the scientific societies.

## Notes

(1)      Ornstein, op. cit., p. 205

(2)      Brown, op. cit., p. 196.

(3)      Ibid.

(4)      E.B. Barnes, op. cit.

(5)      "Annals of Science," VIII (1952), 302-322.

(6)      Ibid., p. 305.

(7)      Joseph Garland, "Medicine as a Social Instrument:
         Journalism," "New England Journal of Medicine,"
         CCXLIV (1951), 838-844.

(8)      "Philosophical Transactions," I (1665), 409-410.

(9)      Ibid., p. 3.

(10)     Ibid., pp. 2-3.

(11)     Ibid., pp. 3-8.

(12)     Ibid., pp. 11-12.

(13)     Ibid., p. 16, II (1666).

(14)    Ibid., II (1666), 143.

(15)    A. Schierbeck, "The Collected Letters of Antoni van
        Leeuwenhoek," "Antoni van Leeuwenhoek," XIX (1953),
        181-188.

(16)    "Philosophical Transactions," II (1666), 163.

(17)    Johannes Walther, "Die Aufgaben der Akademie in
        Vergangenheit und Gegenwart," "Leopoldina" I (1926),
        14.

(18)    W. Röpke, "Die Veroffentlichungen der K. Leopold-
        inische Deutsche Akademie der Naturforscher,"
        "Leopoldina," I (1926), 151.

(19)    Röpke, op. cit., p. 151.

(20)    Callisen, op. cit., XXIII, 953, indicates that eight
        volumes were published, the eighth with a twenty-
        eight page appendix consisting of a catalog of books
        in natural science and medicine.

(21)    The "Union List of Serials" incorrectly enters this
        title under Römisch-kaiserlich Akademie instead of
        under the latest title of the society, and compounds
        the error by stating that it is a translation of its
        "Nova Acta," which is a later series.

(22)    "Repertorium der medicinischen Literatur," 1784, p.
        44.

(23)    "Sammlung von Natur-und Medizin," Preface, Sept.-
        Dec., 1717.

(24)    Barnes, S.B., op. cit., p. 225.

(25)    M. Lion, "Origines du Journalisme Médicale." (Paris:
        Jouve et Cie, 1925).

(26)    "Collection Académique, Partie Etrangere," 1775-
        1779, IV, xxiii-xxiv.

(27)    Cited in S.B. Barnes, op. cit., p. 225.

(28)    M. F. Ashley-Montague, "Edward Tyson and the Rise
        of Human and Comparative Anatomy in England" (Phila-
        delphia: American Philosophical Society, 1943), p. 70.

(29)    Académie des Sciences de Paris, "Inventoire des
        Périodiques," M: 439.

(30)    S. B. Barnes, op. cit., pp. 183-196.

(31)    Dekeyser, op. cit., p. 1756.

(32)    Morgan, op. cit., p. 140.

(33)    Camusat, op. cit., I, 310.

(34)    "Recueil des Mémoires.

(35)    Ibid., Issue No. 1, 1 Feb. 1672.

(36)    Ibid., Issue No. 3, 1 Mar. 1672.

(37)    Ibid., Issue No. 6, 1 Apr. 1672.

(38)    Ibid., Issue No. 7, 11 Apr. 1672.

(39)    Infra.

(40)    Table 2.

(41)    Guitard, op. cit., p. 44.

(42)    D. Mornet, "Les Sciences de la Nature en France"
        (Paris: Armand Colin, 1911), p. 268.  Bolton, op.
        cit., No. 2691, cites the last title as "La Nature
        Considerée sous ses Differents Aspects ou Lettres
        sur les Animaux, les Végetaux, et les Mineraux."

(43)    D. I. Duveen and H. S. Klickstein, "Le Journal Polytype
        des Sciences et Arts," "Papers of the Bibliographic
        Society of America," XLVIII (1954), 402-410.

(44)    Kirchner, op. cit., No. 31.

(45)    S. B. Barnes, op. cit., pp. 219-220.  Barnes says
        the three issues appeared in March, June and July.

(46)    Prutz, op. cit., p. 347.

(47)    S. B. Barnes, op. cit., pp. 211-213.  A monthly
        which appeared in Paris from March, 1703.  Camusat
        in his "Mémoirs pour Servir a l'Histoire du Journaux"
        (Amsterdam: Bernard, 1734), II, 132, cites it under
        the title "Recherches de Mathematiques et de Phys-

ique," but he also states that Parent was a mathematical prodigy and was admitted to the academy in 1669, which would make him prodigious indeed.

(48)     A.G. Weber in the preface to "Auszüge verscheidener arzneiwissenschaftlichen Abhandlungen aus den wochenlichen Hallischen Anzeigen," Halle, 1788. It is cited in the review of the collection in the "Allgemeine Deutsche Bibliothek," LXXXIX (1789), 375.

(49)     Académie Royale de Chirurgie, Paris, "Mémoires," Preface to Volume I, 1743.

(50)     Preface, p. ix.

(51)     "Physikalische Belustigungen," 1751, I, Preface.

(52)     Ibid., pp. 8-9.

(53)     "Physikalische Belustigungen," Vol. III (1753), Preface.

(54)     Walter Artelt, "Die medizinischen Lesegesellschaften in Deutschland," "Sudhof's Archiv," XXXVII (1953), 195-200.

(55)     Max Neuberger, "Die Entwicklung des wissenschaftliche Vereinwesens," "Weiner med. Wochenschrift," L (1937), 666-674.

(56)     Naturforschende Gesellschaft in Bern, 1786.

(57)     G.R. DeBeer, "Some Letters from Jakob Samuel Wyttenbach to Sir James Edward Smith," "Annals of Science," VI (1949), 105-114. Smith was the first president of the Linnean Society founded in London in 1788. Wyttenbach's correspondence with Smith is preserved in the archives of the Society.

(58)     "Der Naturforscher," X, 3.

(59)     Infra.

(60)     B. Barber, "Science and the Social Order" (Glencoe, Ill.: Free Press, 1952), pp. 68-69.

(61)     "Critical Review," I (1756), 511.

(62)     Ibid.

Chapter VI

Original Publication: Society Proceedings

In most cases the titles designated as society proceedings in this study are those which were devoted exclusively to papers which were delivered at the public assemblies of the learned societies, or "presented" to them in either oral or written communications by members or non-members. In this respect they probably do not differ greatly from the organs maintained by many of the organizations of science today, except that our current publications are not as closely identified in their titles with the societies and organizations which support them as was the case in the 17th and 18th centuries. One of the many examples that can be cited as an illustration is the publication of an agricultural society which was established in the last quarter of the 18th century and which issued the communications it received under the title "Letters and Papers on Agriculture, Planting etc. Selected from the Correspondence of the Bath and West of England Society for the Encouragement of Agriculture, Arts, Manufactures and Commerce.*" It is full of practical advice on agriculture and animal husbandry, and in a later period might have well been called the "Gentleman Farmer," as many of its correspondents did in fact sign their offerings. This helps to account for the fact that very few of the titles we have designated substantive journals can be connected with organized societies. This is confirmed by S. B. Barnes in his study. He found that in the period 1665-1730, of the thirty scientific journals he included only six were connected with important academies of science. (1)

In this study we found evidence for society sponsorship for only approximately twenty-five per cent of the titles in the list. This makes it apparent why so many of the 18th century journals had such short lives. Society sponsorship provides an important element of continuity, as is shown in Tables 6 and 7. The comparison is even more striking when we examine the titles which continued in existence for thirty years or longer (Table 8).

## Table 6

### Duration of Society Proceedings[a]

| | General | Medicine | Agriculture | Surgery & Other Medical | Other | Total | Cumulative Percentage |
|---|---|---|---|---|---|---|---|
| 1[b] | 24 | 6 | 10 | 2 | 2 | 44 | 22 |
| 2 | 5 | 2 | 2 | 1 | 1 | 11 | |
| 3 | 4 | 1 | 2 | - | - | 8 | |
| 4 | 3 | - | - | 1 | 1 | 5 | |
| 5 | 3 | 1 | 1 | 1 | 1 | 7 | 37 |
| 6 | 4 | - | 1 | - | 1 | 6 | |
| 7 | 5 | - | 5 | 1 | 2 | 13 | |
| 8 | 2 | - | 2 | - | 1 | 5 | |
| 9 | 5 | - | - | - | 1 | 6 | |
| 10 | 3 | - | - | - | - | 4 | 54 |
| 11-15 | 10 | - | 4 | - | - | 14 | |
| 16-20 | 11 | 3 | 4 | - | - | 18 | |
| 21-25 | 6 | 3 | - | - | 1 | 10 | |
| 26-30 | 7 | 1 | - | 2 | - | 10 | |
| 31- | 29 | 3 | 6 | 1 | 3 | 42 | 100 |
| Total | 121 | 21 | 37 | 10 | 14 | 203 | |

[a]Includes only original publications.

[b]One year or less.

Table 7

Comparison of Duration: Society Proceedings
and Substantive Journals

|  | Society | Substantive |
|---|---|---|
| Five years or less | 37 % | 69 % |
| Over five years | 63 % | 31 % |
|  | 100 % | 100 % |
| Ten years or less | 54 % | 82 % |
| Over ten years | 46 % | 18 % |
|  | 100 % | 100 % |

Table 8

Comparison of Duration: Society Proceedings
and Substantive Journals, II

|  | Society | Substantive |
|---|---|---|
| Thirty years or less | 79 | 96 |
| Over thirty years | 21 | 4 |
|  | 100 | 100 |

The relatively long duration of the society publications helps
to account for the fact that in the accompanying tables (9
and 10) some of the decades show as many active society
publications as substantive journals although they represent
many fewer titles.    For example there were as many (27)
active proceedings of societies in the decade 1750 (Table 1)
as there were substantive journals, although 119 substantive
journals had their origins in the period up to 1760 as against
93 society proceedings which had their origins in the same
period (Table 1).    Although Germany again dominates in
number of publications in this class, the superiority is not
nearly as great as it was with the substantive journals, e.g.
60 original publications in Germany as against 36 in France
and 21 in Italy (Table 10), while the ratios for substantive
journals are 304 in Germany as against 53 in France and 23
in Italy (Table 2).    The translations and abridgments indicated in Table 10 are those from the original publications,
e.g. for the 36 society proceedings published in France there
appeared 19 translations or abridgments, while in Germany,
although 60 titles were published, only 6 abridgments or
translations appeared, and most of these were translations
from the Latin into German, or abridgments in German.

Table 9

Active Society Proceedings by Subject and Decade

| | 1670 | 1680 | 1690 | 1700 | 1710 | 1720 | 1730 | 1740 | 1750 | 1760 | 1770 | 1780 | 1790 |
|---|---|---|---|---|---|---|---|---|---|---|---|---|---|
| General | 2 | 2 | 2 | 2 | 4 | 6 | 11 | 15 | 23 | 30 | 34 | 44 | 47 |
| Medical | - | - | - | - | - | - | 1 | 1 | 1 | 2 | 5 | 6 | 6 |
| Agricultural | - | - | - | - | - | - | - | - | - | 6 | 10 | 10 | 12 |
| Other | - | - | - | - | - | - | - | 1 | 3 | 4 | 6 | 7 | 4 |
| Total | 2 | 2 | 2 | 2 | 4 | 6 | 12 | 17 | 27 | 42 | 55 | 67 | 69 |

Of the scientific and general scholarly societies which had their origins in the 17th century few found it necessary to issue periodic accounts of their activities. They either found adequate outlets in the contemporary general periodicals or else published the results of their work as retrospective accounts in the form of monographs. This was true of the Accademia de' Lincei (Rome, 1600 to 1630) and the Accademia del Cimento (Florence, 1657 to 1667). Ornstein cites a publication of the former society under the title "Gesta Lynceorum," published in 1609, which she calls "by far the earliest recorded publication of scientific endeavors by a society," (2) and Garrison cites another title published in Rome by the same society under the title "Praescriptiones." The first title for which we were able to find definite documentation is the "Saggi di Naturali Esperienze" published by the Accademia del Cimento in Florence in 1666-1667. It was a retrospective review of ten years' work of the society. Like the publications of the Accademia de' Lincei it appeared as the collective work of the society and anonymity is maintained regarding the individual contributions. This influence is apparent in the publications of the Académie des Sciences of Paris, which attempted to maintain the same anonymity in their early publications, and in their "Histoire," an annual publication which began after the turn of the century, and in which they provided a narrative account of the year's activity of the society. The Académie maintained this attitude almost until the end of the century. Bertrand reports in his history of the society:

> Before publishing its work for the first time, the company asked itself whether they should name in the preface those who were responsible for the various discoveries. They were of the opinion that they

Table 12

Soceity Proceedings by Country and
Subject Titles Issued

| | Switzer-land | France | Holland | Sweden | Russia | England | Denmark | Italy | Germany | Other | Total |
|---|---|---|---|---|---|---|---|---|---|---|---|
| **GENERAL SOCIETIES** | | | | | | | | | | | |
| Original | 4 | 25 | 6 | 5 | 5 | 5 | 5 | 17 | 40 | 11 | 123 |
| Trans. and Abridg. | - | 14 | 5 | 7 | 3 | 18 | 2 | 2 | 4 | - | 55 |
| Total | 4 | 39 | 11 | 12 | 8 | 23 | 7 | 19 | 44 | 11 | 178 |
| No. of Societies | 3 | 18 | 6 | 4 | 1 | 5 | 5 | 13 | 20 | 3 | 78 |
| **MEDICAL SOCIETIES** | | | | | | | | | | | |
| Original | - | 2 | 1 | - | - | 5 | 4 | - | 3 | 5 | 20 |
| Trans. and Abridg. | - | 1 | - | - | - | 5 | 1 | - | 2 | - | 9 |
| Total | - | 3 | 1 | - | - | 10 | 5 | - | 5 | 5 | 29 |
| No. of Societies | - | 2 | 1 | - | - | 5 | 1 | - | 3 | 5 | 17 |
| **AGRICULTURAL SOCIETIES** | | | | | | | | | | | |
| Original | 4 | 4 | 1 | - | 1 | 2 | 1 | 3 | 11 | 5 | 32 |
| Trans. and Abridg. | 2 | - | - | - | 2 | 1 | - | - | - | - | 5 |
| Total | 6 | 4 | 1 | - | 3 | 3 | 1 | 3 | 11 | 5 | 37 |
| No. of Societies | 2 | 4 | 1 | - | 1 | 2 | 1 | 3 | 7 | 5 | 26 |

**OTHER**

| | | | | | | | | | | | Total |
|---|---|---|---|---|---|---|---|---|---|---|---|
| Technology | 1 | — | 3 | — | — | 1 | — | — | — | — | 5 |
| Resuscitation | — | — | 2 | — | — | 1 | — | — | — | — | 3 |
| Mathematics | — | — | 1 | — | — | — | — | — | — | — | 1 |
| Surgery | — | 2 | — | — | — | — | — | 1 | 1 | — | 4 |
| Marine | — | — | — | — | — | — | — | — | 1 | — | 1 |
| Mining | — | 1 | — | — | — | — | — | — | — | — | 1 |
| Archeology | — | — | — | — | — | — | 1 | — | — | — | 1 |
| Magnetism | — | 1 | — | — | — | — | — | — | — | — | 1 |
| Bee Culture | — | — | — | — | — | — | — | — | 1 | — | 1 |
| Astronomy | — | — | — | — | — | — | — | — | 3 | — | 3 |
| Inoculation | — | 1 | — | — | — | — | — | — | — | — | 1 |
| Geography | — | — | — | — | — | 1 | — | — | — | — | 1 |
| Total | 1 | 5 | 6 | — | — | 3 | 1 | 1 | 6 | — | 23 |
| Trans. and Abridg. | — | 4 | 1 | — | — | — | — | — | — | — | 5 |
| Totals | 1 | 9 | 7 | — | — | 3 | 1 | 1 | 6 | — | 28 |
| **GRAND TOTALS** | | | | | | | | | | | |
| Original | 9 | 36 | 14 | 5 | 6 | 15 | 11 | 21 | 60 | 21 | 198 |
| Trans. and Abridg. | 2 | 19 | 6 | 7 | 5 | 24 | 3 | 2 | 6 | — | 74 |
| No. of Societies | 6 | 28 | 11 | 4 | 2 | 15 | 8 | 17 | 35 | 13 | 139 |

should not be named, and it was decided that naming
them would be a contradiction, were they also to say
that the discoveries were made in the Academy.
This strange equality, which was decreed but not
maintained, was not without precedent, since the experiments of the academicians of the Cimento at
Florence remained their common property.  The Academy of Paris in appropriating to itself the work of its
members denied to each of them the right to inscribe
them in their own works.

One reads in the proceedings for 18 August 1688: 'The
company, in order to avoid in the future having those
persons who compose it inserting in their own works
particulars of the observations and new discoveries
which are made in its assemblies, have agreed to the
regulation that in the future each of those who wish
to have their works printed will be obliged to notify
the Company and to bring their manuscripts there in
order to have them examined, either by the Academy
or by committees appointed which will be named for
that purpose.  In regard to those works which have already been printed by its members, the Company has
resolved to lay claim to those which belong to them
and whenever the occasion presents itself.' (3)

The Académie later added another regulation which forbade
any of its members to state on the title pages of their works
that they were members of the society without being author-
ized to do so by a committee.  It may possibly be to these
regulations that Ornstein refers when she says that the breakdown of the intentions of the academy to publish their work
as a unit resulted in 1688 in the appointment of a commission
to investigate the work published by members of the academy
to determine whether or not the author was guilty of plagia-
rism. (4)

This anonymity of authorship is also characteristic of
the publications of the Collegium Privatum Amstelodamense,
an organization of medical men which was organized in Amsterdam early in 1644, and which existed sporadically until
1672.  It was similar to a number of other groups formed in
this period which met at intervals to dissect and examine
specimens.  In 1667 the first volume of its publications appeared under the title "Observations Anatomicae Selectores
Amstelodamensum."  Since it was followed six years later
with a second volume with the same title, it deserves consideration as a candidate for the title of first publication of
a serial proceedings by a scientific society.  It was probably

founded early in 1664 by Gerard L. Blasius or Blaes (d. 1692) and its most distinguished member was Jan Swammerdam (1637-1680). (5)  F.J. Cole in his account of this society in his "History of Comparative Anatomy" says of Blaes and Swammerdam that "In their later writings both claim the authorship of a considerable section" of the society's publications. (6)  It appears even at this early date, that despite the selflessness and devotion to science which was demonstrated by anonymity of publication, natural pride in authorship could not help asserting itself.

The publications edited by Bartholin and Denis which were cited earlier are included among the substantive journals although there were nominally associated with organized groups, because it is not clear that the publications resulted from the activities of societies.  This is the case with a number of other publications which describe themselves as the work of a particular society.  In many instances it seems very likely that the society was organized largely for the purpose of issuing a publication, rather than that the publication resulted from the activities of the society.  This appears to be true in the case of what Dekeysser calls the "first medical review in Portugal" although it is obvious from its title that it aspired to a much broader subject coverage: "Zodiaco Lusitanico Delphico, Anatomico, Botanico, Chirurgico, Chymico, Dendrologico, Ictyologico, Leithologico, Medico, Metereologico, Optico, Ornithologico, Pharmaceutico e Zoologico."  The sole issue of this publication appeared in 1749. (7)  It is described on its title page as the work of an Academia dos Escondidos, or "secret ones."  The influence of the humanistic academies is shown both in its title and in the pseudonyms adopted by the members of the society who signed themselves Apollo, Jason, Argos, etc. (8)

An earlier claimant than the "Observationes Anatomicae" to the title of being the first published society proceedings is the "Centurie des Questions Traitées ès Conférences du Bureau d'Addresse" which was published in Paris between 1636 and 1655.  Hatin says of them: "These are evidently the origins of the proceedings, the reports of the memoires of our scholarly societies." (9)  They cannot, however, be regarded in any sense as the proceedings of a soceity.  They were the result of another of the many innovations of the social reformer, Theophraste Renaudot, who inaugurated a series of public forums on various subjects at his Bureau d'-Address.  Brown reports that they were held in low esteem by the literati of the period and spoken of only in the most derogatory terms when they are mentioned at all by contemporary writers. (10)  The forums began some time before the

summer of 1633 and were discontinued after the death of
Richelieu when Renaudot's other activities were also severely
circumscribed.  The first volume of the published accounts
of these meetings appeared in 1636 and the fifth and last volume was published in 1655 after Renaudot's death.  Their
popularity is indicated by the numerous reprints which appeared in the following years.  Brown cites a partial reprint,
which he discovered in the library of Princeton University,
in which the volume is rearranged in the form of a topical
encyclopedia.  The title borne by the reprint provides some
idea of the subjects discussed at the meetings: "L'Académie
des beaux Esprits contenant ce qu'il y a de plus beau et de
plus curieux a scavoir de l'Histoire, de la Morale, de la
Philosophie, de la Theologie, de la Jurisprudence et de tous
les Arts et Sciences."  These volumes exhibit a curious mix-
ture of the medieval and the modern and the confusion of
science and superstition in early 17th Century France.  A-
mong the topics discussed and evidently selected to appeal to
a wide audience:  how animals are born from decay, whether
it is more advantageous for men to have several wives or for
women to have several husbands, whether sterility is more
frequently the fault of the male than of the female, the various terms of conception and why infants born seven months
after conception are more likely to live than those born after
eight, if wine aids or interferes with digestion, and the nature of sleep and what should be its duration. (11)

        In the first phase of its history the Royal Society of
London published monographs rather than serial publications,
and some of the greatest books printed in the 17th century in
England were issued under its imprint. (12)   Malpighi sent
his manuscripts to the Royal Society from Italy and many of
his titles appeared under the Society's auspices.  Weld in his
'History of the Royal Society'' reports that the publication of
Willughby's 'History of Fishes'' exhausted the treasury of the
Society so much that they had to fall into arrears in paying
the salaries of its officers. (13)   The influence of Bacon is
clearly discernable here, since  he had enjoined his readers
to bring together collection on various subjects.  In the stat-
utes adopted at the granting of the Royal charter in 1663,
however, the Royal Society did make provision for the maintenance of a record:

        ...wherein shall be fairly written all such observa-
        tions, histories, and discourses of natural and artifi-
        cial things--as also such philosophical experiments,
        together with particular accounts of their processes as
        shall be ordered to be entered therein. (14)

Soon after this a proposal was made to publish the communications received by the Society (15) but the proposal never
came to fruition.   It was not until 1665 that the secretary of
the Society, Oldenbourg, began the publication of the "Philosophical Transactions" as a private venture, albeit with the
approval and under the surveillance of the Royal Society.
Before the appearance of the first issue of the "Transactions"
the following resolution of the council appears in its records:

> That the  Philosophical Transactions to be composed
> by Mr. Oldenbourg be printed on the first Monday of
> every month, if he have sufficient matter for it, and
> that the tract be licensed under the Charter by the
> Council of the Society, being first reviewed by some
> members of the same; and that the President be now
> desired to license the first papers thereof, being writ-
> ten in four sheets in folio, to be printed by John
> Martyn and James Allestrye. (16)

The Society, nevertheless, soon made it clear that they were
assuming no official responsibility for the publication.   In the
"Advertisement" which appears at the end of the twelfth number, 7 May 1666, the following statement occurs:

> Whereas 'tis taken notice of, that several persons
> perswade themselves, that these Philosophical Trans-
> actions are publish't by the Royal Society, notwith-
> standing many circumstances, to be met with in the
> already publish't ones, that import the contrary; The
> Writer thereof hath thought fit expressly here to de-
> clare, that that perswasion, if there be any such in-
> deed, is a meer mistake; and that he, upon his Pri-
> vate account (as a Well-wisher to the advancement of
> useful knowledge, and a Furtherance thereof by such
> Communications, as he is capable to furnish by that
> Philosophical Correspondency, which he entertains,
> and hopes to enlarge) hath begun and continues both
> the composure and publication thereof:   though he de-
> nies not, but that, having the honour and advantage of
> being a fellow of the said Society, he inserts at times
> some of the Particulars that are presented to them,
> to wit, such as he knows he may mention without of-
> fending them, or transgressing their Orders; tending
> only to administer occasion to others also, to consider
> and carry them further, or to observe or Experiment
> the like, according as the nature of such things may
> require.

When the "Philosophical Transactions" were resumed after the

cessation of the "Philosophical Collections" in 1682, the preface to the first number issued in 1682 reiterates this position:

> Although the writing of these Transactions is not to be
> looked upon as the business of the Royal Society, yet
> in regard they are a specimen of many things which
> lie before them, contain a great variety of useful mat-
> ter, a Convenient Register for bringing in and pre-
> serving many experiments, which, not enough for a
> book, would else be lost, and having proved a very
> good ferment for the setting of uncommon thoughts in
> all parts a-work. (17)

The administrative history and the record of the Royal Society's activities appeared in the retrospective histories which
were published at long intervals, beginning with Thomas Spra
in 1667. Birch in his 'History of the Royal Society of London" includes the records of the Society from 1660 to 1687.
He was followed by Thomas Thomson's 'History of the Royal
Society from its Institution to the End of the Eighteenth Century" (1812) and Charles Richard Weld's "A History of the
Royal Society" (1848).

It was not until 1753 when the forty-seventh volume
covering the years 1751 and 1752 appeared that the Royal
Society began to issue the "Philosophical Transactions" under
its own auspices. They announced in the preface to that volume:

> The Committee appointed by the Royal Society to di-
> rect the publication of the "Philosophical Transactions,"
> take this opportunity to acquaint the public that it fully
> appears, as well from the council-books and journals
> of the Society, as from the repeated declarations,
> which have been made in several former "Transactions,
> that the printing them was always, from time to time,
> the single act of the respective Secretaries, till this
> present XLVII volume. An this information was though
> the more necessary, not only as it has been the com-
> mon opinion, that they were published by the authority,
> and under the direction, of the Society itself; but also,
> because several authors, both at home and abroad,
> have in their writings called them the 'Transactions of
> the Royal Society." Whereas in truth the Society, as
> a body, never did interest themselves any further in
> their publication, than by occasionally recommending th
> revival of them to some of their secretaries, when,
> from the particular circumstances of their affairs, the

"Transactions" had happened for any length of time to
be intermitted.  An this seems principally to have
been done with a view to satisfy the public, that their
usual meetings were then continued for the improvement of knowledge, and benefit of mankind, the great
ends of their first institution by the royal charters,
and which they have ever since steadily pursued.

But the Society being of late years greatly enlarged,
and their communications more numerous, it was
thought advisable, that a Committee of their members
should be appointed to reconsider the papers read before them, and select out of them such, as they
should judge most proper for publication in the future
"Transactions;" which was accordingly done upon the
twenty-sixth of March 1752.  And the grounds of their
choice are, and will continue to be, the importance or
singularity of the subjects, or the advantageous manner of treating them; without pretending to answer for
the certainty of the facts, or propriety of the reason-
ings, contained in the several papers so published,
which must still rest on the credit or judgment of
their respective authors.

It is likewise necessary on this occasion to remark,
that it is an established rule of the Society, to which
they will always adhere, never to give their opinion,
as a body, upon any subject, either of nature or art,
that comes before them.  And therefore the thanks,
which are frequently proposed from the chair, to be
given to the authors of such papers, as are read in
their accustomed meetings, or to the persons, through
whose hands they receive them, are to be considered
in no other light, that as a matter of civility, in return for the respect shown to the Society by those
communications.  The like also is to be said with regard to the several projects, inventions, and curiosi-
ties of various kinds, which are often exhibited to the
Society; the authors whereof, or those who exhibit
them, frequently take the liberty to report, and even
to certify in the public news-papers, that they have
met with the highest applause and approbation.  And
therefore it is hoped that no regard will hereafter be
paid to such reports and public notices; which in some
instances have been too lightly credited, to the dis-
honor of the Society. (18)

Historians are generally agreed that the cause of this change
was a scathing attack upon the Society and upon the "Trans-

actions" delivered by John Hill in his "Review of the Works
of the Royal Society" (London, 1751). Some of the criticism
in Hill's review is reminiscent of the satirical attacks upon
the Society in its formative years, when the playwright
Thomas Shadwell in his "The Virtuoso" (1676) created the
famous figure of the pedant Sir Nicholas Gimcrack who studies the art of swimming on a stool in his home, since, as
he says, he is interested solely in the theory of the matter.
(19) With the formal, albeit rather hedging, sponsorship of
the "Transactions" the Society created a "Committee of Papers" consisting of five members to select papers for publication. They also provided that the "Transactions" should be
distributed gratis to members of the Society, and admission
fee was raised from two to five guineas to finance the change.

The publication activities of the Académie des Sciences
in Paris closely parallels that of the Royal Society. Its first
major publication was the "Mémoires pour Servir a l'Histoire Naturelle des Animaux," a collection of tracts on comparative anatomy which appeared in 1671. It was first issued in a limited edition and distributed by Louis XIV and by
members of the academy, and thus did not have a very wide
distribution. Edward Tyson, the English anatomist, was not
able to see a copy until 1683. (20) It was reissued, anony-
mously, in a public edition, in 1676 and went through several
other editions before it was incorporated into the Académie's
"Histoire et Mémoires" covering the period 1666-1699. In
this the authors of the separate monographs were identified. (21) Until the beginning of the 18th century the Académie published no official proceedings. Its activities throughout the 17th century were reported to the public largely
through the "Journal des Sçavans" which had its inception in
1665, one year before the Académie was officially organized.
The association between the "Journal" and the Académie in
the early part of their history is similar to that which prevailed between the "Philosophical Transactions" and the Royal
Society. Abbé Gallois who edited the "Journal" from January
1666 to January 1674, was also a secretary of the Académie
des Sciences as well as a member of the Académie Francaise.
He was an encyclopedic scholar, which was not unusual in his
day, who was interested in history and philology, but is also
said to have been celebrated as a mathematician, astronomer,
and physician. (22) Louis Cousin who edited the "Journal"
from 1687 to 1707, however, was a lawyer by training, a
classicist and an authority in ecclesiastical history, as well
as a member of the Académie Francaise.

The first published account of the proceedings of the
academy appeared in 1698 in an account written in Latin by

Duhamel, first secretary of the academy. The first edition appeared in Paris under the title "Academiae Scientiarum Historia." It is not clear whether the Académie published any proceedings before this or not. There is some evidence that such a publication appeared between the years 1692 and 1694, although none of the published lists of periodicals includes these volumes. The translator who compiled two collections of abstracts from the society's publications between 1748 and 1762 indicates that they cover the proceedings of the academy from 1692. (23) The Académie made an attempt from 1692 to 1694 to issue monthly memoirs or transactions "after the manner of ours in London; but could not carry them on above two volumes or years, for without great correspondence this can hardly be done." (24) Lister adds that he had purchased two small quartos of the monthly memoirs for twenty livres and also quotes Abbé Gallois as saying that the paper might have been more successful if Leibnitz had contributed to it. Barnes also cites some correspondence of Huyghens to Leibnitz approving of a Dutch reprint of the French memoirs which was appearing in Holland, but it is quite possible that all this talk may have been about the "Journal des Sçavans" rather than of a separate publication issued by the Académie. The published catalog of Boerhaave's library, "Bibliotheca Boerhaaviana sive Catalogus Librorum" (Leyden, 1739), contains an entry for a two volume edition published in Amsterdam of the "Mémoires de Mathematiques et de Physique de l'Académie Royale des Sciences de l'Année 1692 et 93." Perhaps the most conclusive evidence of the existence of these volumes is the statement which occurs in the tenth volume of the retrospective "Histoire et Mémoires, 1666-1699*" which was published by the academy between 1729 and 1734:

> The Académie Royale des Science although established in 1666, did not begin to provide the public with a collection of its memoirs or extracts from its registers until the year 1692. They continued to do so in 1693 but from that year discontinued the collection until 1699. The reasons why the company undertook to issue a series of this sort are stated in an announcement which was placed at the beginning of the volume for that year...

> The long interval between 1666 and 1699 was filled in some manner by a multitude of fragments and singular and curious observations scattered in the "Journal des Sçavans" which was born almost at the same time as the academy.

It was not until 1702 that the Académie des Sciences
began the annual publication of its proceedings beginning with
the year 1699 in which the Society was reorganized.  Between
1729 and 1734 it published a retrospective history and collection of its memoirs covering the years from its origins to
1699, in eleven volumes.  The first two volumes of the series consists of a translation by Fontenelle, the secretary
who succeeded Duhamel, of Duhamel's "Historia" to which he
also added some new material.  The avertissement to the
first volume states:

> The history of the Académie Royale des Sciences
> which we are now publishing was compiled in part
> from the registers of this company and in part from
> M. Duhamel's Latin history.  M. DeFontenelle, the
> perpetual secretary of the Academy, has compiled this
> history from the origin of the Academy until about
> 1679; the other years to 1699, in which the long se-
> ries of the "Histoire et Mémoires" begin, were trans-
> lated into French in an order similar to that which
> M. DeFontenelle followed in the preceeding ones.  One
> can find in these volumes things which were omitted
> by M. Duhamel and reciprocally M. Duhamel inserted
> pieces  which will not be found here, either because
> they were essentially revised, or treated more amply
> by the members of the academy in the volumes which
> follow.

It adds that a five volume quarto edition had been printed in
Holland, but advised the reader that it is greatly inferior to
the edition in hand.  The third volume of the series is in
two parts and is a revision of Perrault's "Mémoires pour
Servir a l'Histoire Naturelle des Animaux" with the addition
of several monographs that had not appeared in the earlier
editions.  Volumes four to nine are devoted to collections of
memoirs and correspondence of the various academicians.
The tenth volume has the title "Mémoires de Mathématique
et de Physique Tirés de Registres de l'Académie Royale des
Sciences Années 1692-1693," which may possibly be a reprint
of the series we discussed earlier.  The last half of the volume is devoted to "Mémoires de Mathématiques et de Physique par MM. de l'Académie Royale des Sciences, Extraits
de Differens Journals etc."  The eleventh volume is an index
to the series.

In the series "Histoire et Mémoires" which the Académie published on an average of two to six years after the
papers had been delivered at their meetings, the Academy

set the pattern for the publication of society proceedings which was followed by a number of other scientific and learned societies on the continent. In the first part or "Histoire" they summarize the contributions for the year covered by the volume. It consists of short essays on specific topics, summaries of reports of investigations made to the society, and the discussions elicited in their meetings. The "Mémoires" consist of selected papers which are arranged roughly in chronological order of presentation and are complete papers rather than the abstracts which appear in the "Histoire." The preface to the volume for 1707 comments on this arrangement:

> The "Histoire" contains much more than the "Mémoires" which are those pieces read before the academy which are considered most worthy of being presented in their entirety...

This division serves two purposes, the preface continues; first, it enables the reader to read in brief form the parts in the "Histoire" which pertain to the "Mémoires," and secondly,

> In general, it is believed that in reporting both to serious scholars and to those who are not, it would be good to present in two different forms the materials which compose this report, in order that the work of the Academy should be better known and that the taste for the sciences should grow. (25)

In 1750 the Académie began a new series devoted to the communications sent them by contributors who were not members of the society. This publication appeared under the title "Mémoires de Mathématiques et de Physique Presentées a l'Académie Royale des Sciences pars Divers Scavans, et Lus dans ses Assemblées.*" This series, which was issued until 1786, was used also for publication of papers which found no place in the regular series. For example, the last volume, published in 1786, contains four papers of Lavoisier on the chemistry and manufacture of saltpeter. (26)

One of the primary devices used by learned and scientific societies for encouraging research and publication was the prize essay. The topics for investigation were announced either in the societies' publications or in the general press. The scholarly and literary journals of the 18th century are full of announcements of questions posed for prizes by the various societies and academies of Europe, as well as abstracts and reviews of the winning essays. This device probably had its origins in the prizes awarded by the national

governments of Europe for the solution of various problems,
such as the discovery of a method of determining correct
longitude at sea, which engaged some of the best minds of
the period.  Collections of prize essays awarded by a particular society were printed as early as 1715 at Bordeaux (27)
and prizes were awarded regularly at the Académie des Sciences in Paris from 1721.  Rouille de Meslay, member of
Parliament, had given the Academy a legacy of one-hundred
thousand livres with an annual income of 4000 livres for this
purpose.  The legacy, it is interesting to note, made provision for publication.

> And the other part of the said income will be em-
> ployed in the following manner:   one fourth for the
> remuneration or fees for the judges, another fourth
> to the secretary of the academy for the expenses of
> the announcements and publications and copies of the
> treatises which will be written. (28)

The income from the legacy could not be used at once because
the will was contested by Meslay's sons who cited this legacy
to the Académie and the sort of research which Meslay had
indicated as suitable for the Académie to pursue as indica-
tions of his lack of mental competence.  The advocat for
Meslay's son stated that it was not only ridiculous to suggest
as a topic for investigation, determination of the composition
of the planets, but that it was equally absurd to investigate
the principles of light and movement.  The legal proceedings
were carried on for four years before they were finally ad-
judicated in favor of the Academy.  The essays which received the Académie's awards were printed as separates, but
they were also collected under the title "Recueil des Pièces
qui ont Remporté le Prix,*" from 1727.

One indication of the influence of a particular society
and its contribution to the dissemination of ideas is the number of reprints and abridgments of its publications which appeared in the course of the years.  There does not seem to
be in existence any complete catalogs of the publications of
either the Royal Society or the Académie des Sciences, but it
is a fairly safe generalization to say that in terms of the distribution of their publications they were the most influential
of their time.  It is difficult to say how many times the proceedings of these two societies were reprinted because editions of the different volumes appeared at various times.
The translations and foreign imprints provide a surer guide
to the degree of penetration of the publications.  Beside the
many abridgments of the "Philosophical Transactions" which
appeared in London, there were editions in English at both

Lübeck (1774-1778) and Wittenberg (1768-1775), and three translations into German, two into French, and one each in Latin, Italian and Dutch of various parts of the series. Beside the many editions of the 'Histoire et Mémoires'' in France, there were several editions in French in Holland, six translations into German, two into English, and one into Italian. (29)

The publishing histories of most of the other societies established in the 17th and 18th centuries cannot be compared to these two leading societies. Of the approximately 220 societies which had their origins before 1790, and which were somehow associated with science or technology, there are over 50 for which we found no record of printed publication prior to 1790. (30) This represents almost 25 per cent of the total number of societies which were uncovered in the course of this study. When we consider that perhaps the principal source of information concerning the existence of the societies is their publications, it appears that this proportion may be even greater. The need and desire to leave a record of their activities was probably one of the greatest motivations which led the societies to publish their proceedings, but it is also true that in some cases societies of scientific men were organized for other purposes than the advancement of science, or at least for purposes which might not lead to the publications of proceedings.

Many of the organizations of professional groups, artisans and tradesmen, which go back to antiquity, existed primarily for regulating their activities and maintaining standards of performance. A charter was granted to the Royal College of Physicians in 1518 ''...imitating the example of well governed cities in Italy and many other nations.'' (31) However, no publications of a serial nature issued from this body until 1768 when the first volume of their ''Medical Transactions'' appeared in London. Somewhat the same role was filled in Paris by the Faculté de Médecine which is even older. It was not until the Société Royale de Médecine was established in Paris in 1778 that the published papers of a medical society appeared in France. One example of a society formed for purposes that might not necessarily lead to the publication of proceedings was the Society of Collegiate Physicians, which existed in London between 1767 and 1798. It was organized to challenge the right of the Royal College of Physicians to restrict membership to those who had obtained their medical degrees either at Oxford or Cambridge. They failed in their initial attempt to force the College to grant them membership, even though they actually made an armed assault on the College. The Society included such

distinguished British physicians as William Hunter and Foth-
ergill.   Papers were read at some of their meetings, but it
was not until 1790 that it was proposed before one of their
gatherings that a selection of these papers be printed.   This
proposal led to the usual round of committees but the plan
evidently never came to fruition. (32)   The Edinburgh Har-
veian Society which was founded in 1782 (33) by Andrew Duncan, was a similar organization.   It was said to be one of
the oldest medical social clubs in Edinburgh.   D'Arcy Power
says:

> Perhaps its survival is due to the fact that it demands
> little of its members since its meetings are held only
> once a year--on the anniversary of William Harvey's
> birthday. (34)

One writer on the "natural history of learned and scientific
societies" suggests that the Scots must have a particular talent
for this kind of organization.

> Some of the Scottish societies of this period were dis-
> tinguished by the conviviality of their proceedings.
> The Harveian Society of Edinburgh founded in 1782,
> was preceded by a Faculty Club comprising a group of
> imaginary physicians who wore wigs and gowns at their
> meetings.   The Society (which for a time was known
> as the 'Circulation') met annually on the anniversary
> of Harvey's birthday 'to commemorate the discovery
> of the circulation of the blood by the circulation of the
> glass.'   Membership was limited to those proposed at
> the Aesculapian Club or the Dissipation Club.   Dr.
> Andrew Duncan, the first president, in the conviction
> that medical men did not take sufficient exercise, es-
> tablished the Gymnastic Society in 1786, where Har-
> veians were to compete with one another at swimming
> or other sports; but 'enthusiasm for this detracted
> from attendance at the Harveian Festival.' (35)

There were other societies of more serious purpose
which left no published record of their activities.   The sole
remaining trace of some of these societies are their manuscript record books or the manuscript collections of their
papers.   Among these we can cite the Gloucestershire Medical Society, which was distinguished by the membership of
William Jenner, and which met three times a year at the
Fleece Inn at Rodborough in the north of Gloucestershire.
The papers of this society, which include several of Jenner's,
remained unpublished until they fell into the hands of Dr. Alfred Henry Carder of Birmingham who allowed an account of

them to be published at the centennary of Jenner's first vac-
cination. (36)   Notice of another such society occurs in the
correspondence of William Cullen who wrote in 1788 to James
Cleghorne:

> Your uncle and I are, I believe, the only surviving
> members of a society which existed at Edinburgh in
> the year 1735, and which laid the foundation of the
> Medical Society, which became more formally incor-
> porated the year after, and as you know has flourished
> ever since, to the great advancement of medical sci-
> ence in this University.  Tell your worthy uncle that
> I have what I consider, and I believe he would con-
> sider, as a curiosity.  It is a manuscript book, in
> which the discourses of the society in 1735 are re-
> corded; and there are I believe some of his juvenile
> performances to be found in it.  At our breaking up
> in the spring of 1735, we drew lots for this book,
> and the fortunate lot fell upon Douglas, the Surgeon of
> the Welsh Fusileers.  This gentleman, after travelling
> about for some years, came at length to Glasgow, and
> died there, leaving me this book as a legacy. (37)

It has been suggested that at least one of these organizations
of students at Edinburgh was formed to give students a place
to practice the preparation and defense of their theses.   This
was the Chemical Society of the University of Edinburgh which
had its origins in 1785.   James Kendall who discovered the
manuscript volume of their papers in the library of the Royal
Irish Academy claims for it the distinction of being the "first
chemical journal." (38)   This claim is tenuous for there are
several earlier contenders which have the merit of having
been published.   Beside the two titles which are listed by
Kirchner, "Kurelle chemische Versuche und Erfahrungen,"
which appeared in only one issue in Berlin in 1756, and the
"Chymische Nebenstunde" of which two issues appeared in St.
Petersburg in 1762 and 1768, there is the whole series of
chemical journals issued by Lorenz von Crell, who can probably be considered the originator of chemical journalism.
The first of this series is the "Chemisches Journal für die
Freunde der Naturlehre, Arzneygelahrtheit, Haushaltungskunst
und Manufakturen *" which started in 1778.

The Royal Medical Society of Edinburgh began as an
association of medical students in 1737.   It was organized for
hearing and discussing dissertations written by its members
in preparation for the formal papers they had to deliver as a
part of their medical training.   The Society did not receive
a Royal Charter until 1778, and although plans were made at

various times for the publication of their papers, no publication of this society appeared in the 18th century. The
necessity for a publication may have been reduced to some
extent by the procedure adopted by the society for the circulation of the manuscript copies of its papers. This procedure is described by Gray in his history of the society.

> A sufficient number of copies of dissertations was
> procured, at the expense of the Society, so that every
> member should receive them in circulation. At the
> commencement of the session the secretary arranged
> the list of circulation according to the seniority of
> the members, who then intimated to him their desire
> to have their names placed on it. The names of
> members, who afterward desired to be included in the
> list, were added to it according to priority of applica-
> tion. The original arrangement was not to be altered
> in any instance, except by the mutual agreement of
> members to exchange their places on the list. The
> Secretary began the circulation every Saturday during
> the session, at 8 o'clock in the morning, by sending
> the papers to the senior member on the list; and the
> papers then circulated among members according to
> seniority, six hours being allowed to each member.
> If a member detained the papers more than six hours
> beyond the time at which he ought to have sent them
> away, he was not to send them to the next member
> on the list, but to him whose right it was to have
> them at the time of delivery. Every member was to
> send the papers at the appointed time, whether they
> had been six hours in his possession or not. If the
> papers were delivered at the abode of any member
> later than the hour appointed for him to have sent them
> away, he was not liable to a fine though they should
> happen to be detained: but he had to endeavor to set
> the circulation right as soon as possible. A book cir-
> culated with the papers, in which were inserted the
> names and addresses of the members who were to re-
> ceive the papers, and the hours alloted to each mem-
> ber for the perusal of them. In another part of the
> book, each member from whom he received the papers
> the hour at which he received them, the name of the
> member to whom he sent them, the hour at which he
> sent them, and his own name. The list of circulation
> of the preceding week were examined every Friday
> night by one of the authors whose dissertations were
> read at the preceding meeting.

For many years the members appear to have conducted

the circulation without assistance.   On 8th November
1783 Mr. Richard Lubbock moved, 'That David the
porter be appointed to carry the papers in circulation
to and from each member's lodgings at the proper
hours'; but, a week later, he withdrew his motion.
An there is no evidence of detailed rules of the
porter's assistance until 1823. (39)

Elaborate arrangements for circulation of papers resulted from the fact that several of the societies made the
writing of papers a condition of membership.   Thus Article
XV of the new regulations of the Académie Royale de Chirurgie de Paris of 18 March 1751 states:

> The councellors are required to furnish one or two
> memoirs a year; if they do not have legitimate rea-
> sons for not doing so, their positions may be de-
> clared vacant. (40)

The Académie Imperiale et Royale des Sciences et Belles-
Lettres de Bruxelles had a similar regulation which required
each of the ordinary members (as distinguished from the
honorary members) to produce at least one memoir a year,
to be placed in the hands of the secretary and to be read at
one of the assemblies.   The regulation adds, that the memoir would not be published without the consent of the author.
(41)   These provide additional evidence that the societies
were formed in large measure to stimulate research and
communication of the results of research.   The societies of
the 18th century were frequently referred to as "literary societies" not because of their concern with belles-lettres, but
because of their concern with scientific literature.   The preface to the first volume of the "Memoirs of the Medical Society of London Instituted in the Year 1773" states this attitude
clearly:

> Nothing has contributed more to the advancement of
> science, than the establishment of literary societies:
> these excite a generous ardour in liberal minds, and
> raise even envy itself into useful emulation.

> In that science, which rational estimation has first
> place in the scale of honour, the science which pro-
> poses the noblest objects for its end, the preservation
> and restoration of health; the improvements which
> have already resulted from the formation of societies
> are well known to the medical world.

> The principal part of our knowledge must be ever de-

rived from comparing our own observations with those
of others. In this view the utility of societies, which
afford an opportunity for the mutual communication of
our thoughts, must be sufficiently apparent. De-
ceased authors cannot solve our difficulties, nor will
the observations made in other ages and climates,
hold always true in our own.

There are some circumstances peculiarly favourable
to a rising society; each member thinking the honour
of the association in some measure dependent upon
himself, is stimulated to the highest exertion of his
powers: unawed by the same, and fearless of being
eclipsed by the lustre of his predecessors, no damp
is cast upon the vigour of that genius, which can
alone produce great discoveries.

Medical papers, which may tend to the advancement
of the science, will be received by the Society; and
such as may be deemed worthy of publication, carefully preserved, until sufficient matter for a volume
shall be collected.

Many useful facts are lost from the want of a proper
opportunity of conveying them to the world; and though,
when considered separately, they may not be of sufficient importance to claim the attention of the public,
yet when a number of them are collected together,
they may become highly deserving of notice: to such
facts, when properly authenticated, the Society will
always be particularly attentive.

In order to excite practitioners to bring those talents
to light, which would otherwise lie buried, and useless
to the community, the Society, on its first institution,
proposed to hold forth honorary rewards to those who
should improve the medical art; 'and it is now resolved to give a Silver Medal annually to the author
of the best memoir that shall be communicated within
the year; which shall be decided by the Fellows of the
Society, who being judges of its merit, cannot be
candidates for the prize.'

The lag between the presentation of the papers to the
society and their appearance in published form varies considerably, but the Académie des Sciences, Belles-Lettres et
Arts de Rouen wins the doubtful honor of having achieved
greatest delay. The history of the society goes back to 1716
when a group of residents of that city formed an organization

to cultivate the sciences and arts.   Not much seems to be
known of that group, the date of their cessation or whether
they gave rise to any publications, but in 1735 it was evidently necessary to form a new group which called itself a
botanical society.   The society was organized by two physicians and in 1740 was joined by the distinguished surgeon
LeCat who seems to have dominated the group.   In the period before the granting of the charter in 1744, no minutes
seem to have been taken of the discussions, but with the
granting of the charter the society was organized on the model
of the Académie des Sciences and the Académie des Inscrip-
tions et Belles-Lettres, and the presentation of formal papers
was inaugurated.   None of these papers seem to have been
published under the auspices of the society, although many
of them appeared in other media.   Gosseaume, the secretary
of the society after its restoration in 1803, to whom the task
fell of collecting and transcribing the remaining memoirs,
tells the story in the preface to the "Précis Analytique des
Travaux" published between 1814 and 1821 and which covers
the activities of the society from 1744 to 1793, when the activities of the society were suspended.

> The Academy from its institution had proposed to
> communicate to the public by means of print, a précis
> of its work.   They felt justly that the account which
> they rendered to the public each year at their public
> meeting filled this intent only imperfectly, and they
> charged several special committees with the selection,
> the examination and the classification of those mem-
> oirs which they proposed to publish.   The government,
> on its side, encouraged these activities by giving the
> Academy the authorization necessary to this end and
> in entrusting them with the censorship of their own
> publications.

> However, none of these proposals met with a single
> satisfactory result.   What could have been the cause?
> Surely, the talents and the zeal of the commissioners
> who were named cannot be called into question.   If I
> can be permitted to express my own sentiments, there
> were too many collaborators assisting in the same
> project, and the multiplicity of instruments retarded
> its progress.   Let us add that the memoirs which
> were stored in different places could not either be
> consulted or compared at the moment of need.   The
> slowness of communication caused the work to languish
> and ended by causing them to be forgotten.

> When at the reestablishment of the academy, this com-

pany did me the honour of entrusting me with its
archives, I could collect in one place under my own
eyes all those memoirs which had escaped the mis-
fortune of circumstances.  I could arrange them and
coordinate them at leisure, and having finished this
preliminary task I could dare to undertake an enterprise which had been beyond those who possessed
means superior to mine. (42)

Of the 2200 memoirs which Gosseaume says were presented
to the Academy between 1744 and 1793, he says that he was
able to obtain only 862.  He assigns several reasons to the
loss of the others: (1) negligence of the members in failing
to deposit copies with the secretary, (2) a fire on 26 December 1762 in which LeCat's files were destroyed, including many of the society's memoirs, and finally (3) the Revolution which made necessary the movement of the papers from
one place to another.  He ends his account with a plea to
anyone who may have in his possession any of the missing
memoirs to return them to the society.

    Some of the apparent lag between the date of founda-
tion of a society and the first appearance of its proceedings
may be a result of the confusion which sometimes exists in
the literature regarding the date on which some of the societies were founded.  One of the justifications is that different
points in the societies' history are sometimes regarded as
foundation dates, and that the predecessors of a given society
are sometimes regarded as the same as the society which
succeeded it in a particular city although sometimes this did
not occur until decades after the original society had ceased
its activities.  The dates proposed in the literature for the
origin of a society may be: (1) the date the society was proposed, or when the group of those interested in organizing
the society first met, (2) the date of the society's first open
meeting, or (3) the date of the granting of the first official
charter.  These discrepancies sometimes account adequately
for the lag between the time the society was founded and the
appearance of its first publication, but in a number of other
cases this explanation does not suffice.  The Académie Royale
des Belles-Lettres founded in Arres in 1737 does not seem to
have published anything until 1785.  Despite its title the pro-
gramme published 6 April 1785 does not seem particularly
literary. (43)  It consisted of the answers to two questions:
(1) what were formerly the branches of commerce in those
countries which at present form the province of Artois, and
(2) would it be advantageous to reduce the number of roads
in the territory of the villages in the province of Artois.

The Massachusetts Medical Society founded in Boston in 1781 did not publish its "Medical Papers" until 1790. Although the preface to this issue expressed the hope that they might soon publish another number, the second half of the volume did not appear until 1806. The Académie Royale des Sciences et Belles-Lettres of Caen which had antecedents going back to 1652 did not publish the first volume of its "Recueil" until 1731, and its "Mémoires" did not appear until 1754. The Societé Royale des Sciences, Belles-Lettres et Arts of Clermont-Ferrand whose date of foundation is given as 1747 (44) appears in the 18th century to have published only the "Séance Publique Pour l'Ouverture du Jardin Royale Botanique in 1782." The Académie des Sciences, Arts et Belles-Lettres founded in Dijon in 1725 (45) published the first volume of its "Mémoires" in 1769 and the second in 1774 after which it was suspended until 1783. They then appeared regularly every half year until 1786 at which time they were suspended until 1820. (46)

Of the twenty-five provincial academies which Guitard (47) lists as having been established before 1790, seven seem to have issued no publications whatsoever in the 18th century, and several of the others are represented only by very occasional publications. One reason for the failure of some provincial academies to publish proceedings was that the publications of the societies in the capital were open to them. Some of them were affiliated with the societies in Paris. (48) The Societé Royale des Sciences at Montpellier, for instance, states in the first volume of its "Histoire" that although its letters patent had been granted in 1706, it had published nothing for a period of sixty years. They considered themselves, the introduction continues, a part of the Académie des Sciences in Paris, and many of their memoirs appeared in the volumes published by the academy. The editor of this first volume accounts for the fact that the volume covering the years 1706 to 1730 is so slim by the fact that he excluded all memoirs published in the Parisian proceedings, as well as by the fact that he has eliminated all those which he feels become outdated with the passage of time. In 1761, at the height of the French enthusiasm for the new English methods of agriculture and for the idea of the application of scientific principles to the improvement of agriculture, the Societé Royale d'Agriculture de la Généralité de Paris was formed. It issued one volume of its proceedings at that time but did not issue another until 1785. A similar pattern is demonstrated by the many provincial agricultural societies which were organized at about the same time. As with the general societies, we find that those who were active in the work of the agricultural societies were closely associated with the in-

dependent journals which were utilized as a medium for publishing their reports.  For example, Palerne, who was
secretary of the Paris society, was one of the collaborators
on the "Journal Économique," a periodical which devoted considerable space to agricultural matters.  (49)

In many cases papers presented before the scientific
societies appeared in the general periodical press.  The use
of the general periodical press may have been the result of
reluctance to wait until the society had "sufficient matter to
form a volume."  Many of the papers of LeCat appeared in
such general journals as the "Journal de Verdun," the "Journal de Trevoux," in the "Journal des Sçavans," and even in
the "Mercure de France."  One publication which is difficult
to account for is a paper of LeCat's which appeared in the
January issue, 1750, of the "Nouveau Magasin François ou
Bibliothèque Instructive et Amusante," a French language
monthly which was published in London.  The paper is entitled, "Dissertation sur les polypes d'eau douce, prononcés
dans une des seances de l'Académie Royale des Sciences de
Rouen."  There is no indication in the publication that it is
a reprint, and if it is indeed an original appearance it would
be interesting to reconstruct the manner in which such a paper found its way into a periodical of this character.  (50)

The experiences of Robert Dossie (1717-1777) who was
an active popularizer of the ideas of the Society for the Encouragement of Arts, Manufactures and Customs, which was
founded in London in 1754, are instructive in this connection.
The papers of the society were not published as a group until
1768 when Dossie issued the first volume of the "Memoirs of
Agriculture and Other Oeconomical Arts."  Prior to this time
the memoirs read before the society were preserved in its
"Guard Book."  Some of the papers were circulated in manuscript, for example, Dossie's 'Instructions for the Manufacture and Assay for Potashes."  His method for the purification of whale and cod oil was awarded a premium by the Society, but it was published in the "Gentleman's Magazine" (51)
and in the "Annual Register."  (52)  Another outlet for some
of the papers Dossie presented to the society was the agricultural periodical "Museum Rusticum et Commerciale" which appeared in London between 1763 and 1766.  (53)

The Dublin Society for Improving Husbandry, Manufactures and Other Useful Arts, founded in 1731, contributed to
the "Dublin News Letter" a section entitled "Weekly Observations."  These were reprinted in 1739 as the "Dublin Society's
Weekly Observations, 1736-1737."  (54)  In the same way the
Edinburgh Society for the Encouragement of Arts, Science,

Manufactures, which was founded by Allan Ramsay in 1754, reported its activities in the "Scots Magazine." (55)  In Germany the Oekonomischen Sozietät zu Leipzig, founded in 1763, did not publish its proceedings until 1771, and its first reports appeared in such newspapers as the "Leipziger Intelligenzblatt," the "Wittenberger Wochenblatt," and the "Dresdner Gelehrten Anzeiger." (56)  The activities of the Akademie der Wissenschaften in Munich and of the Sittlichen und landwirthschaftlichen Gesellschaft in Berghausen, both appeared in the "Annalen der Baierischen Litteratur,*" a review of scholarly activities in Bavaria published from 1781, despite the fact that both societies published their own proceedings.  In some cases although an organ published by the society existed for the presentation of its papers, the general periodical press was utilized in order to bring information more quickly before the public.  For example, the Provinciall Utrechts Genootschap van Konsten en Wetenschappen published its proceedings of June 17 in the issue of the "Algemeene Konst-en Letterbode," a general literary and review journal, on July 4, 1788, although it had been publishing its "Verhandelingen" from 1781.  In the United States because of the lack of media for the publication of scientific articles, the general literary journals frequently served as a place of publication for papers delivered before the societies.  The "American Museum," a general literary journal published in Philadelphia, included in its January number, 1787, a paper by Benjamin Rush entitled "An Account of Dr. Hugh Martin's Cancer Powder, with Brief Observations on Cancers Read in the American Philosophical Society February 3, 1786." (57) The same issue includes also an anonymous article on the cultivation of potatoes which the editor indicates is "published by order of the Philadelphia Society for Promoting Agriculture." (58)

There was another compelling reason for the appearance of papers presented before societies in the general press.  Anyone who was anxious to bring his ideas before the public or felt that he had a priority to protect might place his work in any public medium that presented itself. We still find some workers inserting reports of work in progress in general scientific journals such as "Nature" or "Science," although they intend to present the complete results of their work in a society journal.  Benjamin Rush, for example, could have had his paper inserted in the "Transactions" of the American Philosophical Society, before which it had been delivered, for that society had been publishing this series since 1771.  The Society, however, published only six volumes in its first eighty years.  We do not know all the particulars in this case, but the pattern is presented clearly in the case of

Lavoisier in the recent bibliography of the chemist compiled
by Duveen and Klickstein. (59)  The first of Lavoisier's
papers to appear in Rozier's journal was his memoir on the
purification of water which had been read at a public meeting of the Académie in 1770.  The memoir was not published
in the Academy's proceedings until the volume for 1770 appeared in 1773.  The article in Rozier's journal appeared as
an anonymous account of Lavoisier's work, but Duveen and
Klickstein are of the opinion that it was the result of an understanding between Rozier and Lavoisier.  His paper on the
effect of heat on the diamond read before the Academy on 29
April 1772, which was not published in the "Mémoires" until
1776, appeared in the "Journal" for May 1772.  Similarly his
paper on the calcination of metals, delivered on the 12th
November 1774 was published in Rozier's journal in December of the same year, while it did not appear in the "Mémoires" until 1778.  Such promptness of publication as af-
forded by Rozier's journal would be considered exemplary
even today.  Lavoisier seems to have continued this practice
through 1775, and even published in the journal several reports and papers which although presented to the Académie
never appeared in the "Mémoires."  After 1775 Lavoisier
continued to submit some of his non-academic papers to the
journal.

The ways in which communications got into the publications of the societies depended largely on the nature of the
organization, but the major difference between the journals
which appeared under society sponsorship and those which resulted from the initiative of a single editor or a small group
of editors, is that the society usually made some provisions
for review of the communication before they permitted it to
be published.  The societies were fully aware that they were
lending their prestige and authority to the communication. (60)
Not many of the societies restricted their media to the communications of their own membership; most of them welcomed papers from outsiders as well, though these were usually subjected to different handling than the others.  Usually
papers submitted by non-members were presented to the society through the sponsorship of one of the members who is
frequently mentioned along with the author, a practice which
is still in existence in some of the continental societies.  In
addition there were in many of the scientific societies a class
of membership designated as correspondents, whose major
function was to act as representative of the society in the
provinces or in other countries, but who usually had the privilege of submitting communications to the society.

It is curious that with the elaborate provisions which

many of the societies made for the review of publications they frequently disavowed responsibility for the reliability of the papers themselves. For example, the Literary and Philosophical Society of Manchester in the preface to the first volume of its "Memoirs" in 1785, states:

> The sanction which the Society gives to the work, now published, under its auspices, extends only to the novelty, ingenuity, or importance of the several memoirs it contains. Responsibility concerning the truth of the facts, soundness of reasoning, or the accuracy of calculation, is wholly disclaimed; and must rest alone on the knowledge, judgment, or ability of the authors, who have respectively furnished such communications.

The American Philosophical Society established at Philadelphia in 1729 made similar disavowals in the first volume of its Transactions:

> As soon, therefore, as the Society judged that they had received a sufficient Number of Communications for a Volume, they appointed a Committee, to assist the Secretaries, in selecting out of them such as might be most proper for the public view. And for their direction in the execution of this trust, the following Rules were given, viz. First 'That the grounds of the Committee's Choice of Papers for the Press, should always be, the importance or singularity of the subjects, or the advantageous manner of treating them, without pretending to answer, or to make the Society answerable, for the certainty of the facts, or propriety of the reasonings, contained in the several Papers so published, which must still rest on the credit or judgment of their respective authors.' Secondly 'That neither the Society, or the Committee of the Press, do ever give their opinion as a body, upon any paper they may publish, or upon any subject of Art or Nature that comes before them. (61)

In France the societies had reason for exercising precautions in the publication of their communications for they had an important privilege to protect, i.e. that of publication prior to submission to the censorship. Bouillier states that:

> The academies had privileges which were not of less importance for the printing of works or memoirs published in their name. They had no need of the approval of a censor; it was permitted, as it is stated

in the documents relative to the foundation of the
Academy at Caen, that they could have printed by
whatever printer they chose all those works which
they wished to have appear under their name. (62)

The regulations of many of the societies set up procedures
for handling the communications sent to them.  Those of the
Académie Royale de Chirurgie of Paris of 18 March 1751
provide that:

Article XI:   The memoirs, letters and works which
are addressed to the Academy will first be put in the
hands of the Commissioner for Abstracts who will
prepare an abstract of it in order to render account
of it at the next assembly.  He is also charged to
deal in the same manner with the new books which
appear both in the realm and in foreign countries, especially those which have a relation to surgery.  These
abstracts will be rendered faithfully and without any
criticism on the part of the Commissioners who will
simply report the facts from which one may be able
to profit.

Article XXXIII:   In the weekly meetings the Commissioner of Abstracts will read the letters, memoirs
and other works.  The memoirs will be read twice,
and discussions will be reserved until the second
reading.  For those which merit special attention, a
committee will be assigned to report within a designated time. (63)

Although censorship was not as rigorous in England as
it was in France, at least as far as official sanction was
concerned, (64) society publications had to run the gauntlet
of criticism from the public press.  It is interesting to note
the way in which a general literary magazine, the "Critical
Review," takes the Royal Society to task for one of the issues of the Transactions.  It is another indication that science in the 18th century was still considered a part of the
interest of the educated man.

The Royal Society is doubtless in the right to encourage the ingenious of all classes and denominations to
transmit their discoveries and hints of improvements
in all arts and sciences, whether familiar or obtuse;
and in the course of this communication that Philosophical Body must receive many crude essays that
cannot appear with propriety among the works of the
learned; but, surely, those who superintend the pub-

lication, ought to have a greater regard to the reputation of the Society than to exhibit such abortive productions. (65)

The review makes some technical observations on the paper
of Christianus Hee, Professor of Mathematics and Experimental Philosophy at Copenhagen, stating that his work "...
contains a very defective calculation of the resistance to be
overcome by bodies moved on the surface of the water."(66)
It indulges in an occasional bit of sarcasm as well. In commenting on the articles on the meteorology of Spitalsquare,
London and Tooting in Surrey on the 8th and 9th day of February, the review adds that "...this might have remained a
secret to the end of time, had not those literati kept a register of their thermometers." (67)   On the other hand, it
could also have been pointed out that the societies sometimes
exercised their prerogatives of rejection with even worse results.   For example, the Royal Society in 1797 rejected Jenner's paper on innoculation and it was necessary for Jenner
to have it published privately. (68)

Although some of the societies managed to issue volumes of their proceedings at fairly frequent intervals, on the
whole, they do not seem to have done so. (Table 11).   The
common practice was exemplified by that of the American
Philosophical Society in waiting until "...they had received a
sufficient number of communications for a volume." (69) The
first volume of the Society's "Transactions" was published in
1771, the second in 1786, and the third in 1793.   The American Academy of Arts and Sciences, established in Boston in
1780, published the first volume of its "Memoirs" in 1785.
In the preface they invited potential contributors to send their
papers to the Academy since they were "possessed of a number of valuable papers which would go far towards forming
another volume." (70)   The second volume did not appear until 1793.   Frequency of appearance of society publications is
shown in table 11.

Despite the rejection of authority which had taken
place as a part of the "scientific revolution," the teachings of
antiquity were still regarded as valid sources of information
for the contemporary scientist in the 18th century.   This was
especially true in those fields in which the scientific spirit
had not yet achieved a firm grasp, for example, in medicine.
The medical journalist Baldinger writing on his proposal for
a medical library writes with conviction when he says:

I have believed for a long time that one should not
tie himself to any sect or to any century, but that

Table 11

Average Intervals Between the Appearance
of Volumes of Society Proceedings

| | General | Medical | Agricultural | Other | Total | Per cent |
|---|---|---|---|---|---|---|
| Less than 1 yr. | 5 | – | 4 | – | 9 | 5 |
| 1  year | 23 | 4 | 9 | 6 | 42 | 25 |
| 2  years | 22 | 2 | 6 | 1 | 31 | 19 |
| 3    " | 17 | 1 | 3 | 2 | 23 | 14 |
| 4    " | 7 | – | 1 | – | 8 | |
| 5    " | 4 | 1 | – | 1 | 6 | |
| 6    " | 3 | – | – | 1 | 4 | 17 |
| 7    " | 2 | – | – | – | 2 | |
| 8    " | – | – | – | 1 | 1 | |
| 9    " | 1 | 1 | – | – | 2 | |
| 10   " | – | – | – | – | – | |
| Over 10 years | 3 | 1 | 1 | – | 5 | |
| One volume | 19 | 5 | 7 | 3 | 34 | 20 |
| Total | 106 | 15 | 31 | 15 | 167 | 100 |

one should seek for a general picture of our art from
its beginnings to our own times, in order to put aside
all sectarianism and to make oneself familiar with the
good, the necessary and the useful of all the centuries.

The general symtomatology of Hippocrates which has
lasted for two thousand years is still valid.   The general art of healing was established by Hippocrates and
Galen and has lasted until Hebenstreit and Brendel,
who based their teachings entirely on Greek scholarship. (71)

This was true for some other branches of science as well.
The "Miscellanea Curiosa," first published in 1670, were not
issued in a German translation until almost a century later,
and there is no evidence that this was done for antiquarian
reasons alone.   It is possible, of course, that even in this
earlier period the patterns of obsolescence varied considerably
between the sciences and that while medicine had a low rate
of obsolescence, a new discipline such as chemistry would
exhibit it in a high degree.   There is some evidence of this
in the publication of Lorenz von Crell, who issued his "Chemisches Journal*" at irregular intervals at Lemgo between
1778 and 1781.   Six parts appeared in a three year period.

His "Neuesten Endeckungen in der Chemie,*" 1781-1786, on the other hand appeared every six months, and in the twelfth issue he announces the beginning of a new series with even a shorter interval between issues.

> According to the former organization of my journal these chemical observations which I have collected for my readers, came into their hands only every six months, and often the contributions which were sent had to lie with me for much longer. In this way the praiseworthy curiosity for more knowledge is satisfied only at a late date. In the interim perhaps many spent their energy, time and money on projects which he afterwards found were already, and often even better, dealt with. Or perhaps he could have performed his needed tasks more easily, cheaper and in a better way with the help of the directions from these earlier achievements. (72)

The proceedings of the scientific societies can be considered a response to the commemorative impulse as well as to the desire to provide a record of scientific advances, but they are a much truer repository of original thought and observations than the substantive periodical. The contemporary scientific periodical probably owes more to proceeding than to substantive journals, but the contemporary scientific periodical represents an amalgam of the two media, related to the society proceeding in the respect that it presents original communications and to the substantive journal in its adherence to periodicity of issue and to the sort of derivative journalism represented by abstracts and reviews.

## Notes

(1)     S. B. Barnes, op. cit., p. 123.

(2)     Ornstein, op. cit., p. 75.

(3)     Bertrand, op. cit., p. 55.

(4)     Ornstein, op. cit., p. 157.

(5)     Many of Swammerdam's papers were still unpublished at his death until Boerhaave published them under the title, "Bijbel der Natuur." E. Nordenskiold, "History of Biology" (New York: Knopf, 1946), p. 168.

(6)     (London: Macmillan, 1944), p. 131). (Author's

emphasis.)

(7)      Dekeysser, op. cit., p. 1760, gives 1635 as the date of publication, but he has apparently confused this with the date attributed to the first political news journal in Portugal which appeared in that year.

(8)      A. Silva Carvalho, "Histoire de la Presse medicale au Portugal," "Medicina Contemporanea, LIV (1936), 299-304.

(9)      Cited by Scudder, op. cit., No. 1357, 1500. This is apparently the reason Scudder dates his list from 1633.

(10)     Brown, op. cit., p. 18.

(11)     J. Levy-Valensi, "Histoire de la Presse médicale française au xviie Siècle," "Paris Médicale," Annexe, CX (1938), 110, 157.

(12)     John L. Thornton, "Scientific Books, Libraries and Collectors" (London: Library Association, 1954), pp. 173-174.

(13)     Charles R. Weld, "A History of the Royal Society" (London: J.W. Parker, 1848), I, 310.

(14)     Cited by Ornstein, op. cit., p. 109.

(15)     Ibid., p. 125.

(16)     Cited by Lyons, op. cit., p. 56.

(17)     Cited in Lyons, op. cit., p. 85.

(18)     Cited by G.R. Potter, "The Significance to the History of English Natural History of John Hill's "Review of the Works of the Royal Society," "University of California Publications in English," XIV (1943), 157.

(19)     Dorothy Stimson, "Critical Years of the Royal Society," "Journal of the History of Medicine," II (1947), 283-298.

(20)     Ashley-Montague, op. cit., p. 58.

(21)     F.J. Cole, "A History of Comparative Anatomy" (London: Macmillan, 1944), p. 351.

(22)     Morgan, op. cit.

(23)     W. B. A. von Steinwehr, "Physische Abhandlungen die
         Jahre 1692 ff. enthaltend" (Breslau, 1748-1759), 13
         vols.

(24)     S. B. Barnes, op. cit., p. 210, cited from Martin
         Lister's "A Journey to Paris in the Year 1698"
         (London: Tonson, 1699).

(25)     Année 1707, (2d ed.; Paris: Boudot, 1718).

(26)     D. I. Duveen and H. S. Klickstein, "A Bibliography of
         the Works of Antoine Laurent Lavoisier" (London:
         Dawson, 1954), Items 89-92.

(27)     Académie Royale des Sciences, Belles-Lettres et Arts
         de Bordeaux, "Recueil des Dissertations qui ont Rem-
         porté le Prix." Cited in Deniker, op. cit., pp. 249-
         250.

(28)     Cited in Bertrand, op. cit., p. 177.

(29)     See also Table 10.

(30)     See Appendix II.

(31)     A. M. Carr-Saunders, "The Professions" (Oxford:
         Clarendon Press, 1933), p. 67.

(32)     L. G. Stevenson, "The Siege of Warwick Lane: Together
         with a Brief History of the Society of Collegiate Phys-
         icians," "Journal of the History of Medicine," VII
         (1952), 105-121.

(33)     D'Arcy Power, "British Medical Societies" (London:
         Medical Press, 1939), p. 45. The correctness of
         this date is in question, since Duncan in the "Medical
         and Philosophical Commentaries of the Society in Edin-
         burgh" for the year 1780 notes a meeting of the Har-
         veian Society at Edinburgh at which a prize medal for
         the year 1780 was awarded.

(34)     Ibid., p. 45.

(35)     J. Cohen and others, "Natural History of Learned and
         Scientific Societies," "Nature," CLXXIII (1954), 328-
         333.

(36)　W. LeFanu, "A Bio-bibliography of Edward Jenner, 1749-1823," (Philadelphia: Lippincott, 1951), p. 16.

(37)　J. Gray, 'History of the Royal Medical Society, 1737-1937' (Edinburgh: University Press, 1952), pp. 22-23.

(38)　James Kendall, "The First Chemical Journal," "Nature," CLIX (1947), 867.

(39)　Gray, op. cit., pp. 109-111.

(40)　"Mémoires," 1753, p. vi.

(41)　"Mémoires," I (1777), Historical Introduction.

(42)　Académie Royale des Sciences, Belles-Lettres et Arts de Rouen, "Précis Analytique des Travaux," I (Rouen: Periaux, 1814) 5-6.

(43)　Reviewed in the "L'Esprit des Journaux Français et Étrangers," June, 1785, pp. 292-294.

(44)　Bernard Fay, "Learned Societies in Europe and America in the Nineteenth Century," "American Historical Review," XXXVII (1932), 255.

(45)　Ibid., Fay gives 1740.

(46)　J. Deniker and R. Descharmes, "Bibliographie des Travaux Scientifique" (Paris: Imprimerie Nationale, 1895-1922), pp. 139-141.

(47)　Guitard, op. cit., p. 58.

(48)　F. Bouillier, "L'Institute et les Académies de Province" (Paris: Hachette, 1879), passim.

(49)　L. Passy, 'Histoire de la Société Nationale d'Agriculture" (Paris: Renouard, 1912), p. 53.

(50)　Pp. 1-10.

(51)　XXXI (1761), 495.

(52)　IV (1761), 142-145.

(53)　F.W. Gibbs, 'Robert Dossie (1717-1777) and the Society of Arts," "Annals of Science, VII (1951), 167.

(54)     T. P. C. Kirpatrick, "The Periodical Publications of
         Science in Ireland," "Bibliographical Society of Ire-
         land," II (1921), 41.

(55)     Archibald Clow, "The Chemical Revolution" (London:
         Batchworth, 1952), p. 40.

(56)     K. Kohlsdorf, "Geschichte der Leipziger Oekonomi-
         schen Sozietät" (Leipzig:   Edelman, 1913), p. 11.

(57)     Pp. 34-40.

(58)     Ibid., pp. 47-48.

(59)     D. I. Duveen and K. S. Klickstein, "A Bibliography of
         the Works of Antoine Laurent Lavoisier, 1743-1794"
         (London:   Dawson, 1954).

(60)     The social psychologist Richard Mueller-Freinenfels
         has drawn some interesting parallels between the de-
         velopment of capitalism and modern science which in-
         dicates that both involved the development of systems
         of credit. "...modern science is a capitalization of
         the spirit, a spiritual capitalism, which shows all the
         characteristics of the economic capitalism." "Studies
         in the Social Psychology of Science."  Translated by
         Heinrich M. Bosshard.  "Journal of Social Psychol-
         ogy," IV (1933), 31.  See also Mueller-Freienfels'
         "Psychologie der Wissenschaft" (Leipzig:   J. A. Barth,
         1936).

(61)     Preface to the first volume.

(62)     Bouillier, op. cit., p. 61.

(63)     "Mémoires," 1753, p. vi.

(64)     J. P. Belin, "Le Commerce des Livres Prohibés à
         Paris," (Paris:   Belin, 1913).

(65)     I (1756), 528.

(66)     Ibid.

(67)     Ibid., p. 530.

(68)     F. J. Fulton, "The Impact of Science on American
         History," Isis, XLII (1951), 176-191.

(69)    "Transactions," 1771, Preface.

(70)    "Memoirs," 1785, Preface.

(71)    E. B. Baldinger, "Das neugestiftete medicinische Lese-
        institut zu Marburg," "Neues Magazin für Aerzte,"
        XIII (1791), 340.

(72)    "Neue Entdeckungen," 1786, Preface to No. 12.

Chapter VII

Derivative Publication:   The Abstract Journal


Despite the relatively slow growth of journal publication in the first half of the 18th century there were statements in the literature that the journal was beginning to dom-
inate publishing.  As is shown in Table 12, however, it was
not until much later that the periodical began to assume a
significant role. (1)   Yet even before the number of periodicals had become a trickle, complaints were being raised a-
bout an inundation.   The compiler of a periodical bibliography
as early as 1715, the "Curieuse Nachricht von den Heute zu
Tage grand Mode gewordenen Journal-Quartal-und Annual
Schriften," claimed that bookstores were no longer bookstores but journal stores and that bookdealers had become
journal-dealers. (2)  This opinion was expressed even more
strongly toward the end of the century in the review of a new
journal, the "Medicinisches Practisches Bibliothek:

Table 12

Proportion of Press Output Devoted
to Periodicals Percentages

|  | 1740 | 1770 | 1800 | 1908 |
|---|---|---|---|---|
| Theology | 1.7 | 3.6 | 8.3 | 26.5 |
| Jurisprudence | 1.0 | 3.3 | 9.3 | 20.3 |
| Medicine | 8.0 | 9.9 | 14.8 | 22.7 |

This is truly the decade of the journal, and one should
seek to limit their number rather than to increase them,
since there can also be too many periodicals. (3)

These were but echoes of complaints about the growth of the
literature which have been with us at least since the early
part of the seventeenth century. S.B. Barnes cites Barnaby
Rich, writing in 1613:

One of the diseases of this age is the multiplicity of
books; they doth so overcharge the world that it is

149

not able to digest the abundance of idle matter that is
every day hatched and brought forth into the world.
(4)

One of the explanations for this periodic expression of dis-
may at the bulk of the literature lies in the fact that the
burden of responsibility which the scholar assumes becomes
ever smaller in terms of the subject matter while it tends
to remain the same or grows larger in bulk.  The biochem-
ist today, making the same complaint as the 18th century
scholar, is concerned with a much smaller segment of literature, which is probably equal to the entire output of the
literature with which the 18th century encyclopedic scholar
was concerned.  Goldfriedrich's analysis of the periodical
bibliography, the "Curieuse Nachricht," cited above, shows
that an early seventeenth century scholar interested in the
natural sciences would have been concerned with only 113
titles, in the following categories: (5)

| | |
|---|---:|
| General learned and literary journals | 40 |
| Historical-political journals | 16 |
| Literary-historical-political journals | 7 |
| Theological journals | 22 |
| Philological journals | 5 |
| Journals of jurisprudence | 4 |
| Medical and medical-physical journals | 3 |
| General journals | 5 |
| Journals of newspaper extracts | 3 |
| Moral journals | 2 |
| Philosophical journals | 1 |
| Academic news journals | 1 |
| Journals devoted to academic disputations | 1 |
| Abstract journals | 1 |
| Travel journals | 1 |
| Historical calendars | 1 |
| | |
| Total | 113 |

One of the consequences of the growth of the literature
was the development throughout the 18th century of bibliographic guides and handbooks.  One example of this kind of publication is Johann Traugott Müllern's "Einleitung in die oekonomische und physikalische Bücherkunde,*" issued at Leipzig in
three volumes from 1780 to 1782.  In the preface to the first
volume Müllern stated that he was attempting to do for economics and physics (i.e. agriculture and natural science) what
Miller and Noszelt had done for theology, Westphal for law,
Haller and Murray for medicine, and Gatterer and Meusel
for history.  In his own field he named as predecessors,

Zinken, Moser, Denso, Wöllner and Münchhausen.  Not all
of the authors whom Müllern mentioned can be considered
bibliographers; Murray, for instance, edited a review journal, and Denso is better known as a journalist, but it is
fairly clear that Müllern was not venturing into a new field.
Another indication of the growth of the literature was Müllern's dependence on secondary sources:

> I hope that no over-critical scholar will take me to
> task for the fact that I have made use of critical col-
> lections, journals, learned newspapers, book cata-
> logs, magazines and other periodical works in com-
> piling this book.  I would like to know the person who
> would wish to complete such a comprehensive work
> out of his own brain and his own reading without sim-
> ilar aids. (6)

Johann Georg Hager's "Geographisches Büchersall zum Nutzen und Vergnügen eröffnet*" is a curious hybrid.  In the
preface to his work he failed to make clear just what sort of
a publication he had in mind:

> The scholar has neither money to buy nor time to
> read even the best of the geographic writings.  Johann
> Albert Fabricius who put the learned world eternally
> in his debt, has made known to us 439 monthlies.
> Yet there is not a single one among them that is de-
> voted solely to geography.  There are theological,
> legal medical, philosophical, moral, historical, econ-
> omic, musical and other miscellaneous publications
> and "Bibliotheken" in various languages.  Only a geo-
> graphic "Bibliothek" is as yet unknown to us, although
> it would be as useful and as necessary as the others,
> since we are in this day overwhelmed with geographic
> books. (7)

The "Büchersall" might be described as a periodically issued
bibliographic handbook and abstract and review journal for the
geographer.  It was issued in thirty parts in Chemnitz between 1764 and 1778.  Despite an occasional reference to or
review of the current literature, it was essentially a retrospective survey of the literature.  Yet Hagers included such
journalistic features as letters by the editor.  He promised
his readers an impartial judgment of both old and new geographic writings, reported on the best available maps, and
gave biographical data on the important geographers:

> I am not setting any definite time when I will be fin-
> ished.  ...And who knows where, here and there,

> there will not arise an enthusiast or helper who will
> offer me aid.   Many hands make, according to the
> well-known saying, an early end.   (8)

We are not concerned here, however, with these mar-
ginal forms, but with abstract journals.   Prutz in his history of journalism cited two early examples of this form:
the "Journal du Journal" or "Censure de la Censure," which
he says was published in France as early as 1670, and the
"Monatsextracte" which appeared in Leipzig beginning with the
year 1703.   The last named was made up of selections from
various political journals and did not differ significantly from
some of the early newspapers which were characteristically
made up of news items borrowed from other newspapers.
The first authentic journal devoted exclusively to abstracts
of which we have any information was the "Aufrichtige und
unpartheyische Gedancken über die Journale, Extracte und
Monaths-Schriften, Worrinnen dieselben extrahiret, wann es
nutzlich suppliret oder wo es nothig, emediret werden; nebst
einer Vorrede von der Annelmlichkeit, Nutzen und Fehlern
gedachter Schrifften."   It was edited by Christian Gottfried
Hoffmann (1692-1735) who in the first issue stated the purpose
of the work:

> In the first place I will spare you the task of purchas-
> ing and reading all the monthly publications.   Second-
> ly, when it is necessary and possible I will include
> a collation of the reviews along with a list of the
> books which have been reviewed.   And thirdly you will
> have an adequate report and an extract of those ex-
> tracts.   (9)

Two volumes appeared between 1714 and 1717, each containing
twelve issues, but only in the first volume was the plan followed.   Almost forty different journal titles were abstracted,
including the "Acta Eruditorum," the "Journal des Sçavans,"
the "Giornale de' Letterati" as well as a number of historical-
political journals such as "La Clef du Cabinet des Princes"
and the "Mercure historique et politique."   The second volume
contained principally original reviews and thus should be considered a review journal rather than an abstract journal.   It
seems likely, however, that earlier abstract journals may
have appeared.   Lehmann cites Hoffmann himself as saying:

> It has unfortunately gone so far that we shall soon
> have more extracts and books taken from books than
> real books.   (10)

Hoffmann may, of course, have been referring to the many

contemporary learned journals which devoted a large part of
their space to reviews and reprints or abstracts of articles
printed in other journals.

The foregoing discussion points up the difficulty of
classification of the periodical publications of this period into abstract and review journals. It would probably be more
correct to refer to many of them as "extract" journals. Review journals frequently reviewed periodicals in the same
fashion as books, annotated lists of the contents are provided
and, sometimes, lengthy extracts from the individual articles.
There was so much over-lap among the three categories
(the collection, the abstract journal and the review journal)
that it might have been wiser to consider them a single
group. A broad distinction, however, can be made between
two of the categories on the basis that, on the whole, the
review journals devoted themselves to surveying the entire
literature, while the abstract or "extract" journal, as here
defined, concerned themselves solely with the literature appearing in other periodicals. There were a large number of
publications of this nature in the 18th century, but since we
are concerned principally with scientific journalism, we can
only mention a few of the general journals in this category,
although the 18th century scholar with an interest in science
probably used them freely.

The "Vollständige Einleitung in die Monaths-Schriften
der Deutschen" appeared in Erlangen in 1747. It consisted
of a list of the contents as well as extracts of some of the
articles of a number of learned and belletristic journals published in 1746. (11) The "Allgemeines Magazin der Natur,
Kunst und Wissenschaften,*" issued in Leipzig from 1753,
was probably of greater interest to the contemporary scientist. Of the twenty-nine abstracts included in the first issue,
all but five were of scientific or technological interest. The
editor, in his preface, stated that he had used the "Universal
Magazine of Knowledge and Pleasure," issued in London between 1747 and 1803, as his model. The character of the
"Magazin" is suggested by the fact that the "Universal Magazine" has been referred to as "a 'popular' magazine in the
modern sense." (12) This did not necessarily put it outside
the interests of the serious scientist, since the boundaries
between the popular and the scholarly were not as firmly
drawn in the 18th century as they are today. The "Allgemeines Magazin" devoted itself exclusively to the foreign literature as did also the "Neue Auszüge aus den besten aus-
ländischen Wochen-und Monatsschriften." The "Neue Auszüge"
was issued weekly soon after the foreign sources from which
it drew its material appeared. It covered the fields of medi-

cine, agriculture, politics, fine arts and literature. (13)
Ten volumes appeared at Frankfurt between 1765 and 1769.
The "Esprit des Journaux Français et Étrangers" was probably the best known and the most extensive publication in
this category. Beginning in 1772 it was published successively at Liege, Brussels, Paris, again at Liege and Brussels,
until, at the turn of the century, it was taken over by the
prosperous press at Bouillon which also issued among other
journals the "Journal Encyclopédique." By 1793 it comprised
a collection of 244 volumes to which a four volume author
and subject index were added.

In this discussion of abstract journals we might include a publication which could as easily be called a collection or an encyclopedia, the "Bibliothèque Choisie de Médecine, Tirés des Ouvrages Périodiques Étrangers, avec
Plusiers Autres Pièces Rares, et des Remarques Utiles et
Curieuses.*" It was edited by François Planque (1696-
1765) beginning in 1748 and was continued after his death by
M. J. Goulin. It appeared simultaneously in an octavo edition in 31 volumes and a quarto edition in 10 volumes. It
consisted of an alphabetic arrangement of subjects or topics
with extracts from pertinent journal articles under each heading. For example, under the first subject, "Abces," there
was a brief introduction by Planque, followed by an article
on the subject taken from the "Journal des Sçavans" (1697)
with added comments by the editor; another article on the
same subject from the "Progrés de la Medécine" (1694);
an article on an abcess found inside the body from the "Mémoires" of the Académie des Sciences (1731); and several
articles by Nicolas Blegny on abcess of the breast taken from
his "Nouvelles Déscouvertes" as well as from the translation
of this work which appeared in Latin under the title "Zodaicus
Medico Gallicus" (1680). Under some of the other headings
he included articles from such general literary journals as
the "Nouvelles de la Republique des Lettres," the "Journal de
Verdun," and the "Mercure." There are few modern publications to which this encyclopedia of abstracts can be compared. It served to some extent as a medical subject index
to the general and scientific journals up to the middle of the
18th century.

Among the journals devoted exclusively to abstracts of
the scientific literature were: the "Natuur-en Genees-kundige
Bibliothek," edited by Eduard Sandifort which appeared in
Lausanne during 1783 and 1784. The "Bibliothèque" was is-
sued in three parts, one devoted to medicine and subtitled,
"Bibliothèque de Médecine, de Chirurgie et de Pharmacie."
The second volume was devoted to natural history and chem-

istry and the third volume to chemistry. The preface to
the third volume explained the delay in publication as being
due to the death of its editor, P.R. Vicat, but continuation
was evidently intended since the preface goes on to state:

> If this collection has the good fortune to please the
> public, we will add in the following (issues), in order
> that it may be more useful, proposals for new ex-
> periments. (14)

and later:

> We will add to the third volume of each science a
> subject index to the contents, as well as to the sixth,
> the ninth, etc. Although this "Bibliothèque" makes up
> a part of the "Bibliothèque Medico-Physique du Nord,"
> it can nevertheless be procured separately from the
> two volumes which preceded this one. (15)

Although references to literature other than German appeared in the "Bibliothèque," the sources of these references
were all German medical review journals and collections,
which the editor listed in the preface to the first volume.

Although there are very few of the journals of the
period 1665-1790 which can be classified exclusively as abstract journals, many of the titles which we have included a-
mong the substantive journals were made up in large part of
abstracts from other journals. The reviewer in the "Frankfurter Medicinische Wochenschrift" in commenting on one such
journal which is here classed with the substantive journals,
was moved to remark:

> Among the various methods of the journalist, there is
> indeed no easier and more pleasant one than that of
> putting out a "Magazin, "Archiv," etc., of which ac-
> cording to the "Teutschen Merkur" there are already
> in our German fatherland some 245 journals, maga-
> zines, etc. flitting about, plundering freely and selling
> anew for a good price everything they can find which
> is suitable for their purposes. But good God! what
> will finally happen when we readers are served up
> three times and even more with the same thing in
> three or more periodicals for which we must pay with
> our hard earned money. No, truly, this is too de-
> ceitful a practice, and when it is repeated too often
> then there will be resistance against it. (16)

The indignant editor was obviously referring not only to those

periodicals which we have classed as abstract journals, but
to a great many of the other scientific and technological
periodicals published in Germany and elsewhere on the continent, and if we were to include all the journals which contained a significant number of abstracts, the number of abstract journals enumerated in Table 13 would probably swell
to ten times the number.

Table 13

Number of Titles of Abstract Journals Issued 1665-1790
by Subject and Decade of Origin

|         | 1670 | 1680 | 1690 | 1700 | 1710 | 1720 | 1730 | 1740 | 1750 | 1760 | 1770 | 1780 | 1790 |    |
|---------|------|------|------|------|------|------|------|------|------|------|------|------|------|----|
| General | -    | -    | -    | 1    | 2    | -    | 1    | 1    | 9    | 1    | 3    | 4    | 2    | 24 |
| Medical | -    | -    | -    | -    | -    | -    | -    | 1    | -    | 4    | 1    | 7    | -    | 13 |
| Other   | -    | -    | -    | -    | -    | -    | -    | -    | 1    | 1    | -    | 1    | 2    | 5  |
| Total   | -    | -    | -    | 1    | 2    | -    | 1    | 2    | 10   | 6    | 4    | 12   | 4    | 42 |

The abstract journals as a whole were of relatively
short duration; only 14 lasted 10 years or longer and 24 did
not continue their existence beyond a single year (compare
Table 13 and Table 14). Our observations about the derivative nature of much of German periodical publication in this
period is borne out by the high proportion (60 per cent) of
abstract journals of German origin (Table 15), and holds
true as well for the next form of derivative journalism we
are to consider, the review journal.

Table 14

Active Abstract Journals, Subject and Decade

|         | 1670 | 1680 | 1690 | 1700 | 1710 | 1720 | 1730 | 1740 | 1750 | 1760 | 1770 | 1780 | 1790 |
|---------|------|------|------|------|------|------|------|------|------|------|------|------|------|
| General | -    | -    | -    | -    | 1    | -    | -    | -    | 4    | 5    | 3    | 3    | 3    |
| Medical | -    | -    | -    | -    | -    | -    | -    | -    | 1    | 2    | 1    | 2    | -    |
| Other   | -    | -    | -    | -    | -    | -    | -    | -    | -    | -    | -    | -    | 2    |
| Total   | -    | -    | -    | -    | 1    | -    | -    | -    | 5    | 7    | 4    | 5    | 5    |

Table 15

Abstract Journals by Subject and Country of Origin

|  | Germany | France | Holland | England | Other | Total |
|---|---|---|---|---|---|---|
| General | 13 | 4 | 4 | 1 | 2 | 24 |
| Medical | 8 | 2 | 3 | - | - | 13 |
| Other | 4 | - | 1 | - | - | 5 |
| Total | 25 | 6 | 8 | 1 | 2 | 42 |

Notes

(1)   Gerhardt Menz, "Die Zeitschrift" (Stuttgart: Poeschel Verlag, 1928), p. 19.   Menz took his data from the "Ostermesskatalog," with the exception of the data for 1908 which are from the German National Bibliography.

(2)   Goldfriedrich, op. cit., p. 58.

(3)   "Neues medicinisches Wochenblatt für Aerzte," 1789, p. 211.

(4)   S.B. Barnes, op. cit., p. 2.

(5)   Goldfriedrich, op. cit., p. 56.

(6)   J.T. Müllern, "Einleitung in die Oekonomische und Physikalische Bücherkunde" (Leipzig, Schwikerischen Verlag, 1781-82), II, vii.

(7)   The list by Fabricius to which Hager refers appeared in the third edition of Daniel Georg Morhof's "Polyhistor" (Lubeck, 1732).   A fourth edition of the "Polyhistor" had already appeared at the time Hagers is writing, although he does not seem to be aware of it. The fourth edition included an expanded list of journals by Joachim Schwabe (1714-1784) including some 800 titles.

(8)   Ibid., p. 38.

(9)   Cited in Prutz, op. cit., pp. 43-44.

(10)   Lehmann, op. cit., p. 202.

(11)   Not located in this country.   Prutz, op. cit., p. 48,

says that it did not complete one volume, but Kirchner cites it as being issued from 1747 to 1753 in two
volumes, each with six issues.

(12)     Graham, op. cit., p. 168.

(13)     "Berlinische Sammlungen zur Beforderung der Arz-
         neiwissenschaft," I (1768), 426.

(14)     "Bibliothèque Medico-Physique du Nord," III (1784),
         viii.

(15)     Ibid.

(16)     "Frankfurter Medicinische Wochenschrift," 1785, 699-
         702.    A review of "Magazin für Apotheker, Chemisten
         und Naturalisten," edited by Johann Caspar Elwert,
         Nurnberg, 1785-1787.

Chapter VIII

Derivative Publication:   The Review Journal

The learned periodical press served from its very
beginnings as publicist for the book trade.  S.B. Barnes has
shown that the book sellers were frequently the instigators and
publishers of the learned journals.  Although not many of the
learned periodicals of the 17th and early 18th century were
devoted exclusively to reviewing books, many of them, like
the "Acta Eruditorum" and the "Journal des Sçavans," were
preponderantly book-reviewing media.  Specialized book reviewing media devoted exclusively to the sciences did not
appear until later in the 18th century, but in the age of the
encyclopedic scholar, when everything was grist for the
scholarly mill, the general review journals may have served
adequately in keeping the scientist, the "amateur," or "virtuoso," or "curious," as he was called in that period, abreast
of the new books and journals which were appearing in the
various fields of science and technology.

Although the "Acta Eruditorum," published in Latin for
almost a century, was designed to serve an international cli-
entele, most of the countries of Europe developed their own
book review periodicals in their own vernaculars.  In Denmark the "Dansk Litteratur-Tidende," which appeared under
various titles in Copenhagen between 1720 and 1837, had the
longest duration of any of the learned journals which appeared
in that country.  In England a number of review journals appeared before the end of the 17th century, but most of them
like the "Bibliotheca Universalis," or an "Historical Accompt
of Books and Transactions of the Learned World," which appeared in only one issue in Edinburgh in 1688, and the "Miscellaneous Letters, Giving an Account of the Works of the
Learned," which appeared in 24 numbers in London between
1694 and 1696, were of short duration.  It was not until 1726
when the "Critical Review or Annals of Literature" appeared,
that a review was able to establish itself firmly.  Both the
"Critical Review" and the "Monthly Review," which began its
career in 1749, were widely abstracted in the learned and
scientific journals on the continent.  (1)  In France the "Journal des Scavans" continued to be the major book-reviewing

medium, but many of the reviews published in the neighbor-
ing countries of Holland and Belgium were published primarily for a French audience.  The "Bibliothèque François"
appeared in Paris from 1741 to 1756, and one of the outstanding French reviews of the last half of the 18th century
was the "Année Littéraire," edited by that staunch critic of
the encyclopedists, Freron, and published in Amsterdam between 1754 and 1790.  (2)    Pierre Bayle's "Nouvelles de la
République des Lettres" was widely discussed and much imi-
tated all over Europe.  The Dutch also published reviews in
their own language, including the "Boekzaal der Geleerde
Wereld," which began in 1692, and the "Vaderlandsche Letter-
oefeningen of Tildschrift," published under various titles in
Amsterdam between 1761 and 1876.  In Italy there was a
multiplicity of journals, such as the many "Giornale dei Lit-
terari" which were published at Florence, Modena, Parma,
Pisa, Venice, etc., beginning with perhaps the best known
of the series, the journal of that title edited by Nazeri in
Rome between 1668 and 1681. (3)

        In Germany the lack of political centralization in the
18th century was reflected in the large number of regional
journals.  Every intellectual center or university town in
Germany had its own journal of learned and scholarly news;
many of them were almost like newspapers in their format
and frequency of issue.  Among them:

| | |
|---|---|
| Altonaische Gelehrte Anzeigen. | Altona, 1745-1789 |
| Erlangische Gelehrte Anmerckungen. | Erlangen, 1749-1789 |
| Dressdnische Gelehrte Anzeigen. | Dresden, 1749-1801 |
| Erfurtische Gelehrte Nachrichten. | Erfurt, 1754-1796 |
| Wochentliche Hallische Anzeigen. | Halle, 1729-1810 |
| Frankfurter  Gelehrte Anzeigen. | Frankfurt, 1736-1790 |
| Hallische Gelehrte Zeitungen. | Halle, 1766-1791 |
| Jenaische Gelehrte Zeitungen. | Jena, 1749-1786 |
| Leipziger Gelehrte Zeitungen. | Leipzig, 1715-1797 |
| Miscellanea Lipsiensia. | Leipzig, 1716-1752 |

The most outstanding, perhaps, and certainly the most endur-
ing of these scholarly and review journals, was the "Göttingische Zeitung von gelehrten Sachen*" which started in 1739.
It began as an independent journal under the editorship of
W. B. A. von Steinwehr, whom we encountered earlier as the
translator of the transactions of the Parisian and Berlin academies.  The "Göttingische Zeitungen" was closely associated
with the University and its editors were drawn from the university staff.  In 1753 it came directly under the auspices of
the Gesellschaft der Wissenschaften zu Göttingen. (4)  It appeared twice weekly and reported academic news such as new

appointments in the German universities and reviewed current books appearing in all the countries of Europe. The famed Swiss physiologist and poet, Albrecht von Haller, was closely associated with it from its beginning and after 1747 was for a time its editorial director. At that time Haller submitted to the "Kurator" of the University a plan for the management of the journal. The plan remained in manuscript until it was printed in the volume commemorating the one hundred and fiftieth anniversary of the "Gesellschaft der Wissenschaften zu Göttingen." (5) He continued his connections with the journal even after his return to Berne. Although the statement that he wrote 12,000 reviews for the journal has been shown to be erroneous, (6) it still appears occasionally in the literature. (7)

In addition to the academic and news journals, there were, of course, also German general review journals similar to the "Critical Review" and the "Monthly Review." Among these were the "Allgemeine deutsche Bibliothek,*" issued in Berlin from 1765, and "Allgemeine Literatur Zeitung,*" which started in Jena in 1785. In the first issue of the "Allgemeine deutsche Bibliothek," which is fairly characteristic, included 26 long reviews of which only three are devoted to books of scientific-technological interest: Haller's book on physiology, a volume of the transactions of the Bavarian Academy of Science, and a book on mining. The 91 short reviews in the same issue fell into the following groups:

| | | | |
|---|---|---|---|
| Theology | 43 | Domestic Economy | 4 |
| Fine Arts | 23 | Natural History | 2 |
| Medicine | 9 | Mathematics | 2 |
| Philology | 4 | Other | 4 |

Despite the general nature of the contents of these journals, it is apparent that they frequently contained material of interest to the scientist and physician. Sixty years after the first issue of the "Wochentliche Hallischen Anzeigen," (8) the medical and surgical observations appearing therein were issued as a separate volume; the "Auszüge verschiedener arzneiwissenschaftlicher Abhandlungen aus dem Wochentlichen Hallischen Anzeigen."

The group of journals segregatel for consideration as review journals in this study fall into that classification largely by virtue of the fact that they included reviews of monographs as well as reviews of journals. The reviews of journals frequently included abstracts of original articles so that on that basis they could easily be classified with the ab-

stract journals.  One of the earliest of this genre, for example, the "Weekly Memorial for the Ingenious,*" which appeared in London between 1682 and 1683, devoted a considerable portion of its space to abstracts of articles from the
contemporary learned journals.  F. N. L. Poynter in his article calls it "the first English medical journal" on the
grounds that "at least one-third of its space was given up to
accounts of medical books and papers." (9)  On this basis he
disputes the priority sometimes accorded to the "Medicina
Curiosa" which appeared in 1684.  These disputes illustrate
the pitfalls of attempting to classify the journals that were
issued in this period.  Some of the abstracts in the Fai-
thorne edition of the "Weekly Memorials" (10) are a series
taken from the "Zodiacus Medico-Gallicus," the Latin translation of Nicolas Blegny's "Nouvelles Déscouvertes sur Toutes
les Parties de la Médecine," issued in Paris in 1679.  The
"Zodiacus" is reviewed as if it were an original edition,
which spreads some doubt on Blegny's claims of the widespread appeal and distribution of the journal.  The "Memorials" include in addition to reviews of current books, extracts
from journals of the period such as the "Journal des Sçavans"
and the "Miscellanes Curiosa."

        The first scientific review journal of any extent and
duration is the "Commentarii de Rebus in Scientia Naturali
et Medicina Gestis*" which was published in Leipzig between
1752 and 1798.  It appeared in quarterly issues of about two
hundred pages each, and contained long reviews of scientific

Table 16

Number of Titles of Review Journals Issued 1665-1790
by Subject and Decade of Origin

|         | 1670 | 1680 | 1690 | 1700 | 1710 | 1720 | 1730 | 1740 | 1750 | 1760 | 1770 | 1780 | 1790 | Total |
|---------|------|------|------|------|------|------|------|------|------|------|------|------|------|-------|
| General | -    | 2    | -    | 1    | 1    | -    | 1    | -    | 3    | -    | 3    | 1    | -    | 12    |
| Medical | -    | -    | -    | -    | -    | -    | -    | -    | 2    | -    | 5    | 10   | 5    | 22    |
| Other   | -    | -    | -    | -    | -    | -    | -    | -    | -    | 2    | 1    | 2    | 1    | 6     |
| Total   | -    | 2    | -    | 1    | 1    | -    | 1    | -    | 5    | 2    | 9    | 13   | 6    | 40    |

books, dissertations and journals, especially society proceedings.  It had the advantage that it was printed in Latin and
was therefore accessible to the entire learned world.  The
journal articles are abstracted at some length; for example,
in the first issue, forty-six pages are devoted to review of
the articles in the current "Mémoires" of the Académie des

Table 17

Active Review Journals by Subject and Decade

| | 1670 | 1680 | 1690 | 1700 | 1710 | 1720 | 1730 | 1740 | 1750 | 1760 | 1770 | 1780 | 1790 |
|---|---|---|---|---|---|---|---|---|---|---|---|---|---|
| General | - | 1 | 1 | - | 1 | 1 | 1 | 1 | 2 | 3 | 4 | 3 | 3 |
| Medical | - | - | - | - | - | - | - | - | 1 | - | 2 | 7 | 11 |
| Other | - | - | - | - | - | - | - | - | - | 1 | - | - | 2 |
| Total | - | 1 | 1 | - | 1 | 1 | 1 | 1 | 3 | 4 | 6 | 10 | 16 |

Sciences de Paris. The main section of the journal was devoted to reviews but it also contained short section which
provided reports of academic news and lists of books in the
natural sciences and medicine which had been published in
the previous year but which had not been reviewed in the
current volume. Each volume contained its own author and
subject index and decennial indexes were issued to the first
thirty volumes. These serve, in some measure, as an index
to the scientific literature of the last half of the 18th century.
The fourth and last decade of the journal did not reach completion and thus no cumulated index for the period was issued. It was widely known and honored, as attested in the
preface to the "Medical and Philosophical Commentaries" issued between 1773 and 1795.

To the formula of the "Commentarii" the "Medical and
Philosophical Commentaries" added original articles and is
thus included with the substantive journals in this study. The
first six volumes were issued in quarterly numbers like the
"Commentarii." With the seventh volume the journal frankly
acknowledged its medical character by changing the title to
"Medical Commentaries." Under this title it appeared annually. The preface to the first volume provides insights into
18th century attitudes toward medical journalism:

Medicine has long been cultivated with assiduity and
attention, but is still capable of farther improvement.
Attentive observation, and the collection of useful
facts, are the means by which this end may be most
readily obtained. In no age, since the revival of
learning, does greater regard seem to have been paid
to these particulars than in the present. From the
liberal spirit of enquiry which universally prevails, it
is not surprising that scarce a day should pass without something being communicated to the public as a
discovery or improvement in medicine. It is, how-

ever to be regretted, that the information which can
by this means be acquired, is scattered through a
great number of volumes, many of which are so expensive, that they can only be purchased for the libraries of public societies, or of very wealthy individuals.    Hence, a complete view of all the improvements which are daily made or proposed in medicine,
cannot be obtained without much expense and great
labour.

No one, who wishes to practice medicine, either with
safety to others, or credit to himself, will incline to
remain ignorant of any discovery which time or attention has brought to light.    But it is well known that
the greatest part of those who are engaged in the actual prosecution of this art, have neither leisure nor
opportunity for very extensive reading.    Any expedient, therefore, which would serve, to communicate
new discoveries, without the necessity of examining
a great variety of books, must have some influence in
forwarding the improvement of the medical art.

Different periodical publications, intended as the annals of literature in general, are regularly published
in this island.    These literary journals contain an account of new books in medicine, as well as those in
other arts and sciences.    They will, therefore, in
some degree, answer the end here proposed.    But
they consist principally of characters of books; to
prove the justice of which, excerpts from the books
themselves are sometimes introduced.    It is therefore
evident that they can serve only to enable those who
have leisure for reading to select the most useful publications.

A scheme, better calculated for saving time in reading, and expense in purchasing books, is a concise
view of the books themselves.    It cannot indeed be al-
leged, that, from this or any other plan, the same ad-
vantages will be obtained as from a careful perusal of
original works.    But, by this means, those who have
not leisure for extensive reading, may easily become
acquainted with any thing proposed as a discovery in
medicine, and with the principal arguments by which
it is supported; while those who have, will thus be en-
abled to select such authors as they themselves imagine best deserve attention.

About twenty years ago, an undertaking of this kind

was begun at Leipsic.  This well known and valuable
publication, which is intitled, "Commentarii de Rebus
in Scientia et Medicina Gestis," is still regularly continued, and may be supposed to supersede any similar
attempt with regard to medical publication.   But, the
distance of the authors of that work from this island,
and the number of publications on the Continent of
Europe, are probably the reasons why they take notice of few British books, and of these even not till
many years after they have been published.   Beside
this, from their extensive plan, they can take in but
few books at a time; thus their account even of German books is in general very late.   It may further be
added, that these Commentaries are seldom to be met
with in this country, till a considerable time after
they have been published.   It is evident, therefore,
that they do not answer all the purposes which might
be expected from such a scheme; and that they are of
less service to medical people in the British dominions
than in other countries.

From these considerations we have been induced to
undertake a similar publication in this country, which
we propose to execute on the following plan.   It will
form annually one volume in octavo, consisting of
four parts, one of which will be published quarterly.
Every part will comprehend four sections, treating of
the following subjects:   An account of the best new
books in medicine, and those branches of philosophy
most intimately connected with it;  medical cases and
observations;  medical news;  and a list of new medical publications. (11)

The preponderance of German titles among the review
journals is shown in Tables 18 and 19.   In accounting for the
volume of German publication there are some explanations in
the literature which tend toward the mystical, e.g. Garrison:

The extraordinary preponderance of Germanic titles is
easily explicable by the Teutonic traits of patient industry, methodic persistence and purposeful organization. (12)

Ornstein in her study cites one author who attributes the size
of German publications to a quality he calls "schwerblütig-
melancholicus," and Ornstein herself suggests that the lack of
interested amateurs of science in Germany in this period was
perhaps due to an "innate Schwerfälligkeit of the German which
is never compatible with the versatility of the amateur." (13)

The Germans themselves have a term which perhaps accounts
to some extent for the large number of German publications:
"schreiblustig" a quality which seemed to be well recognized
in the 18th century.   The editor of the "Journal Encyclopédique," in responding to the criticism of the journal by
Freron, who had apparently used the term "German compilation" as a form of abuse, makes the following retort:

> M. Freron, believing that he is striking a terrible
> blow at our journal, calls it a German compilation...
> What then is a compilation?  In what respect is our
> journal more a compilation than the other journals?
> What does he mean by German?  Is it the German
> nation he thinks he is insulting or ourselves?  Does
> M. Freron believe that the intention itself is suffi-
> cient to wound?  He resembles a small angry child,
> who in his tiny fury, has nothing biting to say and
> believes he is making up the defect by words which
> signify nothing. (14)

We do not have an adequate reason for the preponderance of
German publishing.  It seems clear, however, that there was
no direct correlation between the amount of publication and
the local contribution to science in the 18th century.   The
outstanding work in the field of science in the 18th century
was not taking place in Germany, but in France and England.
This may provide one of the reasons for the greater number
of reviews in Germany; many of them devoted a considerable
portion of their space to translating, abstracting and reviewing foreign journals and books.

      Of the total of 40 review journals included in the anal-
ysis  23,  or 58 per cent (Table 18), are medical reviews of
which all but three are in German, and of these three, one,
the "Bibliotheca della più recente Letteratur medico-chirurgi-
ca," published in Pavia between 1790 and 1792, is a translation of the "Bibliothek der neuesten medicinisch-chirurgischen
Literatur," which was issued from Vienna between 1789 and
1792.   This ratio of medical to other specialized reviews is
a corollary to the fact that of the subject specialized periodicals, the medical journals made up by far the largest group.
In addition, not only did the physicians of the 18th century
make up the largest organized group that was interested in
science, but they had the largest group with a professional
stake in the scientific literature.   The old humanistic tradi-
tions that combined the role of the physician with that of the
philosopher, or more exactly, the natural philosopher, continued to exercise its influence throughout the 18th century,
and was reflected in the 18th century physician's interest in

Table 18

Review Journals - Country of Origin

|  | Germany | France | Holland | England | Other | Total |
|---|---|---|---|---|---|---|
| General | 6 | 2 | 2 | 2 | - | 12 |
| Medical | 17 | 1 | - | 1 | 4 | 23 |
| Other | 4 | - | - | 1 | - | 5 |
| Total | 27 | 3 | 2 | 4 | 4 | 40 |

Table 19

Comparison of the Duration of Review Journals
Published in Germany With Those Published
in Other Countries

| Number of yrs. Duration | General | | Medical | | Other | | Total | |
|---|---|---|---|---|---|---|---|---|
|  | G | O | G | O | G | O | G | O |
| 1 | 1 | - | 1 | - | - | 1 | 2 | 1 |
| 2 | - | 2 | 2 | 3 | - | - | 2 | 5 |
| 3 | - | 1 | 1 | 1 | 1 | - | 2 | 2 |
| 4 | - | - | 3 | 1 | 1 | - | 4 | - |
| 5 | - | - | - | - | - | - | - | - |
| 6 | - | 1 | - | 2 | - | - | - | 3 |
| 7 | - | - | 2 | - | 1 | - | 3 | - |
| 8 | - | 1 | 1 | - | 1 | - | 2 | 1 |
| 9 | - | 1 | 1 | - | - | - | 1 | 1 |
| 10 | - | - | - | - | - | - | - | - |
| 11-15 | - | - | 3 | - | - | - | 3 | - |
| 16-20 | - | - | 1 | - | - | - | 1 | - |
| 21-25 | - | - | - | - | - | - | - | - |
| 26-30 | 1 | - | 1 | - | - | - | 2 | - |
| 30- | 3 | - | 1 | - | - | - | 4 | - |

G--Germany          O--Other

all branches of science.   The fact that the term "medical" is
included in the title of a review does not mean that it was devoted exclusively to the subject of medicine.   The "Foreign
Medical Review," for example, published in London between
1779 and 1780, has the subtitle:  "Containing an account with
extracts of the new books published on natural history, botany, materia medica, chemistry, anatomy, surgery, mid-
wifery, and the practice of physic, in every part of the con-

tinent of Europe; together with intelligence of new and interesting discoveries." (15)    The fact that medicine itself was
not fully drawn into the circle of subjects that were being at-
tacked with the new spirit of scientific investigation does not
seem to have been any deterrent to the volume of publication
on that subject.    In fact, a considerable portion of the medical literature of that period seems to be much concerned with
the reiteration and application of traditional medical ideas.
For example, one of the most industrious of medical journalists of that period, Ernest Gottfried Baldinger, in the preface to the first volume of his "Medicinisches Journal, *" says:

> I have resoved to use the hours that I can spare from
> my various official duties in such a way that will per-
> haps not be unpleasant to my friends and many of my
> former students.    I have often wished that I could
> deal more thoroughly with many subjects than is made
> possible by the demands of teaching.    With these sub-
> jects I shall therefore deal more fully as time per-
> mits.    In the first place, to serve as an introduction,
> (the journal) will provide a better knowledge of the an-
> cient physicians, of whom detailed instruction is given
> in few universities, since they all concern themselves
> entirely with modern knowledge.    The sources of our
> art are so little consulted any more, that many stu-
> dents graduate every year who have not in their en-
> tire life seen a volume of Hippocrates.    If a Doctor
> of Theology were ever seen without a Bible, or a Jur-
> ist without his legal code, would that not seem absurd
> But, nevertheless, those who know will attest that
> Hippocrates is just as important to us, and the best
> translations do not supplant the reading of the sources
> themselves.
>
> Besides these essays to clarify some of the teachings
> of the ancients and various of their theories, I will
> discuss literary reports of the most outstanding and the
> best editions of the ancients and their commentaries,
> and also, in time, the outstanding discoveries in our
> art along with the important discussions of the physi-
> cians. (16)

The fact that the various regions of Germany tended
to develop their own journals and reviews does not fully ex-
plain the large number of German titles.    Many, and especially the medical reviews, were published in Göttingen, with
most of them under the imprint of two Göttingen publishers,
Dietrich and Vandenhoek.    Some of the contemporary comments attribute this to the existence of a superior library at

the University.   Usteri, for example, in his review of Arne-
man's "Bibliothek für Chirurgie und practische Medicin,*"
published by Vandenhoek in Göttingen from 1790 to 1793,

> So much which contributes to the value of this "Biblio-
> thek" must be omitted from this review, including the
> excellent and copious extracts and complete notices of
> foreign and expensive works to which the Göttingen
> library provides such adequate access.  (16)

And Richter in his "Chirurgische Bibliothek,*" one of the first
surgical review journals, published in Göttingen by Dietrich
from 1771 to 1797, says that although he will include both
foreign and domestic books in his review, the emphasis will
be on the foreign titles because it is less likely that the German surgeon will have an opportunity to see them.   The Royal Library at Göttingen, he assures his readers, will enable
him to achieve this goal since it obtains copies of the new
books as soon as possible.  (18)   Tode in his review of a
journal which might well be considered competitive to his
own, Murray's "Medicinische practische Bibliothek*" published
by Dietrich between 1774 and 1780, sounds a note of envy
when he says that Murray had the resources of the "Georgia
Augusta" which spares nothing in adding to its collections,
while he had to procure most of the books which he reviews
himself.  (19)   Similarly, Blumenbach, in the preface to his
"Medicinische Bibliothek" which appeared under Dietrich's imprint from 1783 to 1795, says:

> The excellent opportunities which present themselves
> in Göttingen of so readily examining at first hand the
> most important as well as the foreign new books, pro-
> vided this editor with the impetus for issuing this med-
> ical "Bibliothek."  (20)

Baldinger in his proposal for establishing a lending library
for medical books, which we cited earlier, gave as one of
his reasons:

> Since so many journals were written in Göttingen,
> many books were not obtainable for two or three years.
> This was especially true in Göttingen where the pro-
> fessors supervize the library for a part of their in-
> come.   Thus many professors do not buy books at all,
> although several others buy many, e.g. Walch, Böh-
> ner, Pütter, Kästner and others.  (21)

Not all of the journals issued at Göttingen were competitive.   Three of the medical reviews show an obvious se-

quence. The first of these was the "Medicinische Bibliothek,*" edited by Rudolph Augustin Vogel (1723-1774), and
issued under that title between 1751 and 1753 at Erfurt and
Leipzig. After Vogel received an appointment at Göttingen,
the journal came out there with the addition of "Neue" to its
title and continued to be issued until 1773. It appeared six
times each year in issues of approximately 90 pages each,
reviewed the current books in medicine and allied sciences
such as chemistry and botany, and provided an occasional
extract of journal articles from such publications as the
"Gentleman's Magazine" and the "Göttingische Anzeigen," as
well as medical news and a list of medical and natural science books which had appeared in the previous year. It was
followed by the "Medicinische-praktische Bibliothek,*" issued
under Dietrich's imprint from 1774 to 1780, and edited by
Johann Andreas Murray (1740-1791), a professor of medicine
at Göttingen and a director of its botanical garden. After an
interval of three years it was followed by the "Medicinische
Bibliothek,*" edited by Johann Friedrich Blumenbach and published by Dietrich from 1783 to 1795. In the preface to the
first issue Blumenbach promised four issues to make up one
volume a year, but he appears to have had some difficulty in
adhering to his publication program, because he was able to
publish only two numbers in each of the first two years, and
it became more sporadic as time went on. The four issues
of the third volume appeared in 1788, 1789, 1791, with the
fourth and final issue in 1795. The sporadic nature of Blumenbach's review was probably the reason that three competitive medical reviews were issued in Göttingen at about
the same time. Two of these also appeared under Dietrich's
imprint--the "Medicinisch-practische Bibliothek,*" edited by
Christian Friedrich Michaelis (1754-1814) who was able to
publish only three issues of one volume between 1785 and
1786, and Baldinger's "Medicinisches Journal*" which was
published under various titles until 1802 although only the
first nine volumes from 1785 to 1796 appeared under Dietrich's
imprint. When Baldinger went to Marburg he took his journal with him and the last three volumes were published there
under the title "Neues medicinisches und physisches Journal.*"
The third medical review was edited by Justus Arnemann
(1763-1806) who had previously been associated with Schlegel
in the editing of the "Neue medicinische Litteratur" at Leipzig. Arnemann was as remiss as Blumenbach in maintaining
frequency of publication. He hoped to issue a volume every
quarter, but was able to produce only two other issues, the
second in 1792 and the third and final issue in 1793. The review contained approximately 150 pages an issue and appeared
under the imprint of Vandenhoek and Ruprecht.

Two of the other review journals issued at Göttingen appeared with much greater regularity than most of the titles previously cited. One is the "Physicalisch-öconomische Bibliothek,*" edited by Johann Beckmann (1739-1805), professor of "Oeconomie" at Göttingen, and issued by Vandenhoek and Ruprecht in 23 volumes of four issues each between 1770 and 1806. It was devoted principally to agriculture and technology, although Beckmann included reviews of the proceedings of the scientific academies and of books in the natural sciences. Beckmann was the author of another work which is frequently cited as a periodical, the "Beitrage zur Geschichte der Erfindungen,*" which appeared in five volumes of four issues each, at Leipzig, between 1780 and 1805. These fascinating volumes are a sort of bibliographic handbook for technology in general and an encyclopedia of inventions in particular. The "Chirurgische Bibliothek,*" a review journal devoted to the surgical literature, was edited by the celebrated German physician and professor at Göttingen, August Gottlob Richter (1742-1812) in fifteen volumes of four issues each between 1771 and 1797 and issued by Dietrich. Richter promised a cumulated index for each series of six volumes, but they were not issued until 1794 and 1797 when the indexes to volume one through six, and seven through twelve, were published by Witting. The "Frankfurter medicinischer Wochenschrift" in its review of the fifth volume, speaks of Richter's work in the most laudatory terms:

> This Bibliothek comes from the hands of a master and thus does not need our commendations. We indicate it here only in order to have the opportunity to offer the most obligatory thanks to the author as a memorable teacher for what he has done in the service of humanity, on behalf and for the dissemination of this useful science, and in order to be able to ask for the continuation of such an extremely important publication. (22)

We get a glimpse of more polemic medical journalism in a review of the "Medicinische Litteratur für practische Aerzte," issued by Johann Christian Schlegel (1746-1824) in Leipzig from 1781-1794. The review appeared in the "Medicinische-chirurgische Bibliothek" in Copenhagen which was edited by Johann Klemens Tode (1736-1805), who seems to have been well known by his contemporaries for his vituperative abilities:

> Mister Schlegel may be a very fine man, but although his motives may be the best in the world, his powers

are not equal to the burden which he has taken on his
shoulders, even though the Atlas of Göttingen, Mister
Baldinger, to whom he stands in debt, at times seems
to have thrived on it.

I am far from having the slightest jealousy about the
fact that the number of medical critics grow ever
larger. I should rather be proud that the growth to
date has not caused me to lose any credit...

Nevertheless on behalf of the craft of reviewing itself,
it hurts me to see a new reviewer appear who has
neither ability, nor courage, nor respect enough to
perform a useful service for the public. Counter-
feited judgments, borrowed abstracts, bare lists of
contents, naive and pious ejaculations, grave grimaces,
to do honour frequently to fanfares, and to show regard for wooden images will not do it. A true German doctor will no longer be deceived; only the ordinary layman always makes up the majority and he is
thus regarded all too often as the entire people; and
what is really only the echoes of a bagpipe or a cow-
horn is called the voice of the people. The scribbler
and the literary vagabond joyfully lets himself be sum-
moned by such a bagpipe. It doesn't take a great
deal to get a so-called journalist to assist one, and to
become notorious in disrespect of all libraries and in
scorn of all scholars. This connection between so
many learned journalists and the miserable scribblers
thus does the public much harm...(23)

and so on to his:

As has been said, Mister Schlegel in spite of all of
this may be a very fine man, but he is not capable of
setting medical sinners aright, because he is himself
unfortunately one of the greatest of these. This is
shown by his astonished admiration of such people as
Baldinger and Gruner, and especially by his insipid
and distorted judgments and his affected and altogether
un-German diction which demonstrate this to the point
of nausea. (24)

These introductory remarks are followed by a detailed critique of the volume in hand which is interrupted by such occasional interjections as 'Grimacen, elende sinnlose Grimacen.''

After this tirade it is easy to understand why Schlegel

expressed some annoyance in the preface to the third volume
of his journal:

> I had expected that a downpour of invective and abuse
> from the north would fall on my publication.  How-
> ever, I assure this frothing strawsplitter that his in-
> sipid twaddle doesn't bother me in the least, and I
> can only deplore that this reviewer who thinks him-
> self so infallible will not be sufficently exposed in
> these reports. (25)

Despite his avowal of indifference, Schlegel is sufficiently
moved by criticism to defind himself against Tode's accusa-
tions that he had not read a particular book which he reviewed.  It is remarkable that Schlegel should have found it
necessary to defend himself against his charge for in the
case of other review journals in which the editor undertook
to cover an entire field of literature by himself, admissions
of reliance on other review journals and secondary sources
are freely offered.  Schlegel found it necessary in 1787 to
take Justus Arnemann as a collaborator, but other review
journals were inaugurated as the joint efforts of groups of
men.  This was the case with the "Neue litterarische Nachrichten für Aerzte, Wundaerzte und Naturforscher, (26) issued under the direction of the famous medical historian
Kurt Sprengel (1766-1833) in Halle from 1786 to 1789.  In
the preface to the first issue he says:

> Our authors are not always what they should be.
> Their pens are not always occupied with collecting a
> valuable treasure of experiments, nor with publishing
> of what is not known, of what is lacking and with fill-
> ing in lacunae, nor with the further enlightenment,
> better understanding, and correction of what is already
> known.  Often mere necessity, the need to make their
> names known through publication, or economic circum-
> stances--and who can list all the causes of the endless
> writing of books.  Is it any wonder then, that among
> the mass of books with which we are deluged every
> year, that one complains of a meagre harvest of prof-
> it from them...
>
> These thoughts have occasioned a society of physicians,
> surgeons and natural scientists to issue a special liter-
> ary journal for medicine, surgery and the associated
> sciences, chemistry, natural science, and natural his-
> tory.  The society does not in any way ignore the previ-
> ous efforts of many worthy men in this type of work,
> nevertheless, they do not feel that this undertaking is

superfluous, and believe it to be unique at least in
that they have limited themselves to the above sciences of which, on the other hand, they will seek to
provide as complete a review as possible. (27)

The nature of the publication and its administrative organization is more fully explained in the prospectus which appeared
in the surgical annual, "Taschenbuch für die deutsche Wundarzte:*"

> The "Bibliothek der neuesten medicinisch-chirurgischen
> Litteratur" here noted will be issued by more than
> twenty collaborators of whom part are German and part
> are foreigners.  Although the Society flatters itself
> that it is justified in adding to the number of periodi-
> cal works, because of the nature of its fundamental
> plan, it has in addition an even more important mo-
> tive.  The motive lies in the literary needs of a part
> of the Public.  This public is an inseparable part of
> the body politic in Austria, and even in peacetime
> numbers more than seventeen hundred individuals.  The
> location of the cantonements in areas which are inno-
> cent of the Muse, the remoteness of cities where the
> booktrade flourishes, economic conditions and similar
> circumstances have previously perhaps held back most
> of the field surgeons from a necessary familiarity with
> the best new books and basic literature, and we wish
> by means of this journal to eliminate in part this short-
> coming.  The publication office of the "Bibliothek"
> wishes to inform the public of the arrangement of this
> periodical work; the contents will command themselves
> in the period that follows.

> 1. The "Bibliothek" will take notice of publications in
> all branches of medicine.  The main headings of this
> subject are Anatomy, physiology, botany, chemistry,
> surgery, obstetrics, legal medicine, publications of
> mixed contents, notices of smaller works, news.

> 2.  It will provide extracts of the kernel of Latin,
> French, Italian and English publications, from the orig-
> inals, when good translations are not available, since
> it is one of the fundamental purposes of the society to
> observe the most concise completeness by means of
> reviews of those works which are susceptible to or
> worthy of an extract.  Works which are not distin-
> guished by anything noteworthy will be indicated only
> in passing.  By this means the purchase of certain ex-
> pensive books by the field surgeon will be made unnec-

essary.

3.   Since the number of such writings which contain
absolutely nothing new which is useful is not great,
the Society has decided to note all books once, to pass
by the well-known ones with silence, and to extract portions only from the most noteworthy.

4.   Under the heading:   Miscellaneous writings, will
be placed individual observations of medical and surgical content which are noteworthy, reports of researches
on proven remedies, etc.   Where works in pathology
are involved, engraving from the work will be used.
In this manner new instruments and bandages will also be reported.   In order to make the reader acquainted with the foreign literature, the Society has decided to take parts from time to time from the contemporary periodical works; among them: "Giornale
scientifico letterario e delle Arti di una Societa Filo-
sofica;" "Giornale Enciclopedico di Napoli;" "Opusculi
scelti sulle Sciencze e sulle Arti;" the "London Medical Journal,"" Medical and Philosophical Commentaries;"
"Journal de Paris," "Journal de Médecine, Chirurgie
et Pharmacie" (and) the memoirs of the various academies and learned societies.

5.   No author will have occasion to complain of the
method or of the tone of the Journal.   The judgment
of the Society will always be on the matter and not
on the man.   Also the presentation of contradictory
views will never be dictatorial but more often offered
with forebearance and always clothed in modesty. (28)

The journal was issued under the protection of Giovanni Ales-
sandro Brambilla (1728-1800), head of the Viennese surgical
academy and one of the editors was Johann Adam Schmidt,
the secretary of the academy so the journal appears to have
been under official sanction.   In addition to the ambitious
program outlined in the prospectus, the journal also included
reports of military morbidity and other military medical news,
so that it qualifies to be classified as one of the early mili-
tary-medical journals.

The final publication of this genre in the period covered here, is the "Medicinisch-chirurgische Zeitung," a bi-
weekly medical review and news-journal, which began in 1790
and was issued for almost fifty years from Salzburg and Inns-
bruck.   It is said to have had forty to fifty collaborators
drawn from among the members of various academic facul-

ties.  (29)

The comments made in the above chapter that the
journals devoted exclusively to abstracts made up a relatively small part of the amount of literature abstracted or extracted in the scientific and technological periodicals of the
17th and 18th centuries, apply with equal force to the review
journals.  A large part of the contents of the substantive
journals were devoted to reviews and extracts from books,
which again points up the continuing importance of the book
as a medium of scientific communication in this period.


## Notes

(1)     The sub-title of the "Monthly Review" is:  "A Periodi-
        cal Work, Giving an Account, with Proper Abstracts,
        of, and Extracts from, the New Books, Pamphlets,
        etc. as They Come Out."

(2)     Francis W. Gravit, "Notes on the Contents of Freron's
        Periodicals," "Romanic Review," XXXIV (1943), 116-
        126.

(3)     Adolf Dressler, "Geschichte der Italienische Presse"
        (2d ed.; Munich: Oldenbourg, 1933).

(4)     E. Runge, "Aus den Anfangen des deutschen medicin-
        ischen Zeitschriftenwesens." "Medicinische Welt,"
        XI (1937), 950-952.

(5)     Erich Walch, "Albrecht von Haller und die Göttinger
        gelehrten Anzeigen," "Zeitungswissenschaft," III (1928),
        1-3.

(6)     Heinrich Rohlfs, "Eine literarische Legende,"
        "Deutsches Archiv für Geschichte der Medicin," III
        (1880), 270-272.  Rohlfs states that the 12,000 origi-
        nated from a misprint in Blumenbach's biography which
        credited Haller with only 1200 reviews.

(7)     R. Wagner, "Zur Errinerung an Albrecht von Haller,"
        "Gesellschaft der Wissenschaften zu Göttingen, Erste
        Sacularfeir," 1851, p. 7: "It is well known, that
        Haller wrote over 10,000 and according to others
        12,000 long and short reviews and essays in almost
        all branches of literature for our learned journals a-
        lone.  John L. Thornton in his "Medical Books, Li-
        braries and Collectors," (London: Grafton, 1949), p.

94, gives the figure as 13,000.

(8)     Kirchner, op. cit., rejects this title from his bib-
        liography on the grounds that it was a newspaper and
        not a periodical.

(9)     F.N.L. Poynter, "First English Medical Journal,"
        "British Medical Journal," II (1948), 307-308.

(10)    One of two competitive journals with the same title.
        Graham, op. cit., pp. 28-29.

(11)    Medical and Philosophical Commentaries, I (1773),
        Preface.

(12)    Garrison, op. cit., p. 30.

(13)    Ornstein, op. cit., pp. 165, 203.

(14)    "Journal Encyclopédique," III (1759), 138-147.

(15)    Squire Sprugge, in his article "Medical Journalism,"
        "Glasgow Medical Journal," CIX (1928), 110-119, re-
        fers to this publication as the "first medical news-
        paper." However, since he also says that it did not
        appear until 1780, ran for some nine years and then
        changed its title to "Medical Facts and Observations,"
        makes it apparent that he must be referring to the
        "London Medical Journal," 1781-1790.

(16)    "Medicinisches Journal," 1784, Preface.

(17)    "Repertorium der medicinischen Litteratur," 1790, 37.

(18)    "Chirurgische Bibliothek," I (1771), Preface.

(19)    "Medicinisch-Chirurgische Bibliothek, III (1777), 156.

(20)    "Medinische Bibliothek," 1783, Preface.

(21)    Baldinger, op. cit., 337.

(22)    "Frankfurter medicinische Wochenschrift," 1780, p.
        212.

(23)    "Medicinisch-chirurgische Bibliothek," VIII (1781),
        522 ff.

(24)    Ibid.

(25)    "Medicinische Literatur für practische Aerzte," I
        (1781), No. 3, vii-viii.

(26)    The entry in the "Union List of Serials" is incomplete.
        Kirchner, op. cit. , no. 2668, states that a volume
        in 60 issues appeared in 1787 and that this was fol-
        lowed by a volume made up of four issues which ap-
        peared in 1788-1789.

(27)    "Neue literarische Nachrichten," I, 1786, St. 1, pref-
        ace.

(28)    "Taschenbuch für die deutsche Wundarzte," 1789, pp.
        162-166.

(29)    Callisen, op. cit., Vol. XXV, No. 1041.

# Chapter IX

Derivative Publication:   The Collection


   The "collection" has few counterparts in contemporary
scientific communications.   It resembles the anthology of
scientific writings which are published occasionally today.
It also has some features in common with the series of collected reprints which are sometimes issued either by individual authors or institutions.   Although some of the collections were published regularly, (one appeared in weekly issues and two others were monthlies) (Table 23) they have
antecedents which are different from those of the substantive
journal.   Among their predecessors were the collections of
medical cases, or "consilia" which had been issued since the
13th century.   It is probably not wise to insist on a direct
connection between the collections of the 18th century and the
"consilia," because the latter performed a different function.
They were an intrinsic part of the practice of medieval medicine and were compiled as part of the formal requirements
of the physicians' duties, rather than as a means of disseminating knowledge. (1)   The introduction of the collection
in the 18th century was another consequence of the increase
of scientific periodical literature.   Their resemblance to the
substantive journal is largely their mutual difference from the
"book."   The book, at least theoretically, achieves a certain
unity by its adherence to a central idea or subject, while
both the journal and the collection gather more or less disparate
elements.   A more important distinction, perhaps, is that the
"book" is usually the product of an individual author, while
both the collection and the journal are the results of the efforts of many authors.   These distinctions are not clear cut
because the various literary forms of scientific communication, like other processes of organic growth, exhibit a con-
tinuum in which each species represents a more or less arbitrary division.

   The major basis on which the distinction between journal and collection has been made in this study is that of
prior publication.   That is, the "collection" as defined for
this study, is made up of selections from the published literature.   This is also true of the abstract journal, but the

distinction between these two forms can be made on the
basis that while the collection usually reprints items in their
entirety, the abstract journal usually presents the communication in abbreviated form.  Like the abstract journal, one
of the functions of the collection was to provide wider circulation for material already in print, and especially for material in print in languages other than that of the publication
itself.  The collection reprinted more of the older literature
than did the abstract journal, and in this respect had an
attribute in common with the textbook.  This in the eyes of
an 18th century editor was the major function of the collection, to save from obscurity those memoirs which would
otherwise "go lost in the mass of thick quartos." (2)

Germany also dominated this class  of publication
(Table 22).  There does not appear to be any significant
difference, (Table 24), between the duration of serial collections published in Germany and those which appeared in the
other countries of Europe.  Collections tended more toward
irregularity of issue than the other classes of publication.
This and the fact that they were sometimes inaugurated without the intent of indefinite continuation are additional factors
which set them apart from the other forms of serial publication.  The species can perhaps best be defined by examining
some of its individual members.

One example of such a collection is the "Auszüge aus
den besten Französischen periodischen medicinischen, chir-
urgischen und pharmaceutischen Schriften*" which was issued in Leipzig in five volumes between 1780 and 1784.  The
preface to the first volume is worth quoting since it gives us
an insight into some of the mechanics of 18th century scientific journalism:

> The excellent observations of individual scholars often
> are lost when they are not taken up in collections of
> similar essays.  Especially do small works have such
> a fate when they are not included in larger works.
> In addition various difficulties prevent many physi-
> cians, surgeons and chemists of the world from being
> able to communicate their contributions.  Almost all
> of the nations of Europe are aware of this and of how
> our science would suffer, therefore many societies
> and individual scholars have prepared such collections.

> It is true that other sciences can show similar efforts,
> but one must admit that medicine today is especially
> fortunate in this respect, and can show valuable works
> of this kind which are published in Germany, England,

Table 20

Number of Collections by Subject and Decade of Origin

| | 1670 | 1680 | 1690 | 1700 | 1710 | 1720 | 1730 | 1740 | 1750 | 1760 | 1770 | 1780 | 1790 | Total |
|---|---|---|---|---|---|---|---|---|---|---|---|---|---|---|
| General | - | - | - | - | 1 | - | - | 2 | 8 | 5 | 8 | 10 | 1 | 35 |
| Medical | - | - | - | - | - | - | 3 | 1 | 2 | 1 | 5 | 20 | 2 | 34 |
| Other | - | - | - | - | - | - | - | - | 1 | 3 | 2 | 4 | 2 | 12 |
| Total | - | - | - | - | 1 | - | 3 | 3 | 11 | 9 | 15 | 34 | 5 | 81 |

Table 21

Active Collection by Subject and Decade

| | 1670 | 1680 | 1690 | 1700 | 1710 | 1720 | 1730 | 1740 | 1750 | 1760 | 1770 | 1780 | 1790 |
|---|---|---|---|---|---|---|---|---|---|---|---|---|---|
| General | - | - | - | - | 1 | - | - | - | 5 | 6 | 7 | 4 | 3 |
| Medical | - | - | - | - | - | - | 1 | 1 | 1 | 1 | 2 | 7 | 7 |
| Other | - | - | - | - | - | - | - | - | 1 | 3 | 1 | 1 | 4 |
| Total | - | - | - | - | 1 | - | 1 | 1 | 7 | 10 | 10 | 12 | 14 |

Table 22

Number of Collections by Subject and Country of Origin

| | Germany | France | Holland | England | Other | Total |
|---|---|---|---|---|---|---|
| General | 24 | 5 | 3 | - | 3 | 35 |
| Medical | 29 | - | 2 | 1 | 2 | 34 |
| Other | 8 | - | - | - | 4 | 12 |
| Total | 61 | 5 | 5 | 1 | 9 | 81 |

Sweden, France, Holland, Russia, etc. In France for
several years there have been issued many journals,
memoirs, etc., in which new truths of our art are
spread abroad, or are placed in a brighter light, or
are established. Especially was this the case with the
publication which began in Paris under the title "Recueil Periodique d'Observations de Médecine, de Chirurgie et de Pharmacie" in 1754 and since then as the
"Journal de Médecine, Chirurgie et Pharmacie." One
issue of this periodical appeared every month and in
1757 they began in Strasburg to translate it and to issue every year one volume of four issues. Nine volumes of this publication appeared under the title

Table 23

Frequency of Issue of the Collections

|         | Less than weekly | Weekly | Monthly | Bi-monthly | Quarterly | Annual | Bi-Annual | Irregular within year | Irregular longer | One issue |
|---------|------|------|------|------|------|------|------|------|------|------|
| General | -    | 1    | 1    | -    | -    | 3    | -    | 10   | 8    | 10   |
| Medical | -    | -    | -    | -    | 1    | 3    | -    | 11   | 10   | 7    |
| Other   | -    | -    | 1    | -    | -    | 3    | 1    | 1    | 3    | 1    |
| Total   | -    | 1    | 2    | -    | 1    | 9    | 1    | 22   | 21   | 18   |

Table 24

A Comparison of Duration of Collections Issued In
Germany with Those in Other Countries

| Number of years Duration | General | | Medical | | Other | | Total |
|---------|------|------|------|------|------|------|------|
|         | G | O | G | O | G | O | |
| 1     | 7  | 5  | 10 | 3  | 2  | -  | 27  |
| 2     | 3  | -  | 1  | 2  | 4  | -  | 10  |
| 3     | 2  | 2  | 4  | -  | -  | -  | 8   |
| 4     | 3  | -  | 4  | -  | -  | -  | 7   |
| 5     | -  | -  | 2  | -  | -  | -  | 2   |
| 6     | -  | -  | -  | -  | -  | -  | -   |
| 7     | -  | -  | 1  | -  | -  | 1  | 2   |
| 8     | 2  | -  | 1  | -  | -  | -  | 3   |
| 9     | -  | -  | -  | -  | -  | 1  | 1   |
| 10    | 2  | -  | 1  | -  | -  | 1  | 4   |
| 11-15 | 4  | 1  | 3  | -  | 2  | -  | 10  |
| 16-20 | 1  | 1  | 1  | -  | -  | -  | 3   |
| 21-25 | -  | -  | -  | -  | -  | -  | --  |
| 26-30 | -  | 1  | -  | -  | -  | -  | 1   |
| 31-   | -  | 1  | 1  | -  | -  | -  | 2   |

"Sammlung auserlesener Wahrnehmungen aus der Arzneywissenschaft Wundarzney-und Apotherkunst." Its
title and its policy both regarding the French periodicals and the translations changed from time to time.
In the beginning the French journals included essays
from the English and German periodicals which were
also available in German translations, but since the
Edinburgh Essays came out separately in German and

in French, this work was excluded and its place given over to the "Mercure de France" and the "Journal Économique."

With the tenth volume of the "Neuer Sammlung auser-lesener Abhandlungen aus allen Theilen der Arzneywissenschaft" or with the nineteenth volume of the entire series the German translations ended in 1775, in which the 19th volume of the "Journal de Médecine," published in 1763, appeared. One is amazed that one had to wait so long for a translation and that they could permit the latest reports to fall so far behind in Germany, especially since this work is so important and interesting for all branches of medicine. At the end of the 19th volume, twenty-four parts of the French text remained untranslated and they appeared in Germany twelve years too late or too slowly, and one might almost believe that a special effort had been made to make this publication as unimportant as possible for our countrymen. Not only did the new discoveries and reports appear so late, but they were all translated without any selection, unimportant things, essays which contained common and well-known matters, controversies and refutations of which the German could not have the slightest benefit, descriptions of mineral springs in France to which certainly no German physician would send their patients, descriptions of remedies which we could not buy, and which were pompously made known in France by quacks. This beautiful and important publication was so over-laden with such unimportant stuff that one was given cause to wonder whether these essays could bear fruit on German soil. One could forgive these errors, one would readily purchase the good with the bad, if they had only made it a rule to issue a volume a year and if they had not remained so far in arrears.

In time ever new institutes arose in France which sought to broaden the scope of medicine and had the same goals as the "Journal de Médecine." Recently the physicians of Paris have joined together in a society and made their observations known in the 'Histoire" and the "Mémoires" of the Société Royale de Médecine. In the same city the "Gazette de Santé" is issued and by means of the "Gazette Salutaire," issued in Bouillon, they seek to make the physician, surgeon and chemist acquainted with the publications appearing in all of Europe. This last publication has an advantage over many other similar publications since one

can tell at a glance what strides medicine has taken
in the previous year in all its branches as well as
what each one has contributed to these advances.

All these works mentioned, as well as similar periodicals, will be used as a basis for the issue of this
publication, and my view is to select interesting essays from these publications, selections from important new works, but to omit what is not useful for our
German physician.  Above all I loathe the continual
bickering of the French physician and surgeon which
is found in almost every issue of the "Journal de
Médecine," etc.  An essay is published in one issue
and the next one appears which contradicts the first
with much bitterness.  Of what use to us is this idle
talk and bickering, especially since they have not the
slightest influence on the practical aspects of our science?  Bitter and useless contradictions and attacks
betray only too often the proud man, a mean heart
and rude manners.

Above all am I fond of the truthloving and humani-
tarian tone of the "Gazette Salutaire" which permits
itself no bitterness, presents without decoration what
it accepts as the truth, values all highly whether it
is written by a Frenchman or a foreignor, and makes
no vicious attacks on anyone.  Certainly this method
is a surer and more pleasant way to bring the wan-
derer back to the truth, than by partisanship that sets
one against another.  From this publication will I especially seek to make my reader acquainted with the
work of the foreignor and the reports of the newest
things. (3)

The "Auszüge" appeared in a volume a year and included
translations of selected parts of the French medical periodicals, reviews of the shorter French tracts and lists of new
books in German as well as in the other languages.

One of the most extensive of these collections was
"Sammlung auserlesener Abhandlungen zum Gebrauche prak-
tischer Aerzte,*" which began in Leipzig in 1774 and continued until 1835.  It appeared in quarterly issues of approximately two hundred pages each.  Each volume included an index, and collective indexes to series of volumes were published periodically.  Its program was stated in the preface to
the first issue:

The purpose of this collection is to provide better

circulation for the best and newest essays which concern practical medicine, whether they are parts of
larger works or are published separately and thus
make them better known to our physicians.    It will
therefore contain only those essays which are closely
related to practical medicine and which are found in
such foreign writings which the largest number of
physicians have neither time or opportunity to examine.    For example the essays in the"London Observations" and the "Medical Essays" will be excluded,
since these have already been translated by scholarly
physicians and are already in the hand of most practical
physicians or at least should be.    Instead, other short
new writings which are of noteworthy content and
which are printed in a foreign language will be brought
together in this collection.    The point in time from
which we begin will be the year 1770 and we will attempt to bring out at least four issues a year. (4)

Despite this public avowal of contemporaneity and versatility
the first issue of the collection consisted of four essays on
lactation of which three had appeared before 1770.    The matter of the date of the material was taken up again in the
preface to the second issue:

Since our main purpose in this publication is to bring
to the attention of the German public those writings of
foreign learned societies which pertain to practical
medicine and which have not been translated into German, this second collection includes the pertinent
writings from the "Philosophical Transactions" which
have been issued since 1770, and also the writings of
the Parisian Academy and of the learned society in
Haarlem.    The continuation of these will appear in
subsequent collections in which we will also include
some observations issued before 1770 since these are
so little known among us.    We have also included in
the present collection various of the newest and most
noteworthy of the smaller English tracts.    Surgical
cases and everything not immediately the concern of
the practical physician do not belong in this collection,
especially since the surgical papers appear in Professor Richter's "Chirurgische Bibliothek," which should
be brought to the attention of all physicians and surgeons. (2)

This series met a need among the German physicians
as evidenced not only by its long continuation, but also by the
fact that a second edition of the first six volumes appeared in

Leipzig in 1785.

Another German collection which lasted almost as long as the "Sammlung" was the "Hamburgisches Magazin, oder gesammlete Schriften zum Unterricht und Vergnugen aus der Naturforschung und den angenehmen Wissenschaften überhaupt,*" which appeared as a monthly from 1747 to 1781. It was much broader in scope than the "Sammlung," taking all of natural philosophy for its province. It was intended to be popular as indicated by the title and in the preface to the second volume (6) where the editors apologize for including an article by Bernouilli on the mathematics of games of chance, and ended this apologia with the assurance to the reader that this would not happen too often.

Many of the collections that were issued in this period were more limited in the range they attempted to cover than the two titles above. The "Ausgesuchte Beiträge für die Entbindungskunst," issued in Leipzig from 1788 to 1789, is devoted solely to articles on obstetrics. These articles, furthermore, were all selected from another collection which had also appeared in Leipzig, from 1778 to 1794, the "Sammlung der auserlesensten und neuesten Abhandlungen für Wundarzte." This double distillation, or collection from a collection, leads us to believe that there must have been some justice to the remarks of the reviewer of another such publication in the "Frankfurter Medicinischen Wochenschrift:"

> It is merely a collection of essays which have already been printed in other collections or singly and which in this way have been brought into circulation again. As long as book dealers have good fortune with such ventures one should not be surprised to be continually blessed--or better, taxed--with such hasty collections. The choice, however, in this magazine is not bad for the most part...The high price of this magazine will not help it very much. This little volume sells for one florin and fifty-six kronen. And still they can't find honoraria to pay the author! (7)

The most outstanding collection of the 18th century was the series started in Dijon in 1752 and later published in Paris which attempted to bring together in one series most of the scientific journal publication and the proceedings of the scientific societies of the 17th and 18th centuries. Its full title provides some idea of its ambitious scope, "Collection Académique, Composées des Mémoires, Actes, ou Journaux des plus Célèbres Académies et Sociétiés Littéraires Étrangères, des Extraits des Meilleurs Ouvrages Periodiques, des

Traites Particuliers,  et des Pièces Fugitives les plus Rares
Concernant l'Histoire Naturelle et la Botanique, la Physique
Experimentelle et la Chymie, la Médecine, l'Anatomie,
Traduits en François et Mis en Ordre par un Société de
Gens de Lettres." It included among its editors and trans-
lators some of the most distinguished names in French science. It was issued in two series, one devoted to publications which had appeared in France and the other to journals
and proceedings which had originated abroad.  "The work will
be entirely in French," says the preface to the first volume,

> Because the French language has become by a sort of
> general agreement the current language of Europe,
> and because, by the wisdom and precision which
> characterize it, it must also be regarded as the lan-
> guage of philosophy. (8)

One will bind in this collection, the preface continues,

> all the memoirs which have been written in foreign
> languages, translated or abstracted with care by per-
> sons who are both versed in these matters and in the
> languages represented.  The purpose of the collection
> is to bring together those contributions to science
> which are dispersed in a multitude of books which are
> both difficult to read and difficult to assemble in one
> place.  Extracts from printed books will be omitted
> since they represent only a superficial idea of the ob-
> servations contained in them.  The superstitious and
> the fabulous found in many of the transactions will
> likewise be excluded since there are wonders enough
> to be found in experimental observations.  Mathematics
> will likewise be omitted since it seems to the editor
> that mathematics have become intelligible to only a
> small number of people.  The collection will therefore
> confine itself to natural history, experimental physics
> and medicine.

This monumental project was inaugurated by Jean
Berryat (d1745), a physician in ordinary to the King and the
intendant of mineral waters for France.  He was a correspondent of the Académie des Sciences and a member of the
society at Auxerre, but he is remembered principally as the
originator of the "Collection Académique," of which he lived
to see the completion of only two volumes.  The work was
continued by such well-known names in French science as
Buffon and Daubenton, who translated part of the selections
from the "Philosophical Transactions."  The collection as a
whole consists of two parts, one devoted to an abridgement

of the "Mémoires" of the Académie des Sciences de Paris,
the "Partie Francaise" which appeared in sixteen volumes
between 1754 and 1787, and a "Partie Étrangere" which make
up the thirteen volumes issued between 1755 and 1779.  The
later section contains translations of the publications of the
major European scientific societies, and  selected periodicals
published outside of France.  It is most complete for the literature of the 17th, but its coverage of the literature of the
18th century is very sketchy, as one can see from the analysis which follows:

## COLLECTION ACADÉMIQUE, PARTIE ÉTRANGERE

Volume I:  Devoted to physics, containing translations and
extracts from the following:

1. "Saggi de Naturali Esperienze" of the Accademia de
   Cimento, 1666-1667, from the Latin translation of F.
   Van Musschenboek, 1731, along with the translation of
   Mussenbroek's comments and additional bibliographic
   references.
2. Extracts from the "Journal des Sçavans," 1665-1686,
   consisting only of original contributions, and one extract from the "Journal d'Allemagne."

Volume II:

1. "Philosophical Transactions," 1665-1678, with subject
   index.

Volume III:

1. "Miscellanes Curiosa Medico-Physics Academise Naturae Curiosorum," 1670-1686.

Volume IV:    Natural History

1. "Philosophical Transactions," 1665-1683.
2. "Philosophical Collections," one article.
3. "Miscellanea Curiosa Medico Physica," 1670-1686.
4. "Giornale dei Litterati" (Nazari)," 1669-1673.
5. "Acta Medica et Philosophica" (Bartholin), 1671 and
6. Selections from the dissertations and other writings of
   Steno, Redi and Thomas Willis.

Volume V:

1. "Biblia Naturae," of Jan Swammerdam, which says
   the annotation, is here translated into French for the

first time.

## Volume VI:  Experimental Physics.

1.  "Philosophical Transactions," selections.
2.  "Journal des Sçavans," 1688-1692.
3.  "Miscellanes Curiosa Medico-Physics," 1670-1702.
4.  "Acta Medica et "Philosophica,"1671-1679.
5.  "Acta Eruditorum," 1682-1699.

## Volume VII:  Medicine.

1.  "Journal des Sçavans," 1687-1699.
2.  "Philosophical Transactions," 1679-1694.
3.  "Giornale dei Letterati" (Nazari), 1668-1670.
4.  "Acta Medica et Philosophica," 1671-1679.
5.  "Acta Eruditorum," 1682-1693.
6.  "Nouvelles de la Republique des Lettres"(Bayle), 1684-1687.
7.  "Miscellanea Curiosa Medico-Physica," 1687.
8.  "Mercure Galant," 1672-1692.
9.  "Acta, Academia Philo-Exoticorum Naturae et Artis," Brescia, 1686.

## Volumes VIII and IX:

1.  Akademie der Wissenschaften, Berlin, "Histoire et Mémoires," 1745-1753.

## Volume X:

1.  Accademia delle Scienze del l'Instituto di Bologna, "Commentarii."

## Volume XI:

1.  K. Svenska Vetenskapsakademien, Stockholm, 'Hand-lingar."

## Volume XII:

1.  Akademie der Wissenschaften, Berlin,'Histoire et Mémoires."

## Volume XIII:

1.  "Société Royale de Turin, Mélanges de Philosophie et Mathématiques," 1759-1769.

The above list is significant from two points of view -- the limited number of titles included, and the retrospective nature of the selection.   Berryat makes it clear that he regards this collection as a highly selective one, limited to the most significant contributions:

> If all the 'physicians' agree in these truths [the necessity for studying the past record in science] then they also complain of the great difficulties which they encounter in collecting the good works on each subject of physics.   The majority of these works, where they are not detached pieces, subject to loss and oblivion, are issued in immense volumes which in truth are preserved by their mass alone, but they include the diverse work of a large number of scholars, embracing at the same time almost all the fields of science, so that in order to procure the necessary tracts one is obliged to acquire a large number of volumes of which one does not have the slightest need.   Besides among these volumes there are those which are very rare; perhaps an assemblage of all these collections are not to be found in a single library in Europe. And even when these volumes are more commonly found, those which are available only in foreign languages are useless for the majority of readers, and one cannot profit from them without being familiar with a large number of the living languages, so that one loses in the study of words, time that could be better employed in the study of objects. (9)

The "Collection Académique" does not provide a very complete repository of the scientific advances of the 17th and 18th centuries.   It does, however, provide an extremely valuable key to a large part of the literature of this period.   It is made even more valuable by the four volume index to both series which was issued between 1775 and 1776 by the Abbé Rozier. Rozier's index also provides a key to the various publications of the Académie des Sciences de Paris to the end of 1770. In the introduction to the first volume of the index, Rozier explains its genesis:

> Being continuously occupied in leafing through the volumes of the Académie des Sciences in working on the journal, "Observations sur la Physique, sur l'Histoire Naturelle et sur les Arts," I have often lost precious time before finding the desired article...The purpose of this "Table" or "Dictionnaire," or this Concordance (the name is of little importance, if it is found useful) is to collect under a single point of view and in alpha-

betic order, each individual subject, according to the
titles of the memoirs, the dissertations and the observations, etc. and to simplify as much as possible
progress in research, in recalling with a single characteristic word of the title, to be able to find the desired object which one wishes to know, and to see at
a single glance everything which has been written on
the same subject.  In a word it is a veritable con-
cordance, almost or entirely similar to the concord-
ance to the Bible, or the index to Horace. (10)

The subject index makes up the bulk of the four volumes.  It
is in what might be called an alphabetic catchword arrangement, the entry word being some key word in the title.   The
citations are given in parallel columns along the side of the
page, each column representing a different series of the
Académie's publications, and headed with the following code
letters:

ADS 'Histoire et Mémoires'' of the Académie.
SE    ''Mémoires de Mathématiques et Physique.''
PR    ''Prix,'' an eight volume collection of the prize essays
         submitted to the Académie.
MAC ''Machines et Inventions.''
ART ''Arts et Métièrs'' (at that time covering only seven
         folio volumes).
COL ''Collection Académique.''

The last half of the fourth volume is devoted to a bibliography of the authors appearing in the various collections of the
Académie, but covering their other publications as well.
Thus under Haller's name we find not only a list of some of
his poetical works, but also the information that he contributed to the 1715 volume of the ''Mémoires,'' an observation
on a dog that could articulate approximately thirty words.

The ''collection'' is a rather unique device of this period of history.  It can in one way be considered transitional
between the encyclopedic scholarship of the Middle Ages which
sought to bring all knowledge together into a single compendium and the fragmentation of scholarship which was beginning
to take place at the beginnings of the modern era.   The collection was the result of many factors in the 18th century,
among them, (1) the inadequacy of the bibliographic control
of the literature of science in this period, (2) the breakdown
of a common medium of communication, a role which Latin
had previously filled, and (3) the ineffectiveness of the systems of distribution for the scientific literature.  By bringing
together periodical articles in their entirety and reprinting

them from various sources, they found a solution for these
problems which may have been more helpful in the 18th century than they would be today because of the changes in the
ratios between the costs of materials and labor.  A similar
solution was found for the problems of distributing academic
dissertations as we shall see in the chapter which follows.

## Notes

(1)     See especially D. P. Lockwood, "Ugo Benzi, Medieval
        Philosopher and Physician, 1376-1438' (Chicago, Uni-
        versity of Chicago Press, 1951), for a detailed an-
        alysis of the function of the consilia, and a penetrat-
        ing insight into medieval medical scholarship and au-
        thorship.

(2)     Tode in his review of the "Auszuge aus den besten
        medicinischen Schriftstellern der vorigen Jahrhundert,"
        edited by Christoph Jacob Mellin, in his "Medicinische
        chirurgische Bibliothek," II (1775), 131.

(3)     "Auszuge aus den besten Franzoischen periodischen
        medicinischen, chirurgischen und pharmaceutischen
        Schriften," I (1780), Preface.

(4)     "Sammlung," St, 1 (1774), Preface.

(5)     "Sammlung," St. 2 (1774), Preface.

(6)     1747.

(7)     1782, pp. 554-556.   Review of the "Magazin für
        Pharmazie, Botanik und Material Medica."

(8)     "Collection Académique," Volume I of the 1755 edition.
        (Dijon: François Desventes, 1755), p. xxxvii.

(9)     "Recueil de Memoires, oux Collection de Pieces Acad-
        emique," (Dijon: Desventes, 1754), I, pp. i-iv.

(10)    "Nouvelles Table des Articles Contenus dans les Vol-
        umes de l'Académie Royale de Paris" (Paris: Ruault,
        1775), I, v.

# Chapter X

## Collections of Disputations, Dissertations and Other Academic Publications

Ornstein in her study of the rise of modern science in the 17th century (1) has indicated that the role of the university in fostering the development of scientific ideas in that period was minimal, and that most of the activity and interest in this field took place outside the university. While we can cite no studies to document such a statement for the 18th century, we have only to remember the work of Priestly and Lavoisier to realize that significant work in sciences was taking place outside the universities. Nevertheless, a picture of 17th and 18th century scientific and technological serial publication would not be complete without at least a brief glance at a form of literature which was derived from the activities of the universities, and which contributed a portion of the content of the scientific periodicals and serial collections of this period.

Medicine as a discipline of study had been a part of the curricula of the universities almost since their establishment in the Middle Ages. Vesalius in the 16th century and Linnaeus in the 18th, to mention only two, made their significant contributions when they were members of university faculties, and many other university faculties were associated with important scientific discoveries.

The literature with which we are concerned here is that literature which was produced as a by-product of the instruction and other activities of the 17th and 18th century university, the printed disputations, dissertations, and academic addresses which were produced in such large numbers in this period. Ernest Gottfried Baldinger, one of the outstanding medical journalists of the last half of the 18th century, is said to have had 13,000 dissertations devoted almost entirely to medicine in his library. (2) He made great efforts to collect them systematically and in a bibliography of a part of his collection which he printed in one of his journals, he left a description of these activities:

> From the year in which I began to study medicine, I
> began almost at once to gather academic writings on
> all branches of our art, but especially for semeiotics,
> materia medica, pharmacy and general therapeutics.
> From other branches of medicine I have attempted to
> obtain only the important publications. (3)

He states that from the universities of Erfurt, Jena, Halle,
Leipzig, Göttingen and Marburg he is usually able to make
these acquisitions himself, but that at Strasburg, Erlangen,
in Holland and in Sweden he has purchases made for him.
He instructed his friends in all of the universities of Germany and abroad to obtain the new medical dissertations for
him as they appeared and also whatever old ones appeared
on the market.   At auctions he made a practice of buying
complete collections of dissertations and giving away those
that were duplicated in his own collection.   He makes a point
of the fact that all his dissertations are bound separately.
If they happen to be bound together in volumes when he purchased them, he had them separated and arranged in order.
"Since if one wants to read twenty dissertations it is necessary to borrow twenty volumes which contain perhaps a hundred dissertations," (4)   an objection, he fails to note, which
could also be offered against journal articles.   There were
probably few other collections of dissertations as large as
Baldinger's, but we meet frequently in the literature of the
period notices of auctions of libraries which included sizeable
collections.   For example, in one such notice which appeared
in the "Medicinisch-chirurgische Zeitung," a library which
contained 1,454 medical dissertations was offered. (5)

Dissertations and other academic writings appear to have
played a much larger role in the dissemination of scientific
literature in the 17th and 18th century than they do today, although it is difficult to say how much new and significant information they transmitted.   The general impression, albeit a
rather superficial one, is that it was more or less a ceremonial literature, a literature contrived to respond to the
needs of an academic occasion, or in response to the requirements of the academic curriculum.   As a student of the theses
of the Faculty of Medicine of Paris says in her study:

> A certain solemnity is required in conferring a de-
> gree; the formality of the thesis was the response to
> this need. (6)

They were more or less a carry-over of the medieval tradi-
tions of the disputations which were as important as a display
of oratorical and logical skill as they were for presenting in-

formation. This idea of a ceremonial literature might perhaps be applied with profit to some of the scientific literature of the 17th and 18th century literature, if not to the
literature of our own day. It might be interesting to inquire
how much of the literature is produced to fill up the inter-
stices of a program, or as an act of observance of a particular event, which while they serve the necessity for public avowals may not require preservation.

Published dissertations seem to have been as difficult
to come by in the 18th century as they are today. Schlegel
in his review of a collection of dissertations which he himself edited, makes a complaint which is reiterated many
times in the literature of this period:

> Everyone who loves literature knows how frequently
> the academic publications which appear in the Dutch
> academies come to Germany. A principal reason may
> very well be that which the worthy Professor Sandi-
> fort has offered in Leyden, that these publications are
> almost never available for purchase, and are often
> not to be found even in Holland. (7)

It was to allay these difficulties of acquiring dissertations
and to bring together collections of selected academic writings
in order to achieve wider circulation that many of these serial collections were begun. In his bibliography of 17th and
18th century periodicals Garrison lists some 120 titles under
the heading: "Serial Collections of Dissertations, Cases and
Observations." Many of his titles were published after 1790,
and others have been considered under another class of publication. Still other titles from this list have been omitted
because they are non-serial in nature, or because they are
the collected writings of a single individual. We have included only 38 titles of serial collections of academic publications in this study (Table 25), which probably represent
only a portion of all such collections which appeared in print.
We must also remember, that dissertations were reviewed
at length in the review journals, abstracted in the abstract
journals, and included in collections of other academic writings.

Only a few more than one-fifth of the serial publications of dissertations were issued for more than five years,
and only six of them seem to have observed any regularity
at all in their appearance (Tables 26 and 28). They are
more akin to the "collections" discussed in a previous chapter
than to any of the other classes of publications, since most
of them appear to be collections of previously published dis-

Table 25

Number of Academic Collections by Subject
and Decade of Origin

| | 1670 | 1680 | 1690 | 1700 | 1710 | 1720 | 1730 | 1740 | 1750 | 1760 | 1770 | 1780 | 1790 | Total |
|---|---|---|---|---|---|---|---|---|---|---|---|---|---|---|
| General | - | - | - | - | 1 | - | 3 | 1 | - | 1 | 1 | 1 | 1 | 9 |
| Medical | - | - | - | - | - | - | 1 | 2 | 6 | 3 | 10 | 7 | 1 | 28 |
| Other | - | - | - | - | - | - | - | 1 | - | - | - | - | - | - |
| Total | - | - | - | - | 1 | - | 4 | 4 | 6 | 4 | 11 | 8 | 2 | 38 |

Table 26

Active Academic Collections by Subject and Decade

| | 1670 | 1680 | 1690 | 1700 | 1710 | 1720 | 1730 | 1740 | 1750 | 1760 | 1770 | 1780 | 1790 |
|---|---|---|---|---|---|---|---|---|---|---|---|---|---|
| General | - | - | - | - | 1 | - | 1 | - | - | 1 | 1 | 1 | 2 |
| Medical | - | - | - | - | - | - | - | - | 2 | 1 | 4 | 6 | 4 |
| Other | - | - | - | - | - | - | - | - | - | - | - | - | - |
| Total | - | - | - | - | 1 | - | 1 | - | 2 | 2 | 5 | 7 | 6 |

Table 27

Academic Collections, by Subject and Country of Origin

| | Germany | France | Holland | England | Other | Total |
|---|---|---|---|---|---|---|
| General | 8 | - | - | - | 1 | 9 |
| Medical | 21 | 3 | 2 | 1 | 2 | 29 |
| Other | 1 | - | - | - | - | 1 |
| Total | 30 | 3 | 2 | 1 | 3 | 39 |

sertations. Some of them presented in translation dissertations which were available only in their original Latin form.
One example of this kind of publication is J.H. Pfingsten's
"Analecten zur Naturkunde und Oeconomic für Naturforscher,
Aerzte und Oeconomen" which appeared in 1789. Others appear to be review and abstract journals devoted exclusively
to academic publications, e.g. the "Bibliothek von Anzeigen
und Auszugen kleiner academischer Schriften," which appeared in Jena between 1789 and 1792 in three volumes of

Table 28

Academic Collections, Frequency of Issue

| | Less than weekly | Weekly | Monthly | Bi- annually | Quarterly | Annual | Irregular within yr. | Irregular longer | One issue | Total |
|---|---|---|---|---|---|---|---|---|---|---|
| General | - | - | - | - | - | 1 | 4 | 2 | 2 | 9 |
| Medical | - | - | - | - | - | 5 | 9 | 12 | 1 | 27 |
| Other | - | - | - | - | - | - | 1 | - | - | 1 |
| Total | - | - | - | - | - | 6 | 14 | 14 | 3 | 37 |

twelve issues each. Most of them, however, were collections in Latin of the original dissertations brought together by individuals who were desirous of preserving them. In his autobiography Johann Peter Frank (1745-1821), one of the pioneers in public health, discusses the generation of one such:

> Then I prepared for the benefit of my students a collection of the best polemic treatises that had been published in Latin at German universities, which I annotated and in which I included my own Latin publications. The first volume of this work appeared in 1785 under the following title: "Delectus opusculorum medicorum antehac in Germaniae diversis Academiis editorum, quae in Auditorum commodum collegit, et cum notis hinc inde aucta recudi cusavit Joannes Petrus Frank."

> I continued this collection in the following years and closed it in 1793 with the twelfth volume. It was reprinted at Venice and in part at Leipzig. (8)

Later in his biography he speaks of another collection, this time of his own papers:

> In connection with these academic addresses that I gave in Pavia, I must note that formerly at this famous university when the academic dignity was confered, the professors used to make only a brief speech praising such a candidate. Through my example I sought to transform this custom into a more useful one, in that I tried to choose scientific subjects for my public addresses. Soon I found the desired imitation and my learned colleagues often made public

addresses that I regret have not yet appeared in print. Most of my aforementioned memoirs that had appeared up to 1790 were collected in one volume and published at Leipzig under the title "Joannis Petri Frank etc. Opuscula medici argumenti antehac seorsim edita, nunc collecta," Lipsise, 1790. A number of these memoirs were also translated from Latin into German, and in part included in collections of selected memoirs for practicing physicians and surgeons. (9)

The dissertation collections seem to fall into several major groups, (1) general collections devoted to the dissertations of several universities and covering many subjects, e. g. the "Acta Academica Praesentem Academiarum, Societatum, Litterarium Gymnasiorum et Scholarum," issued in six volumes (Leipzig, 1733-1738). One such publication which began as a general collection, the "Gründliche Auszüge aus den neuesten juristischen, medizinischen, historischen, physikalischen und mathematischen Disputationibus" of which six issues appeared at Leipzig between 1736 and 1737, in 1738 formed two series, one devoted to the sciences and the other to the humanities, the "Gründliche Auszüge aus medicinischen, physicalischen und mathematischen Disputationen," in four volumes at Leipzig between 1737 and 1741, and the "Gründliche Auszüge aus juristischen und historischen Disputationibus," issued at Leipzig from 1738. (2) The second major class consists of general collections of dissertations which originated at a single university, e.g. "Collectio Dissertationum Inauguralium Lugduno Batavorum," edited by F. J. de Overkamp at Frankfurt am Main in 1767. (3) The third group consists of collections of dissertations on a single subject, either drawn from many universities, e.g. "Adversaria Argumenti Physico-Medici," Erlangen, 1779-1790, or from a single university, e.g. "Dissertationes Medicae Selectiones Pragenses," Prague and Dresden, 1775 and 1793.

One fact is worth noting in this brief glance at the serial dissertation collections is that many of the individuals who edited and collected them were also editors of scientific journals. Johann Traugott Schlegel who edited a medical review was also responsible for the appearance of the following three dissertation collections: "Sylloge Selectiorum Opusculorum de Mirabili Sympathia" (Leipzig, 1787), "Thesaurus Semiotices Pathologicae" (Stendaliae, 1788-1802), and "Thesaurus Pathologico-Therapeuticus" (Leipzig, 1789-1793). Of the last title he says in his review:

I cannot determine in advance how many volumes of this thesaurus will appear little by little; this will

depend entirely on the approval which my undertaking
receives from the public. (10)

Philip Ludwig Wittwer (1752-1792) who was editor of one of
the first medical historical journals, the "Archiv für die
Geschichte der Arzneikunde in ihren ganzen Umfange" (Nuremberg, 1790), also edited a collection of medical dissertations from the University of Nuremberg, the "Delectus Dissertationum Medicarum Argentoratenisum" (Nuremberg, 1777-
1781), in four volumes.   Christian Gottfried Gruner (1744-
1815), editor and translator of many medical periodicals and
society proceedings in the 18th century, was responsible for
the following dissertation collection, the "Delectus Dissertationum Medicarum Jenensium" (Altenburg, 1778-1785), and
the "Kritische Nachrichten von kleinen medicinischen Schriften in-und ausländischer akademien in Auszugen und Kurzen Ur-
theilen dargelegt" (Leipzig, 1783-1788).   The last title is an
abstract and review journal devoted to reviewing and abstracting German and foreign medical dissertations.   In commenting on this journal in his review in the "Journal de
Médecine et Chirurgie," the editor says:

> One regrets that M. Gruner has chosen to publish in
> German, and we invite him to continue his publication
> in Latin. (11)

Johann Hermann Pfingsten whom we cited above as the editor
of an abstract journal for dissertations, was editor of a
number of other journals in science and technology.   Ernest
Gottfried Baldinger, one of the most prolific of the 18th century medical journalists, besides editing a collection of medical dissertations in Latin, the "Sylloge Selectiorum Opusculorum Argumenti Medico-Practici" (Göttingen, 1776-1782), issued the following extract journal, the "Auszüge aus den
neuesten Dissertationen über die Naturlehre, Arzneywissenschaft und alle Theile derselben' (Berlin and Stralsund, 1769-
1772).

These collections seem to have fallen into disfavor by
the end of the century.   Usteri in his review of Johann
Georg Reyher's "Auszüge medicinischer Probe- und Einladungs-
schriften," of which two issues appeared in Schwerin and Wis-
mar (1790 and 1791), says:

> I greatly wish that this periodical dedicated to academ-
> ic writings might have better fortune and continuity
> than many of its predecessors. (12)

The reviewer in the "Medicinisch-chirurgische Zeitung"

speaks of the fall from esteem of such collections and the
lack of attention which is being paid to this kind of literature. He attributes this to "...the neglect of the printer who
seldom goes to the Fair with this sort of wares..." and to
the "...growing ignorance of the new physicians and the bar-
bers and apothecaries guilds to the Latin language." (13)

Notes

(1)     Ornstein, op. cit.

(2)     Walter Artelt, "Die medizinischen Lesegesellschaften
        in Deutschland," "Sudhof's Archiv," XXXVII (1953),
        200.

(3)     E.G. Baldinger, "Verzeichnis semiotischer akademi-
        scher Schriften," "Neues Magazin für Aerzte," XII
        (1791), 246.

(4)     Ibid.

(5)     II (1790), 128.

(6)     Anna Delage, "Histoire de la These de Doctorat en
        Médecine d'Apres les Theses Soutenues Devant la
        Faculte de Médecine de Paris" (Paris:  Ollier-Henry,
        1913), Preface.

(7)     "Medicinische Litteratur für practische Aerzte," XII
        (1787), 211-213.

(8)     Johann Peter Frank, "Biography," (translated from the
        German by George Rosen), "Journal of the History of
        Medicine," III (1948), 284.  In 1785 Frank, after leav-
        ing the University of Göttingen, had joined the medical
        faculty at Pavia.

(9)     Ibid.

(10)    "Neue Medicinische Litteratur," I (1788), 131.

(11)    1785, p. 64.

(12)    "Repertorium der medicinischen Literatur," 1790, p.
        42.

(13)    "Medicinisch-chirurgische Zeitung," II (1791), 315.

# Chapter XI

## Almanacs and Annuals

As we have seen in our brief survey of the antecedents of scientific journalism, the almanac antedates both the newspaper and the periodical as a form of publication. The popular agricultural and health almanac "Le Grand Calendrier et Compost des Bergiers" was issued throughout the 16th and 17th centuries. Guitard in his study cites an issue in Paris as early as 1488 under the title "Le Compost et Kalendrier des Bergiers." But this is only one of a species represented by a large number of examples which appeared in the long period preceeding the advent of scholarly periodicals. Guitard also cites two other early almanacs which were issued by physicians and which contained hygienic advice, the "Almanach Jehan de Lespne, Docteur en Médecine, Calculé sous le Meredional de la Cité et Ville du Mans," published in Paris in 1534, and the "Magnum et Perpetuum Achalman," which he describes as a satire against the calendars which marked days for purges, and bloodletting, published at Anvers in 1551. These were a great number of similar publications which came out under the direction of physicians, in fact:

> The majority of those published in the sixteenth century had physicians as their authors. By consulting the calendar one knew whether it was propitious to permit oneself to be bled or bathed, whether to be purged in the morning or in the evening. Conventional signs indicated which days were appropriate and which were inappropriate for each one of these grave operations. (1)

This type of almanac continued to appear throughout the 17th and 18th centuries. In addition general almanacs frequently contained material of medical interest. One example is the "Göttingisches Taschenbuch zum Nutzen und Vergnugen," issued by Dietrich at Göttingen from 1775 to 1811. Some of the articles in the 1790 edition of the "Taschenbuch" are fairly typical; an essay on remedies against eye diseases, an extract from a Göttingen dissertation on animal magnetism, and a description of a method of keeping food cool in the summer.

Periodical bibliographies frequently distinguish this class of publication by the interval between issues rather than the content, so that they might more aptly perhaps be called "annuals" rather than almanacs. Sometimes they are grouped with the large number of astronomical almanacs issued on this period, and with the astronomical data books which succeeded them. In the group of titles in this class which we have included for analysis, we have selected only those which seemed likely to have some substantive content of a scientific or technological nature, although the forty-six titles included probably represent only a small porportion of those which might well qualify for inclusion. The bibliography of Grand-Carteret (2) which provided the source of many of the titles in our list, includes 88 titles in the 17th century and over 1200 in the 18th. We have selected only a few of those which did not seem entirely astrological in character, or did not appear to be issued entirely for the amusement and entertainment of the general population. In the preface to his bibliography, Grand-Carteret presents his criteria of selection under the following three categories: (1) title, he included all those volumes which have the generic titles, e.g. "Calendrier," "Almanach," "Étrennes," "États;" (2) content, i.e. whether or not they contained calendar inserts; and (3) frequency, whether they were annual publications such as agendas, annual directories, and reports on civil affairs and conditions. "In a word," he says,

> the almanac and the annual, the two forms of the book designed to record the events of the past, provided each year the information and documents necessary for all the classes of society or for special groups of the public. (3)

His list is therefore a rather mixed-bag which includes titles of the most frivolous nature, from the special almanac for the hairdresser and dancer to the astronomical data books issued by the astronomical observatories. The astronomical almanacs or ephemerides are, of all these groups, perhaps of the greatest scientific interest, but we have included only a few of the titles where there was evidence that they also contained original memoirs as well as the data tables and charts. Included, for example, is the "Connoissance des tems, ou Calendrier et Ephemerides du Lever et Coucher du Soleil, de la Lune et des Autres Planets," which was issued in France from 1679, although it did not begin to include astronomical memoirs and news until 1766. (4) A similar title is the "Effemeridi Astronomiche...Calcolate pel Meridiano di Milano," issued in Milan from 1774 to 1873.

The special almanacs in gardening, hygiene, agriculture and other subjects although they were not significant
media for the dissemination of scientific information provide
insight into the state of popular interest in and knowledge of
scientific subjects.   The "Almanach des Ballons, où Globes
Aerostatiques, Étrennes du Jour Physico-Historiques et
Chantantes," which appeared in Paris in 1784, right on the
heels of Montgolfier's first ascension in a balloon, is made
up of a description of a series of experiments with balloons
and a history of previous attempts at balloon ascension.   It
concludes with several anecdotes and three songs inspired by
the occasion of which the following verse is a fair example:

> The wind became his postillion,
> And a cloud was his pavillion.
> He was oer' whelmed by all with praises,
> For by his secret so marvelously fine
> One is taken to the gods to dine,
> As to the angels his cage raises. (5)

There are almanacs for the building trades, "Almanach des
Batimens...Contenant les Noms et Demeures de Messieurs
les Architects, Experts-Bourgeois, Experts-Entrepeeneurs
de Batimens, Greffier" etc., issued in Paris, 1774 to 1792,
(6) and for the miner, "Chursachsische Bergwerks-Calender,"
Marienberg, 1773-1783, (7) but the majority of the titles included in this study fall into the subjects either of health
and hygiene, or agriculture and gardening.   One of the functions of the agricultural almanacs was to spread the new rational and experimental methods in farming, and some of
them had leading French scientists as collaborators.   The
"Bon Jardinier Almanach," which was issued in Paris for
most of the last half of the 18th century at various times in
its career had the assistance of such men as De Jussieu,
Pepin and Duhamel du Monceau. (8)

Two major groups can be distinguished among the
medical and hygienic annuals and almanacs.   One group is
made up of the popular health almanacs which bear such titles
as "Étrennes d'un Medicin; Ouvrages où l'on Donne les Moy-
ens sur de Remedier Promptement aux Differents Accidents
qui Menaçent la Vie," which was issued in Paris from 1775,
(9) and "Etrennes Salutaires ou Précis de ce qu'il est à
Propos d'eviter et Faire pour se Conserver en Bonne Santé
et Prolonger sa Vie," which was printed in Holland, but which
was also available in the bookshops of Paris. (10)   Another
one in this class is the popular "Almanach de Santé," which

Table 29

Almanacs, by Country of Origin and Subject

|  | Germany | France | Holland | England | Other | Total |
|---|---|---|---|---|---|---|
| General | 4 | 2 | - | - | - | 6 |
| Medical | 5 | 8 | - | 1 | - | 14 |
| Botanical | 2 | 4 | - | - | - | 6 |
| Agricultural | 3 | 4 | - | - | - | 7 |
| Other | 6 | 4 | - | 1 | 2 | 13 |
| Total | 20 | 22 | - | 2 | 2 | 46 |

Table 30

Scientific and Technological Almanacs
by Subject and Decade of Origin

|  | 1670 | 1680 | 1690 | 1700 | 1710 | 1720 | 1730 | 1740 | 1750 | 1760 | 1770 | 1780 | 1790 | Total |
|---|---|---|---|---|---|---|---|---|---|---|---|---|---|---|
| General | - | - | - | - | - | - | - | - | - | - | 3 | 2 | - | 5 |
| Medical | - | - | - | - | - | - | - | - | 1 | 3 | 3 | 7 | - | 14 |
| Other | - | 1 | - | - | - | - | 1 | - | 2 | - | 11 | 10 | 2 | 27 |
| Total | - | 1 | - | - | - | - | 1 | - | 3 | 3 | 17 | 19 | 2 | 46 |

Table 31

Active Scientific and Technological Almanacs
by Subject and Decade

|  | 1670 | 1680 | 1690 | 1700 | 1710 | 1720 | 1730 | 1740 | 1750 | 1760 | 1770 | 1780 | 1790 |
|---|---|---|---|---|---|---|---|---|---|---|---|---|---|
| General | - | - | - | - | - | - | - | - | - | - | 1 | 2 | 2 |
| Medical | - | - | - | - | - | - | - | - | - | 1 | 1 | 2 | 1 |
| Agricultural | 1 | 1 | 1 | 1 | 1 | 1 | 1 | 1 | 1 | 1 | 3 | 3 | 3 |
| Botany | - | - | - | - | - | - | - | 1 | 2 | 2 | 2 | 3 | 3 |
| Other | - | 1 | 1 | 1 | 1 | 1 | 1 | 1 | 2 | 2 | 4 | 7 | 8 |
| Total | 1 | 2 | 2 | 2 | 2 | 2 | 2 | 3 | 5 | 6 | 11 | 17 | 17 |

was issued by Gardane, editor also of a weekly medical news journal, the "Gazette de Santé." Gardane, incidentally, was also a member of the Parisian Faculty of Medicine and the Royal censor assigned to Rozier's journal. Gardane an-

nounces the appearance of the almanac in his "Gazette" in the
following terms:

> Containing an abridgement of the means for being
> well, the manner of governing oneself the first days
> of an illness in the absence of gentlemen of the art
> [of medicine]; the precautions necessary to take in
> order to preserve one's health while travelling; a list
> of the principal mineral waters in the realm, their na-
> ture and effects; abridged information of the proper-
> ties of remedies and their virtues against most of the
> common accidents of life, some useful recipes against
> the diseases of infants, the manner of taking care of,
> grooming and treating horses while travelling, as well
> as the preservative care necessary for the diseases of
> animals, along with a table of contents of the "Gazette
> de Santé." (11)

The other major group is made up of those annuals and almanacs which seem to be directed toward an audience of
physicians. Representative of this class is the "État de
Médecine, Chirurgie et Pharmacie en Europe," issued in
Paris from 1766. It included short articles, reviews of medical legislation and lists of medical publications issued in the
preceeding year. Another such title is the "Nouvelles Instruc-
tives Bibliographiques,*" issued under various titles by Retz,
who was one of the physicians to the King of France. The
first volume, issued in 1785 in Paris, is prefaced with a
sort of engagements calendar or date book for the physician
to record the names and addresses of his patients and their
symptoms, along with a list of the maladies common to any
particular month. The volume also includes a section devoted to reviews of medical books which had appeared in the
previous year, an obituary section giving short biographies
and a list of the publications of the physicians who had died
in 1784, a list of the courses in medicine and in the allied
sciences offered in Paris in the current year, and finally a
list of the physicians practicing in Paris. The volumes were
issued every year at least until 1791, although after the first
volume there was more emphasis on providing abstracts from
the medical literature, and the calendar portion was eliminated, so that it became almost the equivalent of an annual
review of the medical literature.

The most popular German publication of this genre
was the "Almanach für Aerzte und Nichtaerzte,*" which as
the title indicates was addressed to both physicians and laymen. It was edited by Christian Gottfried Gruner (1744-
1815) who was for forty years a professor at the University

of Jena.  It was issued annually in a volume of from 250 to
300 pages and usually contained a calendar as well as a list
of the important dates in medical history beginning with the
creation of the world.  In his reviews of the medical literature of the year Gruner frequently finds occasion to unburden
himself of caustic comments about the state of literature in
general and of medical journalism in particular:

> It has become a business in which the assiduous
> writer is merely provided with his necessary bread
> by the sacrifice of his rest, his health and his honor,
> and the profit is left for the speculative business men.
> Therefore, most of the publications are merely the
> work of busy fingers, and very few are products of
> the intellect, deep thought, or mature and extensive
> experience.  Everyone writes of his observations and
> experiences, the youth, the adult, and the greybeard,
> and assumes a venerable mien as if he were the very
> Aesculapius of his time...Many who are dissatisfied
> with the mass of knowledge achieved by the mother-
> land, look for treasures of wisdom in Italy, France
> and England, whereas they could find it more cheaply
> and more completely in the works of their country-
> men.  The blind esteem of the German for the for-
> eign and the Anglomania of the physician is throttling
> the development of national ability and is preventing
> them from becoming themselves, experts, discoverers,
> and supporters of a rational art of medicine.
>
> One translates without taking the trouble to decide
> whether the foreign product is worth the cost and the
> effort.  Every miserable little publication which is is-
> sued by an unknown Briton, a wretched surgeon, or
> empiric apothecary, is admired, honored, commended,
> translated, and generally obeyed by German physicians.
> (12)

He goes on to say that although there have been some distinguished contributions by British physicians, not a hun-
dredth part of their writings deserve to be translated.  In addition the emphasis on British literature brings with it a neglect of the study of German climate and customs and their
effects on the practice of medicine.  The rest of the essay
is devoted to a polemic against the state of medical literature
in general:

> The majority of physicians are surfeited to the point
> of illness by the reading of journals.  Journals, news-
> papers, magazines, or however the horde of publica-

tions is called, now fill most of the libraries and
most of the heads...Many physicians are zealous to
become the owners or the directors of a journal or
a learned newspaper in order to use this privilege to
exalt their friends and allies and to attack those that
oppose them. (13)

Gruner's almanac, itself, is a pot-pourri of short catechisms
on health, short popular articles, e.g. on opium as a universal remedy, a description of a cannibalistic individual,
medical news items from all the countries of Europe, and
surveys of the medical literature.    Evidence of its popularity
is provided by a satire which appeared in 1787.    Schlegel
notes it in his "Neue medicinische Litteratur," but includes it
under the heading, "A Review of Some Nauseating Publications." (14)

Gruner's comments bear out the impression we arrived at earlier in this study, that the German literature of
this period was largely derivative.    The predominance of
French titles in this group (Table 29) is undoubtedly a result
of the use of Grand-Carteret's list as a source for this study,
but it is also perhaps an indication that this type of literature did not lend itself particularly to reprinting or abstracting, although abstracts of articles from the almanacs did appear occasionally in the scientific periodical literature.    The
almanacs were largely addressed to laymen and were predominantly popular in their appeal, and therefore were not
as frequently used as were the general literary periodicals
for primary communication of scientific information.

## Notes

(1)     Guitard, op. cit., p. 65.

(2)     John Grand-Carteret, "Les Almanachs Français"
(Paris: Alisie, 1896), p. x.

(3)     Ibid., p. viii.

(4)     Ibid., No. 19.

(5)     Ibid., No. 759.

(6)     Ibid., No. 504.

(7)     Bolton, op. cit., No. 1287.

(8)      Passy, op. cit., pp. 5-6.

(9)      Grand-Carteret, op. cit., No. 551.

(10)     Ibid., No. 372.

(11)     "Gazette de Santé," I (1774), 116.

(12)     "Almanach für Aerzte und Nichaerzte," 1782, pp. 137-
         138.

(13)     Ibid., p. 149.

(14)     "Neue medicinische Literatur," 1787, p. 138.   The
         satire is entitled "Almanacum perpetuam für Aerzte
         und Nichtaerzte im Jahr 1787 ad aeternam rei me-
         moriam dem Hrn. Dr. Christian Gottfr. Gruner in
         Jena zugeeignet."

# Chapter XII

## Scientific Literature and the General Periodical

Although we have excluded from the review most of
the general and literary periodicals of the 17th and 18th centuries, a history of the scientific and technological periodical
press in that period would be most incomplete without some
discussion of their contribution to scientific communication.
The fact that a large number of the special journals with scientific content were directed to a more or less general and
unspecialized audience had its corollary in the fact that the
general and unspecialized periodicals contained some scientific content. It would be very easy to distort the picture
of the amount of scientific emphasis in the general periodicals of the 18th century by placing too much importance on
the "scientific articles" which appeared in the general magazines. A considerable proportion of this content undoubtedly
was similar to the "scientific" content which appears in our
general press in response to popular interest and curiosity
today. On the other hand it is probably also true that the
difference between the articles written for the laity and those
that were written for the initiated was not as great then as
the differences are today. In other words an accurate picture of the relationship between the articles on science and
medicine appearing in the general journals and the specialized journals of the 18th century cannot be obtained by comparing them with the scientific and medical articles in our
general and special periodicals today, but with their contemporary counterparts. The Age of Enlightenment was a period
of widespread interest in matters relating to science and it
was inevitable that this interest should be reflected in the
general periodical press. A study of the popular interest in
scientific literature in this period provides an interesting
sidelight into intellectual and cultural history, but we are concerned here with the contribution which the general periodical
press made to a more specialized form of scientific communication.

It would be important in this connection to have some
data on the proportion of the periodical press which was devoted
to science, and to be able to compare it with similar data about

contemporary publishing. Unfortunately we lack this kind of
data in this study. The analysis which Kirchner made of the
whole range of German periodical publication in the period up to
1790 is, however, suggestive. Of the 3494 titles which Kirchner
included in his bibliography, only 910 or 26 per cent fall into
categories which might be considered of interest in the history
of science and technology. Of this total 440 are classified as
general scholarly periodicals and thus fall outside the scope of
this study. The remainder, 470 or 13 per cent of the total, includes such groups as finance journals which are of interest to
us because some of the journals in this group contain material
relating to technology, and the large group of economic journals
which includes agricultural periodicals. Of the total, 1101, or
almost one-third of all the titles, are designated by Kirchner as
journals of popular education, entertainment and light reading.

Table 32[a]

Subject Classification of German Periodicals
in the Period Up to 1790

| Subject | Science | Total |
|---|---|---|
| General scholarly journals | | 440 |
| Finance journals (includes technology) | 49 | 49 |
| Masonic journals | | 13 |
| Historical journals | | 343 |
| Historical-political journals | | 155 |
| Legal journals | | 115 |
| Journals of art and aesthetics | | 13 |
| Literary journals | | 323 |
| Journals of the occult | | 4 |
| Mathematical journals | 4 | 4 |
| Medical journals | 149 | 149 |
| Journals of military science | | 19 |
| Music journals | | 38 |
| Natural science journals | 160 | 160 |
| Economic journals (includes agriculture) | 104 | 104 |
| Pedagogical journals | | 117 |
| Philosophical journals | | 37 |
| Technological journals | 4 | 4 |
| Theological journals | | 294 |
| Moral weeklies, journals of entertainment, etc. | | 1101 |
| Total | 470 | 3494 |

[a]Adapted from Kirchner, op. cit.

We get some additional perspective on the proportion of the periodical press which was devoted to scientific subjects when we examine an 18th century subscription catalog such as the "Liste Genérale per Ordre Alphabétique des Journaux, Anciens et Modernes, Nationaux et Étrangers, qui Circulent dans Toute la France," which was published by the Bureau du Bibliographie Universel in Paris in 1790. The preface to the list states that it is incomplete especially for the provinces and requests the publishers of those periodicals which are not listed to inform the Bureau so that their publications may be included in subsequent editions. Of the 120 or so titles which are included in the list there are only 10 which appear to have any scientific or technological interest. The list does not contain any of the society proceedings that were current at the time, and it is therefore possible that the titles selected for inclusion might have been only those which were thought to have interest for a general readership.

On the level of analysis attempted in this study we have unfortunately no data on the degree of what Bradford calls "scattering" (1) which prevailed in the subject literature of the 18th century. A limited amount of evidence is provided by an analysis of the abstracts which appear in an abstract journal devoted to obstetrics, gynecology and pediatrics, the "Annalen der Geburtshülfe, Frauenzimmer-und Kinderkrankheiten,*" published at Winterthur between 1793 and 1794. It was edited by Johann Jacob Römer (1763-1819) who had been Usteri's collaborator in the "Magazin für Botanik." The volume covering the literature for 1790 and issued in 1793 contains 132 abstracts from 33 journals. One journal, devoted to the same subjects as the "Annalen," Johann Christian Stark's "Archiv für die Geburtshülfe, Frauenzimmer-und neubegorner Kinderkrankheiten" provides 34 of the articles, or 26 per cent. The scattering of the rest of the articles is shown in Table 33, where it can be seen that although many more articles are extracted from the medical journals, the ratio of articles to journals is almost the same for the medical journals as it is for the general journals. While too great a weight cannot be placed on this evidence, the fact that the general science journals provided a larger average number of articles per journal than the medical suggests that a greater degree of scattering of scientific articles prevailed in the 18th century than Bradford found in his study of the current literature. The one mitigating factor, of course, is that many fewer journals were involved in the earlier period. One fairly reliable indicator of the amount of scientific material in the general periodicals is the number of times articles from the general journals were ab-

Table 33

Sources of Articles Abstracted in Volume One
of Annalen für Geburtshülfe

| | Obstetrics | | Medicine | | General Science | | General | |
|---|---|---|---|---|---|---|---|---|
| Journals | Number | Per cent | Number | Per cent | Number | Per cent | Number | Per cent |
| Journals | 1 | 3 | 22 | 67 | 4 | 12 | 6 | 18 |
| Articles | 34 | 26 | 69 | 52 | 18 | 14 | 11 | 8 |

stracted in the scientific journals of the period. The medical journals, especially the German ones, frequently abstracted and reprinted articles that appeared in the general
English literary magazines such as the "Gentleman's Magazine." The reviewer in the "Frankfurter medicinische Wochenschrift" prefaced his review of this journal with a few apolo-
getic remarks:

> We hope our readers will not consider us guilty of
> bad taste when we seek to make them acquainted with
> such an interesting foreign monthly. However, we
> shall borrow only the medical articles, or those which
> we consider suitable for our weekly. (2)

Vogel, in his "Neue medicinische Bibliothek" made no apolo-
gies for reprinting some of the "practical and useful articles"
which appear in the English journal, and adds that he hopes
that they will be especially useful to those who either cannot
obtain the journal or else are unable to read English. (3)
He acknowledges also that he used it freely as well as the
"Monthly Review" for reviews of foreign books which he found
difficult to acquire in Germany. Such subjects as health and
medicine being closer to the public interest perhaps than
astronomy and physical theory were more likely to be abstracted from the general literary journals. The Swiss natural science journal "Archiv gemeinnutziger physische und medicinische Kenntnisse*" thus abstracted a long article from the
"Journal von und für Deutschland" on the promotion of health,
and an article over thirty pages long from the "Deutsches
Museum" on the subject of smallpox and inoculation. The
subject of animal magnetism which greatly engaged the public
in the last quarter of the 18th century was a frequent topic
of contributions and essays in the general journals. The
"Magnetisches Magazin für Niederdeutschland,*" a collection
of such essays issued in Bremen from 1787 to 1790, indicated as sources of the articles in the first issue the following general journals, the "Berlinisches Monatschrift," the

"Hamburgische Unpartheyische Correspondent," the "Hannover-
isches Magazin," the "Altonaer Mercur," and the "Journal des
Luxus und der Moden."

The editor of a periodical devoted to essays on mathematics and to the presentation of mathematical problems and
their solutions, published in London from 1745, stated:

> The editor of the "Gentleman's Magazine" having been
> solicited by several ingenious mathematicians to in-
> sert in it so many of their pieces as would have dis-
> gusted the far greater part of his readers, whose turn
> of mind leads them to delight in a very different kind
> of amusement, he was under a necessity of disregard-
> ing those correspondents.   But while he complied
> with the taste of the polite and gay, the politician and
> the patriot, he thought himself indispensably obliged
> to consider likewise his friends of a more philosophi-
> cal disposition, and therefore he readily joined in a
> scheme for publishing such productions once a quarter
> in a separate pamphlet; nothing of this kind being now
> on foot periodically, except the "Philosophical Trans-
> actions" and the annual "Diaries;" the former of which,
> however well executed, must be acknowledged very
> improper for initiating youth; and in the latter too
> little room is allowed for solutions at large to ques-
> tions worthy of consideration:   A defect and incon-
> venience, which it is the intention of this work to pro-
> vide against. (4)

The editor of the "Journal de Médecine, de Chirurgie et de
Pharmacie" gave as his reason for starting his journal that:

> The newspapers and the mercuries were always until
> the present the sole means by which the public could
> be provided with this information; but two inconveni-
> ences result, 1) these periodical designed to be in
> everyone's hands become dangerous for certain indi-
> viduals when they find therein articles which deal with
> medical or surgical matters in which they have not the
> necessary background, and 2) this sort of observation
> was lost for a large part of those who would be in-
> terested in knowing about them, because not everyone
> is able to keep in his library all the journals and be-
> side in this immense collection there are only very
> few of which they would have need. (5)

The general press, of course, was used for reporting and
discussing events and proposals connected with the science

and technology of the day, especially when the issues were
most immediate and closely concerned the general population.
(6)    For example, many of the documents relating to the
controversy on the use of inoculation against smallpox in
colonial New England are to be found in the general periodical press.    Zabdiel Boylston's report on the use of inoculation and a list of the number of people inoculated appeared
in the "New England Weekly Journal." (7)    On the other hand,
the physician also had an interest in the general press which
transcended his strictly medical interests.    The editor of the
"Neue medicinische Wochenschrift" in reviewing the popular
journal, "Journal des Luxus und der Moden," wrote:

> We believe we have every right to summon this jour-
> nal before the seat of judgement, in that all species
> of luxuries and manners have an influence on health.
> It is therefore the duty of the physician to examine
> and to judge whether or not many luxuries and man-
> ners do not have a detrimental influence on human
> health, and in those cases to warn society of the
> dangers involved.    There are also frequently in this
> publication lessons on dietetics, which the physician
> should evaluate in order to determine whether medical
> heresies are being introduced, which go contrary to
> the genuine precepts of medical teaching.    Many of the
> essays and reports are useful in themselves for the
> physician, especially the physician to the beau monde.
> We shall not comment on that part of the journal
> which does not concern us. (8)

In an earlier period when much credence was put in unsub-
stantiated reports of natural events and phenomena, the general periodical press provided material for comment by the
physican and scientist.    We see evidence of this in a curious
dissertation of the one-time editor of the "Miscellanes Curiosa," Michael Bernard Valentini.    The title of his dissertation, "De Novellarum Publicarum Usu et Abusu in Rebus
Physico-Medicis, (9) which he wrote at Giessen about 1680,
where he was both a student and later a member of the faculty
seems provocative and promises a thorough-going examination
of the function of journalism in science.    Upon examination,
however, it appears to be merely a conglomeration of medical, scientific, pharmaceutical and meteorological news drawn
from many of the newspapers printed on the continent.    Emphasis was on the strange character of the events related
and the material seems to be presented in no recognizable
system or order.

Events and developments in science and the activities

of scientists and scholars, are, of course, a part of social
history, and it is inevitable that events relating to these activities should have found their way into the general press.
One of the principal documentary sources for Linnaeus' activities in Germany is the "Hamburgische Berichte von neuen
gelehrten Sachen," one of the general learned journals of the
period, (10) which must be consulted for some of Linnaeus'
contributions of that time. (11)   It would be interesting both
in terms of contemporary journalism as well as the journalism of the 17th and 18th century to study the means by which
a particular scientific communication finds its way into a
particular medium, but there is enough evidence at least in
relation to the earlier period to venture the guess that like
love it is frequently as much a matter of propinquity as of
rational choice.   There are probably few cases as dramatic
or as important as Mendel's classical paper on genetics
which remained buried in the publications of his local scientific society for forty years, but there are undoubtedly many
other papers which were overlooked or ignored because they
appeared in media that were unusual channels for communication of scientific papers.   Some of Diderot's mathematical
papers were published in the "Mémoires de Trevoux" in 1761,
and his discussion on the construction of an organ was believed not to have been published in the 18th century until it
was recently "discovered" to have been printed in the "Mercure
de France."   Gaspard Monge's work on the theory of caloric
written in 1783 did not appear in print until it was published
in a rather obscure French literary journal in 1790, the
"Journal Gratuit." (13)   A few of the Italian scientists of
that period, as we have seen earlier, were drawn by the
prominence and the prestige of the Royal Society of London
to send their communications to the editor of the "Philosophical Transactions," but others do not seem to have shown a
similar interest in an international audience.   The lithotomist
Tommaso Alghisi (1669-1713), for example, published a series of communications on medical and anatomical subjects
in the "Giornale dei Letterati d'Italia" in 1713.   They were
in the form of letters addressed to Antonio Vallisnieri (1661-
1730) a professor of medicine at Padua and an active investigator in embryology, entomology, parasitology and botany.
A large number of Vallisnieri's own contributions in these
fields appeared in the general journal "Galleria di Minerva"
which was published in Venice between 1696 and 1717. (14)

It is probably true that most of the scientific literature which found its way into the general or local press had
very little significance for the progress of science, but this
is a judgment of history rather than a contemporary judgment
and actually has little bearing on the matter.   That is to say

the scientist or scholar did not always make his decision on
which medium to send his communication on the prejudgment
of its eventual significance.   The following case involves a
rather obscure French physician but provides an illustration
of how the local and provincial press in France was used
as such a medium.   Pierre Dorion (1722-1777) received his
medical degree from the University of Montpellier and spent
most of his professional life in the provincial city of Saint-
Gilles.   All of his published writings that his biographer is
able to find appeared in a newspaper in his area called the
"Affiches de Poitou."   From about 1773 until his death in
1777 Dorion contributed a weekly article to this publication,
consisting largely of popular articles on medical subjects,
but also of occasional original observations in the natural
science, or reports of medical case histories. (15)   It is
possible that an important contribution, if Dorion can be said
to have made one, might have reached the capital and might
have been abstracted in other journals of wider circulation,
but it is equally likely that if such a contribution had been
made it would have remained unresurrected until attention was
called to it by his modern biographer.

        In other cases it appears very probable that although
other more specialized media were open to him, an author
may have chosen one of the general publications in response
to his desires to achieve a wider audience than could be af-
forded by the specialized journals.   Thus Lalande chose the
"Mémoire de Trevoux" to publish his advertisement announc-
ing the return of Halley's comet and inviting all interested
parties to participate in observing it.   Similar articles appeared in the "Mercure de France," "Observateur Litteraire,"
"Année Littéraire" and the "Journal Éncyclopédique." (16)
For similar reasons Lavoisier's paper on the methods of increasing the water supply of Paris, although it was read before the Académie des Sciences did not appear in any of the
publications of the Académie but was published instead in the
"Mercure de France," where it was likely to have attracted
and influenced many more people than otherwise would have
been exposed to it. (17)   The reason why Lavoisier inserted
one of his important papers on the decomposition of water in
the "Journal Polytype" is a little more obscure.   Lavoisier's
bibliographers attribute it to the fact that he was interested
in the process by which the journal was printed, and that he
was considering the use of the process in the dissemination
of agricultural information.

        There is little doubt that it was the desire to encour-
        age and promote the success of Hoffmann's process
        which caused Lavoisier to use the "Journal Polytype"

as a medium for the publication of so important a
scientific memoir. (18)

In other cases it is not always so clear that there was a rational choice behind the author's decision to include his communication in a particular journal.  His choice would naturally be restricted by the available outlets, and in a period
when scientific journals were few it is not surprising that
many scientific papers found their way into the general periodicals.

## Notes

(1)     S.C. Bradford, "Documentation" (London: Lockwood,
        1948), pp. 111-112.

(2)     LVIII (1785), 152.

(3)     1754, Preface to the first issue.

(4)     "Miscellanea Curiosa Mathematica," 1745, Preface to
        No. 1.

(5)     Preface to Vol. I (1754), 2d ed., Paris, 1783.

(6 )    Eberhard Buchner, "Aerzte und Kurpfuscher, Kultur-
        historsich interessante Dokumente aus alten deutschen
        Zeitungen (17. und 18. Jahrhundert)" (Munich: Langen,
        1922).  An anthology of articles of medical interest
        and medical news from the German newspapers of  the
        period.

(7)     Fulton, op. cit.

(8)     1789, p. 194.

(9)     This work is cited by Storz (op. cit.) in his list of
        critical studies on journalism, but his reference is
        taken from Schwarzkopf.  Storz claims to have been
        unable to find a copy in Germany or elsewhere, despite
        strenuous efforts to do so.  The text examined for this
        study appears in a collection of Valentini's publications
        which appeared under the title "Medicina Nova-Antiqua
        Tradens Universal Medicinae Cursum, e Scriptis Hip-
        pocraticis ad Mentem Modernorum Erutum.  Ed. 2.
        Accedunt Miscellanes Curiosa et Fructifera de Novel-
        larum Publicarum Usu et Abusu in Rebus Physico-
        Medicis.  Dissertatio Melico-Medico de Pulsu, etc.

(Frankfurt a. M., 1713). It is possible, of course, that despite the similarity of titles this may not be the dissertation to which Storz refers.

(10)   F. Verdoorn, "The Development of Scientific Publications and Their Importance in the Promotion of International Scientific Relations," "Science," CVII (1948), 493.

(11)   Felix Bryk, "Linnaeus im Auslande" (Stockholm, 1919).

(12)   L.G. Krakeur and R.L. Krueger, "The Mathematical Writings of Diderot," Isis, XXXIII (1941), 219-232.

(13)   Rene Taton, "A Propos de l'Oeuvre de Monge en Physique," "Revue d'Histoire des Sciences," III (1950), 174-179.

(14)   R.R. Landes, "Tommaso Alghisi:  Florentine Lithotomist," "Journal of the History of Medicine," VII (1952), 325-349.

(15)   M. Badouin, "Une Journaliste medicale de Province avant la Revolution," "La France Medicale," LIV (1912), 161-163, 181-184, 206-208, 221-223, 241-243.

(16)   P. Brunet, "La Vie et l'Oeuvre de Clairaut," "Revue d'Histoire des Sciences," VI (1953), 1-17.

(17)   Cochrane, op. cit., p. 41.

(18)   D.I. Duveen and H.S. Klickstein "Le Journal Polytype des Sciences et des Arts," "Papers of the Bibliographical Society of America," XLVIII (1954), 402-410.

# Chapter XIII

## Bibliographic Control of the Periodical Literature in the Seventeenth and Eighteenth Century

In the Baconian scheme the accumulation of data is but the first step in the advancement of knowledge. The importance that Bacon placed on the organization of data is revealed by the number of "Mystery men" which he assigned to almost purely bibliographic functions. The relative importance of the roles of accumulating and organizing data has been well recognized by many men of science but it has perhaps been best expressed by a great practicing scientist of the 19th century, Helmholtz, who in one of his lectures to the laity said:

> I have already noticed the enormous mass of materials accumulated by science. It is obvious that the organization and arrangement of them must be proportionately perfect, if we are not to be hopelessly lost in the maze of erudition. One of the reasons why we can so far surpass our predecessor in each individual study is that they have shown us how to organize our knowledge.
>
> This organization consists, in the first place, of a mechanical arrangement of materials, such as is to be found in our catalogues, lexicons, registers, indexes, digests, scientific and literary annuals, systems of natural history, and the like... Works of this kind form, so to speak, our intellectual principal, with the interest of which we trade; it is so to speak, like capital invested in land. The learning buried in catalogues, lexicons, and indexes looks as bare and uninviting as the soil of a farm; the uninitiated cannot see or appreciate the labour and capital already invested there; to them the work of the ploughman seems infinitely dull, weary and monotonous. But though the compiler of a lexicon or of a system of natural history must be prepared to encounter labour as weary and as obstinate as the ploughman's, yet it neet not be supposed that his work is of a low type, or that it is by

any means as dry and mechanical as it looks when we
have it before us in black and white. In this, as in
any other sort of scientific work, it is necessary to
discover every fact by careful observation, then to
verify and collate them, and to separate what is important from what is not. All this requires a man
with a thorough grasp both of the object of the compila
tion, and of the matter and methods of the science,
and for such a man every detail has its bearing on
the whole, and its special interest. Otherwise dictionary making would be the vilest drudgery imagin-
able. That the influence of the progressive development of scientific ideas extends to these works is obi-
ous from the constant demand for new lexicons, new
natural histories, new catalogues of stars, all denot-
ing advancement in the art of methodizing and organizing. (1)

That scholars early saw the importance of organizing the literature for use is shown by the long history of the development of bibliography before the introduction of the periodical.
Part of Leibniz' plan for the reorganization of the book trade
in Germany included a proposal for the establishment of a
central or a universal library which would maintain a universal index to the literature. (2)  The plan in retrospect reads
like a proposal for one of our bibliographic centers of today,
except that Leibniz went one step further and advocated that
the whole enterprise should be crowned with the maintenance
of a universal encyclopedia of knowledge, which is reminiscent of H.G. Wells' proposal for a "permanent World Encyclopedia in which knowledge is mobilized, kept up to date
and presented in a form for the perpetual use of intellectual
people." (3)

     The index, one of the earliest locating tools for litera-
ture, was already a well established device when the first
periodicals appeared on the scene, and it was merely a logical and perhaps almost inevitable extension of their use to
apply them to the first journals. Thus the very first volume
of the "Philosophical Transactions" was issued with an index.
It consisted of two parts, the first a sort of alphabetico-
classified index with a "stichwort" form of entry and a system of cross references.  Periodical indexing, however,
seemed to present some new problems, and the entire index
does not seem to have been carried out systematically.  The
other part of the index which is described in the volume as
the "more natural method" is a curious form of classified arrangement whose logic is not readily apparent from the order
of the entries.  It does not seem to have been very successful

for it is not continued in the subsequent volumes, which
contain only the alphabetic subject indexes.

The next logical extension of the index to single volumes of periodicals was the index to series of volumes of
the same title or the cumulated index. A large number of
these were issued throughout the 18th century (4) like the
Abbé de Claustre's "Table Générale de Matières Contenues
dans le Journal des Savans de l'Edition de Paris" which was
issued in Paris in ten volumes, between 1753 and 1764, (5)
and F.H. Maty's "A General Index to the Philosophical
Transactions from the First to the End of the Seventieth
Volume" which appeared in London in 1787. In this section
of our review, however, we are not concerned with the cumulative indexes to individual titles, but with the next development in periodical indexing, the collective indexes, or
indexes to a series of periodicals, although it is true that
these steps do not necessarily follow in strictly chronological
order.

Before discussing the first collective periodical indexes that we have been able to find, it may be worthwhile
to glance at two medical review journals which may be regarded in some way as being intermediate between this form
and the abstract or review journal. The first is "Die Entdeckungen der neuesten Zeit in der Arzneygelahrtheit" which
was issued by the German physician Philip Gesner (1738-
1801) in Nördlingen between 1778 and 1788. The first volume which appeared in 1778 covered the literature appearing
in 1770 and 1771. Tode cites part of Gesner's preface to
the volume in his review in the "Medicinische-chirurgische
Bibliothek:"

> Discoveries! A whole volume of discoveries in two
> years? No, the volume contains more than the title
> indicates. Not only discoveries in the narrow sense,
> but also those teachings, observations, experiments
> and researches of the years 1770 and 1771 which ap-
> pear to me to be important, useful, unknown, new,
> newly established or corrected.
>
> My goals are not achieved if I find it necessary to
> point them out.
>
> A number of the publications I have myself seen and
> abstracted. Most of the abstracts, however, are from
> the best journals, and frequently literally transcribed,
> even when I had the book in hand and had read them
> through, since that is in accordance with my plan.

> A better selection and greater coverage each in its
> place, would have given the work a greater useful-
> ness.  Perhaps the volumes which follow will achieve
> this ideal. (6)

After citing the sources which Gesner used in compiling this
work, Tode has the following comments to make:

> To be sure one could add many others which Herr
> Gesner could have used.  Also this book does not
> make the journals from which he has drawn his ma-
> terial completely dispensable for the reader.  The
> most useful aspect of his undertaking lies in its col-
> lection and arrangement of the noteworthy [facts], and
> by placing the reader in the position of being able to
> find everything quickly and to have at a glance a view
> of the progress of the Art in two years.

> Therefore, it is to be wished that Herr G. will perse-
> vere in such a splendid plan, and will issue as soon
> as possible the [review of the literature] of the subse-
> quent years, for which Heaven grant him health, schol
> arly leisure, many books, and above all patience. (7)

Although it has not been possible to examine the volume in
question it appears fairly certain that Gesner was attempting
something quite different from the other abstract and review
journals.  The infrequent and tardy appearance of the individual volumes probably severely limited its usefulness; the
second volume covering the literature for the years 1772 and
1773 did not appear until 1782.

The other title in this category is the "Repertorium
der medicinischen Litteratur*" which approaches the collective
index more closely than Gesner's publication.  It was issued
in five volumes in Zurich between 1790 and 1795 by the Swiss
physician Paul Usteri (1768-1831).  Usteri beside his medical activities as a practitioner and a member of the medical
school faculty, was also active in Swiss politics and for a
time a member of the Senate.  He was also a member of the
Swiss natural science society and from 1812 served as its
president, a position he held until his death.  Besides founding a political journal, the "Republikaner," with Hans Conrad
Eschner, he also, with the assistance of Römer founded one
of the outstanding botanical journals of the 18th century, the
"Botanische Magazin," which after 1790 he edited alone as the
"Annalen der Botanik." (8)  In fact it is difficult to see how
he found time for such an activity as the "Repertorium," but
he is only one example of the extraordinary productivity of

some of the scholars of this period which makes it appear
an age of giants.

The "Repertorium" reviewed the medical literature issued in the previous year and was issued in an annual volume of from 250 to 300 pages.  For each book or journal
title cited, Usteri gives brief annotations and indicates in
which journal the title has been reviewed.  In most instances
he gives a list of the contents of each journal and the individual papers therein.  The reviews vary considerably in
length, sometimes extending over several pages and sometimes confined to a brief comment, e.g. "an unimportant
quack pamphlet." The author index to each volume cites the
authors of the individual articles in the journals reviewed
and is thus tantamount to a collective periodical index to the
literature.  In the preface to the first volume he indicates
the program he intends to follow:

> One cannot help being aware of the mass of periodical
> publication which exists in Germany today even if one
> is not in love with journal reading.  A large part of
> it is devoted to the dissemination of useful knowledge,
> and is valuable for busy men to keep up with the ad-
> vances of his age.  However, in this enormous growth
> of the products of foreign and domestic scholarship,
> there is no periodical which presents from year to
> year, methodically and encyclopedically, a detailed re-
> view of the new comments, observations, experiments
> and discoveries in that subject with which I occupy
> myself, and which relates these discoveries, etc. to
> the already existing mass of knowledge.

> It would be extremely valuable if we had such a publi-
> cation for every science, composed by an individual
> who is truly expert, who has thought all of it through,
> who knows what the ages have already contributed in
> his field, what remains to be done in the future, what
> lacunae still exist, and, what is more important, what
> parts seem to be filled in, but are in reality without
> substance and provide no substance;  an individual who
> knows the ties between his subject and all the other
> subjects of human understanding, what has been done
> and discovered in them, and who knows how to apply
> and to use this knowledge.

> This is a noble ideal for the success of which no ex-
> pense would be too great, but the hope for its realiza-
> tion is unfortunately all too small.  It appears to me,
> therefore, that it might be useful to attempt to approach

this ideal and to partially supply these needs, so that
our ideal may perhaps be fulfilled by degrees.  In the
field of medicine only one attempt of this kind is
known to me and that is Herr Hofrath Gesner's "Entdeckungen der neuesten Zeit in der Arzneygelahrtheit."
Anyone who knows the difficulties involved in such an
undertaking cannot deny Gesner their thanks.  Never-
the less, it is to be regretted that he was always one
decade in arrears in his work, and that he did not
carry out his project in a different way and according
to a different plan.

I am one of those who would like to make the attempt
and I have decided to begin with the year 1789 (instead of going back to where Gesner left off) in order
to make the work easier for myself.  I will issue a
review every three years, the first covering the advances in medicine in 1789, 1790 and 1791, which will
appear in 1792.  The present Repertorium will be
continued as a preliminary step to that work and will
appear at each Christmas Fair in a single volume
covering the literature of the previous year.  I have
decided to include only the important works which appeared in 1789.  These publications which appeared
toward the end of the year will not be included until
the 1790 volume appears, but this is compensated for
by the inclusion of a number of works which appeared
toward the end of 1788.  More important than this is
the accusation of incompleteness which will undoubtedly be made against me, since I am aware that many
publications, especially the foreign ones are not included.  I can only promise greater completeness in
the coming years, and that a supplement which I intend
to issue every three years in the same arrangement
as the present volume will supply the omissions.

In this three-year supplement I will also include more
annotations of reviews of the particular books which
appeared in various periodicals and newspapers.  I
receive many of these because it is often interesting
and important to know what this or that man thinks of
a particular book, or what judgment has been given by
one or another of the journals. (9)

At this point Usteri lists some twenty journals along with the
abbreviations used in the text of his work, and then continues:

...and others which appear less regularly such as
Metzger's "Annalen," the "Bibliothek für Physiker," the

"Frankfurter medicinische Annalen," etc. of which the abbreviations are self-explanatory. These titles will also be found in their complete form in their proper place in the "Repertorium."

I have given the titles of all the publications as completely as possible, as well as the place of publication, the publisher, and in most cases the size of the book. The accompanying annotations about the contents or opinions are partly my own and partly borrowed from journals and newspapers in those cases where they agree with my own opinions. A greater detail in the analysis, especially of the larger works, is not possible.

The publications are arranged systematically, as can be seen. I might have used a more general classification and it may be considered superfluous to have so many subdivisions in presenting a review of the advances in science, but it is also true that the individual essays included in the magazines and collections could more usefully be placed under their own rubrics. (10)

The main body of the work consists of a classified arrangement of the titles included under the following heading and there is only an author index to the entire work:

| Subject | Number of Publications |
|---|---|
| 1. Methodology of medicine; teaching and practice | 11 |
| 2. Literature and history of medicine | 11 |
| 3. Biographical notices | 7 |
| 4. Academic reports | 4 |
| 5. Critical journals | 18 |
| 6. Journals and periodical publications | 26 |
| 7. Collections of academic and other publications | 9 |
| 8. Anatomical publications | 9 |
| 9. Physiological publications | 51 |
| 10. Pharmacology and pharmacy | 80 |
| 11. General therapeutics and symptomatology | 13 |
| 12. Collections of medical observations | 19 |
| 13. Publications on pathology and therapy | 110 |
| 14. Surgery | 37 |
| 15. Obstetrics, gynecology and obstetrics | 31 |
| 16. State medicine | 27 |
| 17. Veterinary medicine | 12 |
| 18. Animal magnetism | 20 |

| Subject | Number of Publications |
|---|---|
| 19.   Medical disputations | 8 |
| 20.   Folk medicine | 40 |
| Total | 553 |

Usteri repeated his promise of a triennial review in the next volume of the "Repertorium," but finally in the preface to the third volume states that he has given up the project:

> The frequent and public demands that I should con-
> tinue this repertory is a real indication that such a
> work when it covers a series of years is a valuable
> aid for every scholar.   Who would not wish that
> such a journal had been in existence for fifty years
> or since the beginning of the century.   Perhaps a
> plan will be created to bring this about, and if there
> is enough demand, perhaps I shall be able to under-
> take this work myself.   The time has already ar-
> rived for my promised 'Pragmatische Uebersicht der
> Fortschritte der Arzneykunde in den Jahren 1789,
> 1790 und 1791.'   That I cannot do this I owe to my
> many duties and the lack of  time.   Other works,
> however, have been planned with which my work
> perhaps can be dovetailed.   Aside from this I am
> now the editor of the "Real repertorium der Allge-
> meine Litteratur Zeitung" which will perhaps make
> my work unnecessary. (11)

The "Allgemeine Litteratur Zeitung" was a literary review journal issued daily in Jena from 1785, and Usteri's reference to himself as the editor of the index of that journal is curi-ous, since it appeared eventually under the editorial direction of Johann Samuel Ersch who was the compiler of a genuine collective periodical index which will be discussed below.

A certain amount of foolhardiness is always involved in claiming the title of "first" for any bibliographic, or, for that matter, any other event.   Thus the honor of issuing the first collective periodical index has been at different times accorded to Beutler, Ersch, Reuss and Beughem.   One's claims in these cases can usually be safeguarded by intro-ducing the correct adjectival modifiers, but from the point of time the honor falls easily to the indefatigable bibliographer of the turn of the 17th century, Cornelius a Beughem.   Beu-ghem's first periodical index was "La France Scavante, id est Gallia Erudita, Critica et Experimentalis Novissima" which was published in Amsterdam in 1683.   It is, being de-voted to the knowledge of all Gaul, divided into three parts,

a chronological part in which the contents of each issue of
the "Journal des Scavans" is listed under the date of issue,
an author index listing in alphabetical order the authors of
the books reviewed, and finally a classified subject index in
six groups.   Despite its title it is an index solely to the
"Journal des Sçavans" covering the years 1665 to 1681.

Beughem's next periodical index was more ambitious
in scope and covered in the first volume nine journals issued
between 1665 and 1686:

1.    Ephemerides eruditorum Gaelice, 1665-1686, i.e. the
      "Journal des Sçavans."
2.    Acta Philosophica societatis regiae in Anglia, 1665-
      1686, i.e. the "Philosophical Transactions."
3.    Ephemerides eruditorum Italice, 1668-1680, i. e. the
      "Giornale de' Letterati" of Nazari.
4.    Joan. Bapt. Dionysu Memoriae et Congerentia super
      artes et scientiae, 1672, 1673 et 1674, i.e. the
      "Mémoires et Conferences" of Jean Baptiste Denis.
5.    Memoriae Ingeniosorum, London, 1682, i.e. the
      "Memoirs for the Ingenious."
6.    "Acta eruditorum," 1682-1686.
7.    Novitataes Reipublicae literariae, 1684-1686, i.e. the
      "Nouvelles de la Republique des Lettres" of Bayle.
8.    Mich. Bern. Valentini Historia Litteraria Academiae
      Naturae Curiosorum, 1684-1686.
9.    Bibliotheca Universalis et Historica, 1686, i.e. the
      "Bibliothèque Universelle et Historique" of LeClerc.

This is a true serial periodical index, since Beughem issued
four additional volumes up to 1710, covering the journals issued up to 1700.   The title of the series which appears on
all the volumes, with the exception of a slight modification in
the second volume is "Apparatus ad Historiam Literariam
Novissimam.*" It was issued at Amsterdam, the first volume in 1689 and the fifth and last in 1710.   The arrangement
of each volume is alphabetical by author.   Since most of the
journal titles he indexed were largely book review journals,
the majority of the entries are book titles with an indication
of the journal in which the review appeared.   In many cases
it is difficult to tell whether the citation is to a book title
or to an original article, except that in the case of book
titles he seems also to note the format in which they were
issued.   It is very defective as an index to the original papers which appeared in the journals, and Beughem seems to
have been most unsystematic about noting the original contributions.   For example, many of Robert Boyle's original papers in the "Philosophical Transactions" are noted under the

author's name, but none of Leeuwenhoek's papers are listed although some 120 extracts from his letters were printed in the "Transactions" in the period covered by the indexes. (12) One reason which suggests itself is that Beughem may not have considered them important enough to index, or that in his eyes these fragmentary contributions had not yet achieved the same dignity which was accorded to the book. The fifth and last volume contains a cumulated author index and a large section devoted to "addenda et corrigenda" so it seems apparent that Beughem did not intend to continue his index beyond 1700.

There is an interval of eighty years between the last volume of Beughem's index and the next periodical index we were able to find. This indicates either that the problem of indexing the periodical literature was not very pressing, or else that the solution to the problem was being found through other means. The bibliographic handbooks such as those cited earlier included references to the periodical literature. In addition, we must remember that the subject bibliographies that were issued in that period, such as the monumental bibliographies of Haller, took cognizance of the periodical literature. The review and abstract journals and the various collections of journal articles may also have helped to fill the gap. The "Allgemeines Sachregister über wichtigsten deutschen Zeit-und Wochenschriften," which is sometimes cited as the "first" collective periodical index, was rather limited in scope and did not last beyond one issue, although the editor, Johann Heinrich Christoph Beutler, states in his preface to the volume that this is the first publication of its kind and that it will be followed by a series of indexes covering other periodicals. It appeared in Leipzig in 1790. The eight periodicals which Beutler indexed all seem rather negligible from a scientific point of view:

> Ephemeriden der Menschheit
> Schlozer's Staatanzeigen
> Deutsche Museum
> Gottingische Magazin der Wissenschaft
> Deutsche Merkur
> Schlozer's Briefwechsel
> Hannoverische Magazin
> Berliner Monatschrift

The principal value of the publication is perhaps not the subject index to periodicals but the part which lists the periodicals issued in Europe in the period 1700 to 1790 and which covers the last 360 pages of the volume. The subject index to the eight periodicals covers 573 pages and there is in addi-

tion a 48 page supplement which lists the names of the authors mentioned in each journal in an alphabetic arrangement under the title of the journal.

Johann Samuel Ersch (1766-1828) has been called the
"father of modern bibliography" (13) and his "Repertorium
über die allgemeinen deutschen Journale und andere periodischen Sammlungen für Erde beschreibung, Geschichte und
die damit verwandten Wissenschaften" issued in three volumes
at Lemgo between 1790 and 1792, has been called the first
bibliography of the contents of periodicals arranged systematically. (14) His claim to either of these titles is open
to some dispute, but he was unquestionably one of the most
active of the bibliographers in the last decade of the 18th
and the first decades of the 19th centuries. He began his
career as a student of theology at Halle where he collabo-
rated with Fabri in issuing the "Geographisches Magazin,"
the "Historisch-geographisches Monatschrift" and the "Sammlung von Stadt-Land und Reisebeschreibungen." When Fabri
went to Jena, Ersch followed, and with Hammerdorfer assisted in editing the "Allgemeine politische Zeitung." Meusel's handbook to German literature, "Gelehrten Teutschlands,"
stimulated him to prepare a supplement to that work entitled
"Verzeichnis aller anonymen Schriften und Aufsatze in der
viertem Aufgabe des Gelehrten Teutschlands" which appeared
at Lemgo in 1788. Additional supplements appeared in 1794
and 1796. After Meusel's death he took over the editorship
of the handbook which was issued under his name as the
"Handbuch der deutschen Literatur seit der Mitte des achtze-
hnten Jahrhunderts" (Amsterdam, 1812-1814). At one time
or another he was connected as editor or in some other ca-
pacity with the "Neue Hamburger Zeitung," the "Britische Annalen," "Minerva" and the "Allgemeine deutsche Bibliothek."
He returned to Jena in 1800 where he was appointed Librarian
of the University. After a short sojourn in Halle as Professor of Geography, he returned again to Jena, this time to be
named the first librarian of the newly reorganized university.
He was also one of the founders of the "Allgemeine Encyclo-
pedie" of which he edited the first seventeen volumes. In
addition to the handbook on German literature he edited also
a handbook on French literature which was issued under both
French and German titles, as "La France Literaire, Contenant les Auteurs français de 1771 a 1796," and "Das gelehrte Frankreich oder Lexicon der Franzosischen Schriftsteller von 1771 bis 1796," issued at Hamburg between 1797
and 1798. In both of his handbooks he took some cognizance
of the periodical literature, although he did not attempt to index it in any detail, e.g. in "La France Literaire" after the
list of monographs and separate publications of an author, he

frequently notes whether the author has published any papers
in the periodical literature and sometimes gives the titles of
the journals in which they appeared.

Someone with misguided generosity has credited Ersch
with the responsibility for the "Allgemeine Sachregister über
die wichtigsten teutschen Zeit-und Wochenschriften, (15)
which, as we have indicated, rightly belongs to Beutler.
Ersch, however, did edit as one of his major bibliographic
works an index to the contents of the literary journal, the
"Allgemeine Literatur Zeitung" which appeared in three series under the title "Allgemeines Repertorium der Literatur"
in Jena from 1793 to 1807, the first series covering the literature from 1785 to 1790 and appearing from 1793 to 1794,
the second the literature from 1791 to 1795, published from
1799 to 1800, and the third the literature from 1796 to 1800,
published from 1806 to 1809.  As the "Allgemeine Literatur
Zeitung" attempted to be comprehensive in its coverage of
the European literature including that which appeared in the
periodicals, the "Allgemeines Repertorium" is tantamount to
an index to the European literature of the last fifteen years
of the 18th century.  Like his "Handbuch der deutschen Literatur," Ersch made this index available to the public in
several separate subject sections.

Jeremias David Reuss (1750-1837) perhaps does not
belong in this discussion since his major index was issued
outside the time span of our study.  In addition it is a retrospective rather than a current index, although this characteristic can be attributed to some of the other indexes we
have discussed.  However, he is sometimes cited as the author of the first periodical index, a claim which can be justified only if one is careful to add that it is devoted solely to
the proceedings of scientific societies, and that it covers the
century preceding that in which it was published.  Like Ersch
he began his career as a literary historian and bibliographer
and ended it as a librarian.  In 1789 he was appointed professor of "Gelehrtengeschichte" and assistant librarian at the
University of Göttingen and from 1814 he served at the same
university as its chief librarian.  Like Ersch, he also published a national bibliography, "Das Gelehrte England, oder
Lexicon der jetzlebenden Schriftsteller in Grossbrittannien,
Irland, und Nordamerika, nebst einen Verzeichnis ihrer
Schriften vom Jahre 1770 bis 1790," which also appeared under the title "Alphabetical Register of all the Authors Actually Living in Great-Britain, Ireland and the United Provinces
of North-America with a Catalogue of Their Publications"
(Berlin and Stettin, 1791).  It is much more valuable than
Ersch's handbooks as an index to the periodical literature,

since he gave it much more recognition than Ersch did in
his "La France Litteraire." Among the titles which Reuss
indicated that he had analyzed for this work are the following:

Archeologia, or Miscellaneous Tracts Relating to Antiquity.
Asiatic Researches.
Duncan's Medical Commentaries.
Essays and Observations, Physical and Literary.
Gren's Journal der Physik.
Hunter's Georgical Essays.
London Medical Journal.
Memoirs of the American Academy of Arts and Science,
    Boston.
Medical Communications.
Medical and Philosophical Commentaries by a Society of
    Physicians in Edinburgh.
Medical Observations and Inquiries by a Society of Physi-
    cians in London.
Medical Transactions published by the College of Physi-
    cians in London.
Nautical Almanac for the Year 1771-1789.
Philosophical Transactions.
Sammlung auserlessener Abhandlungen zum Gebrauch prac-
    tischer Aerzte.
Sammlung auserlessener und neuesten Abhandlungen für
    Wundaerzte.
Sammlung zur Physik und Naturgeschichte.
Transactions of the American Philosophical Society.
Transactions of the Royal Society of Edinburgh.
Transactions of the Royal Irish Academy.

His "Repertorium Commentationum a Societatibus Litteriis
Editarum" published by Dietrich in Göttingen from 1801 to
1821 is a classified subject index to the publications of the
learned societies issued before 1800.   It began the task that
was later taken over by the Royal Society of London in their
"Catalogue of Scientific Papers."

    There were, of course, other methods of organizing
the periodical literature for use, as we have seen in our survey of the abstracting and review journals.   The reviewing
journals in those cases in which they reviewed the journal
literature extensively were tantamount to periodical indexes,
especially when they were issued with cumulativ indexes.
And since the 18th century scientific journals made such a
widespread practice of extracting articles from other journals, collective indexes to individual journals would in effect
provide a control of a much wider area of the literature than

that provided by the original contributions to the journal in question. Another mode of organizing the journal literature was in the form of abridgments of individual titles such as those issued for the "Philosophical Transactions" and the "Mémoires de Trevoux," and some of scientific societies, so that even with the paucity of collective periodical indexes, the 18th century scholar was not entirely at a loss in his efforts to find what he wished out of the mass of periodical literature.


Notes

(1)     H. Helmholtz, "Popular Lectures on Scientific Subjects" (New York: D. Appleton, 1895), pp. 12-13.

(2)     Goldfriedrich, op. cit., pp. 36-38.

(3)     Cited in A. F. C. Pollard, "The Mobilization of Knowledge and the 'Permanent World Encyclopedia' of Mr. H. G. Wells," "Transactions of the 14th Conference of the F. I. D.," II (1938), 161-167.

(4)     See Daniel C. Haskell, (comp.) "A check List of the Cumulative Indexes to Individual Periodicals in the New York Public Library" (New York: New York Public Library, 1942).

(5)     A separate cumulated index to the Holland edition was compiled by T. B. Robinet (Amsterdam, 1765).

(6)     VII (1779), 364.

(7)     Ibid.

(8)     F. Rudio, "Festschrift der Naturforschenden Gesellschaft in Zurich," 1746-1898 (Zurich: Zurcher and Furrer, 1896), pp. 75-78.

(9)     "Repertorium der medicinischen Litteratur," I (1790), Preface.

(10)    Ibid.

(11)    "Repertorium der medicinischen Litteratur," III (1793), Preface.

(12)    Clifford Dobell, "Antony van Leeuwenhoek and His "Little Animals" (London: John Bale, Sons and Dan-

ielson, 1932).

(13)   F.R. Bertheau, "Kleine Chronologie zur Geschichte
       des Zeitungswesens in Hamburg von 1616 bis 1913"
       (Hamburg:  Lutcke und Wulff, 1914).

(14)   Lehmann, op. cit., p. 202.

(15)   "Nouvelle Biographie Générale" (Paris: Didot, 1872),
       pp. 314-315.

## Chapter XIV

## Summary and Conclusions

Despite the elaborate structure of modern scientific communication, with its multiplicity of media and complicated apparatus for attempting to control them, there have been few attempts to examine the whole complex critically. One of the basic prerequisites for the design of an adequate and efficient system of communications in the sciences should be an analysis of the various functions such a system does and should serve. This study makes no attempt at such a critical appraisal, but aims rather at providing some of the historical background against which such an appraisal might be made. One of the best approaches to the analysis of an institution is an historical examination of its origins and development.

The changes in intellectual approaches to phenomena, which occurred by degrees starting with the latter part of the Middle Ages, brought with it a change in attitudes toward the existing body of knowledge. One of the influential spokesmen for this new attitude was Francis Bacon, who in his writings exemplified two attitudes which set the stage for the appearance of the scientific periodical. One was a critical re-evaluation and rejection of the literature of the ancients and the scholastics, which created the necessity for a new body of literature. The second was the emphasis on observation and experiment as the major modes of arriving at new knowledge, resulting in a tendency toward short communications, since an observation or an experiment has a unity in itself, in distinction to the organized and self-consistent systems of knowledge which were the goals of earlier scholarship.

Periodicity in print had been well established in the century preceeding the introduction of the journal. The state of the general periodical press at the beginnings of scientific journalism provided the background against which the scientific journal developed. Among the antecedents and contemporary forms of communication which influenced and shaped the scientific periodical were scholarly correspondence, the

234

annual book catalogs, the manuscript and printed news letters, the calendar and the almanac, and finally and primarily the newspaper. Scholarly correspondence and the
book catalog provided a model for the content and the newspaper and almanac suggested the format and methods of distribution. The editors of the early learned journals had their
prototypes in those men who constituted themselves communications centers for the scholarly world and through whose
hands a great deal of the early correspondence passed. These
were men like Mersenne, Peiresc, Haak, Collins and finally
the two journal editors Oldenbourg and Mencke. The nature
of the correspondence in the period preceding the introduction of the learned periodical anticipated the contents of the
learned journal; it was impersonal in tone, and contained
scientific news and notices of new books. Early periodicals
might in a sense be considered printed letters addressed to
a wider audience than could be reached by the written letter.

This study is based on an analysis of a list of scientific and technological periodicals published in the period
1665 to 1790, i.e. from the time of their origins until the
beginnings of the French Revolution. The various definitions
of the periodical throughout its history reflect current publication practices, but are generally characterized by two factors, miscellaneous content and periodicity of issue. The
periodical falls between the book and the newspaper; it is
usually addressed to a more limited audience than is the
newspaper, and is not as firmly bound to the events of the
day. The periodical resembles the book more than the newspaper in the range of ideas in which it deals.

The journals which had their origins in the period
1665-1790 can be divided into two major groups, which can
be designated by several groups of opposing terms, e.g. primary and secondary, original and derivative, the literature
of record and the literature of dissemination; these terms
reflect the two roles of the medium as a repository and as a
vehicle. These two roles have never been clearly differentiated either in the long history of the scientific periodical or
in our current publication practices. In the first group we
include those journals which were, for the most part, published independently and which contained original matter.
These have been designated substantive journals. This group
includes also the publications established to report the proceedings of the learned societies. The second group includes
those journals which were established largely to provide access to materials that were not readily available by means of
translation, summaries or reprinting. In this group we have
designated as special classes, the abstract journal, the re-

view journal, and the collection.

Although forty-eight per cent of the total number of titles analyzed in this study fall into the group designated as substantive journals, this figure does not represent the total of original publication which was taking place in this period. Most of the journals in this group in addition to the varying proportion of original material they presented, devoted a considerable portion of their space to derivative publication as well, in the form of reprints of articles which appeared in other journals, abstracts of journal articles and book review. In fact the principal characteristic which distinguished the group of substantive journals as a whole is the fact that the were not devoted exclusively to derivative publication.

The substantive journals as a whole can be divided into three groups, (1) those which were composed largely of original contributions, (2) those in which original contributions played a minor role, and (3) those journals which were devoted principally to the dissemination of established ideas and to popular and practical education. The first group makes up the smallest portion of the total, since there were few journals in the 17th and 18th centuries directed exclusively to scientific audiences and which contained significant original contributions. Most of the journals were composites of all the elements of scientific journalism, original contributions, abstracts, reviews and news items. A large proportion of the group designated as substantive journals fall into the third category and were devoted primarily to the spread of new scientific ideas among the educated laity. They reflect the growing popular interest in the natural sciences which characterizes the period of the Enlightenment.

Those titles designated as the proceedings of scientific societies make up one fourth of all the titles on the list. The earliest publications of the scientific societies were non-serial in nature and characterized by anonymity of authorship. Many of the societies were dilatory in establishing organs for communicating the work of their members; the Académie des Sciences did not establish a serial publication until the end of the 17th century and the Royal Society of London did not assume official sponsorship of the "Philosophical Transactions" until almost a hundred years after it had been established. Of the 220 scientific and learned socieites which were recorded as having their origins before 1790, almost 25 per cent provided no printed record of their activities in this period. One explanation which is suggested is that some of the societies were established for purposes other than the communication of information. In other cases the presence

of other outlets for the communications of society members,
such as the general literary journals, and the independent
substantive scientific journals, made the need of society organs less imperative. Although some of the societies managed to issue volumes with some degree of regularity, on the
whole this class of publication was characterized by lack of
regularity in appearance. The existence of a society which
in itself provided a means of continuity for a publication
made regularity of issue less necessary than with the independent journal which had to rely largely on this factor to
maintain its identity.

Approximately 25 per cent of the total number of periodical titles included in this study can be characterized as
purely derivative forms of journalism. They fall into the
following classes: abstract journals, review journals, and
collections or anthologies. Although it is difficult to apply
any of these categories rigorously to the journals of this
period, since few of the journals represent any of these categories in pure form, the following definitions were suggested.
The abstract journal included those journals which devoted
themselves largely to extracting or reviewing articles from
other periodicals, as distinct from the review journals which
devoted themselves for the most part to reviews and abstracts of books. A large proportion of the early journals
devoted a considerable portion of their space to extracts and
reprints from other journals, but journals devoted exclusively to abstracts of journal articles did not appear in any number until the middle of the 18th century. The necessity for
abstract journals was reduced to some extent by the existence
of bibliographic handbooks and by the fact that many of the
substantive journals as well as many of the general literary
journals devoted a considerable portion of their space to this
type of material.

The journals classified as review journals were those
which devoted themselves for the most part to reviewing
books, although in many cases journal issues were reviewed
in the same manner as books, frequently with brief abstracts
of the articles. In the period before the appearance of the
"Commentarii de Rebus in Naturali et Medicina Gestis," the
scholar interested in science, had to depend largely on the
general review journals for this type of literature. General
review journals appeared in almost all of the intellectual
centers of Europe. They were found in great numbers in
Germany, where the lack of political centralization was reflected in the multiplicity of journals of this kind. Medical
review journals mde up by far the greatest proportion of the
scientific review journals. Among the suggested explanations

is that the physicians made up the largest and almost the
only professional group interested in science.  This is reflected also in the large proportion of the subject specialize
journals which were devoted to medicine, which were exceeded among the specialized journals only by those devoted
to theology.

The "collection" or anthology of articles and selection
from other publications is one of the few forms which existed in the 18th century to which we find few parallels today.  One of their major functions was to preserve and disseminate literature which was either inaccessible or in a
language foreign to the country in which they appeared.  The
resemble the textbook in that they both represent a form of
progressive distillation of the literature; although the textbook presents the distillation in the form of a new synthesis
the collection attempts to accomplish this goal by presenting
the material in the original words of the author.

Collections of dissertations and other academic writings were segregated for separate consideration since they
represent a different type of literature than that which appeared in the general scientific collections.  It is suggested
that the dissertation, produced largely as a by-product of
the activities of the 17th and 18th century university, represents a type of ceremonial literature whose purpose may not
be essentially to instruct but to serve as an act of public or
formal observance of an event.  It is pointed out that many
of the editors concerned with the collection of dissertations
were also those concerned with other forms of serial publication.

The almanac preceded both the periodical and the
newspaper.  It continued to be issued in a more or less un-
modified form, but many of the titles which appeared in the
18th century with the title "almanac" are to be regarded as
annual periodicals.  Some of them beside the usual content
of many of the scientific periodicals contained such typical
almanac features as a calendar to historical events, or a
diary for recording daily occurrences.  Most of the publications in this class fall into two groups, those related to
health and hygiene and those concerned with agriculture and
gardening.  Although most of these titles were of decidedly
popular appeal, a few of the medical almanacs or annuals
seem to be directed as much to an audience of physicians as
to laymen.

Because of the general interest in science among the
educated laity in the 18th century, a considerable number of

the general and literary journals included material of interest to science and technology.  Some of the earliest scientific contributions were made through such general learned
journals as the "Journal des Sçavans" and the "Acta Eruditorum."  One factor which contributed to this situation was
the lack of a class of specialized scientists and the fact that
the gap between the scientist and the educated layman had
not yet become great enough to create a communications
barrier between them.  This is borne out by the frequency
with which the general journals were abstracted and reviewed in the scientific press.  On occasion the scientist
was led by his desire to seek a larger audience to insert an
original communication in the general journals, but for the
most part such insertions resulted from the relatively few
scientific channels of publication that were available.

Although an attempt was made by Cornelius a Beughem
to issue a serial index to periodical publications as early as
1683, there were no systematic attempts to provide indexes
to the periodical literature until almost the end of the 18th
century.  This condition was mitigated to some extent by
the fact that indexes were issued to some of the abstract and
review journals which in effect provided an index to the literature which was abstracted and reviewed in these journals.
The collections which brought together large groups of articles from a variety of sources provided another means of
organizing and controlling the literature, and thus served to
some extent in lieu of periodical indexes.

Quantitative analysis does not provide us with much of
the important information we desire about the nature of the
17th and 18th century periodical.  The inference which we
have drawn that very few of the titles in our list presented
significant contributions to science is a subjective impression
based on an examination of a few issues out of the bulk which
this kind of literature represents.  Our conclusions about the
ratios between derivative and original publication are also
based on impressions, but we feel that even a closer examination of the scientific journal literature of this period would
support the observation that by far the largest part of this
literature represented not original research or contributions
but a derivative form of journalism which served the purpose
of the dissemination of information.  Only a small part,
therefore, of the apparatus of scientific journalism in the
17th and 18th centuries was devoted to the primary record.
The local and parochial nature of the majority of 18th century
journals is apparent and can be deduced also from the fact
that articles were reprinted so frequently in different journals.  The primary function of the scientific journal in this

period was that of providing a vehicle for the dissemination of information rather than a repository for the storage of new scientific ideas.

The role which the scientific periodical played in the 17th and 18th centuries evolved in a large measure as a result of its antecedents in the newspaper, the almanac, scholarly correspondence, and the other forms of communication which preceded it, which by extension created the pattern for the development of the format of the scientific periodica In this period it served an audience that differed considerab in its needs and in its characteristics than the audience it serves today. Although there have undoubtedly been some changes both in format and in modes of management of the scientific periodical, the point is sometimes made that these changes have not been commensurate with the changes in the complexity and the organization of science that have occurre in the ensuing centuries. By forcing the periodical to play a double role, that of a repository for information and as a vehicle for the dissemination of knowledge, it is possible that we have forced upon it an impossible task, which is now threatening it with complete breakdown.

# Bibliography

Abderhalden, E. "Die Organization der medizinischen Literatur," "Medicinische Klinik," V (1909), 1021-1023.

Academie des Sciences, Belles-Lettres et Arts de Rouen, "Précis analytique des Travaux." Rouen: P. Periaux, 1814.

Adler, H. "Die medizinische Publizistick in Wien." In: "Ein halbes Jahrtausend. Festchrift des 500 jahrigen Bestandes der Acta Facultatis Medicinae Vindobonnensis." Vienna, 1899. Pp. 171-175.

Aldridge, A. O. "Benjamin Franklin and Jonathan Edwards on Lightning and Earthquakes," "Isis," XLI (1950), 162-164.

Allen, Eric W. "International Origins of the Newspaper; the Establishment of Periodicity in Print," "Journalism Quarterly," VII (1930), 307-319.

Allen, Phyllis. "The Royal Society and Latin America as Reflected in the Philosophical Transactions," "Isis," XXXVII (1947), 132-138.

Allen, W. E. "Repositories for Scientific Publication," "Science," LVI (1922), 197-198.

Amdur, M. K. "Dawn of Psychiatric Journalism," "American Journal of Psychiatry," C (1943), 205-216.

Anderson, Fulton H. "The Philosophy of Francis Bacon." Chicago: University of Chicago Press, 1948.

Andrade, E. N. da C. "The Presentation of Scientific Information," "Proceedings, Royal Society of London," B, CXXXVI (1949), 317-333.

Apel, Bert. "Die Entwicklung des Nachrichtenwesens der Presse in Bayern von den Anfangen bis zur Gegenwart." Unpublished dissertation, University of Erlangen, 1950.

241

Artelt, Walter.  "Die medizinischen Lesegesellschaften in
    Deutschland," "Sudhof's Archiv," XXXVII (1953), 195-
    200.

Ashley-Montague, M.F.  "Edward Tyson, M.D., F.R.S.
    (1650-1708) and the Rise of Human and Comparative
    Anatomy in England."  Philadelphia:  American Philo
    sophical Society, 1943.

Aspinall, A.  "Statistical Accounts of the London Newspapers
    in the 18th Century."  "English Historical Review,"
    LXIII (1948), 201-232.

Bachman, Albert.  "Censorship in France from 1715-1750.
    New York:  Institute of French Studies, 1934.

Badouin, Marcel.  "Une Journaliste medicale de Province
    avant la Revolution,"  "La France Medicale," LIX
    (1912), 161-163, 181-184, 206-208, 221-223, 241-
    243.

Barber, Bernard.  "Science and the Social Order."  Glencoe,
    Ill.:  Free Press, 1952.

Barker, C.  "The Founding of the New Haven County Medi-
    cal Association," "Yale Journal of Biology," VI (1933/
    34), 323-331.

Barnes, Eugene B.  "The International Exchange of Knowl-
    edge in Western Europe, 1680-89."  Unpublished Ph.D
    Dissertation, Graduate Library School, University of
    Chicago, 1947.  pp. 151.

Barnes, Sherman B.  "The Beginnings of Learned Journalism
    1665-1730."  Unpublished Ph.D. dissertation, Graduate
    School, Cornell University, 1934.  Pp. 338.

-----.  "The Editing of Early Learned Journals," "Osiris,"
    I (1936), 155-172.

-----.  "The Scientific Journal, 1665-1730," "Scientific
    Monthly," XXXVIII (1934), 257-260.

Barwick, G.F.  "A List of the Magazines of the 18th Century,
    "Transactions of the Bibliographical Society," London,
    X (1908-9), 109-140.

Bates, Ralph S.  "Scientific Societies in the United States."
    New York:  Wiley, 1945.

Bather, F.A. "Scientific Publication," "Nature," CVIII
(1921), 144.

Belin, J.P. "Le Commerce des Livres Prohibés a Paris
de 1750 à 1789." Paris: Belin Freres, 1913.

Belling, John. "On the Advancement of Science by Published
Papers," "Nature," CXVI (1925), 539.

Bernal, J.D. "Lessons of War for Science," "Report on
Progress in Physics," X (1944-5), 418-436.

-----. "Publication and Classification of Scientific Knowledge," "Nature," CLX (1947), 649.

-----. "Social Function of Science." London: Watts and
Co., 1954.

Bertheau, Franz R. "Kleine Chronologie zur Geschichte des
Zeitungswesens in Hamburg von 1616 bis 1913."
Hamburg: Lutcke und Wulff, 1914.

Bertrand, Joseph L.F. "L'Académie des Sciences et les
Académiciens de 1666 a 1793." Paris: Hetzel, 1869.

Blumer, G. "The First Medical Transactions in America,"
"Yale Journal of Biology," VI (1933-34), 299-305.

Blunck, Ilse. "Die Anfange der landwirtschaftlichen Fach-
presse," "Zeitungswissenschaft," XI (1936), 252-254.

Bolton, Henry C. "A Catalogue of Scientific and Technical
Periodicals, 1665-1895. Smithsonian Miscellaneous
Collection," Vol. XL (1897).

Bonno, Gabriel. "Liste chronologique des Periodiques de
Langue française au xviiie Siècle," "Modern Language
Quarterly," 1944, pp. 3-25.

Bouillier, Francisque. "L'Institute et les Académies de
Province." Paris: Hachette, 1879.

Boyer, J. "La Creation du premier Journal scientifique,"
"Nature" (Paris), LXXV (1947), 243-244.

Brasch, F.E. "The Royal Society of London and its Influence
upon Scientific Thought in the American Colonies,"
"Scientific Monthly," XXXIII (1931), 337-355.

Brierley, William B. "Scientific Publication," "Nature," CVIII (1921), 41-42.

Brodman, Estelle. "The Development of Medical Bibliography." Baltimore: Medical Library Association, 1954.

Broeckx, Corneille. "Coup d'Oeil sur les Institutions Medicales Belges depuis les dernieres Années du xiiie Siècle." Bruxelles: Société Encyclopédique des Sciences Medicales, 1841.

Brown, Harcourt. "Scientific Organizations in Seventeenth Century France." Baltimore: Williams and Wilkins, 1934.

Brunet, P. "La Vie et l'Oeuvre de Clairaut," "Revue d'Histoire des Sciences," VI (1953), 1-17.

Bryk, Felix. "Linnaeus im Auslande: Linnés gesammelte Jugend-Schriften autobiographischen Inhaltes aus den Jahren 1732-38." Stockholm: The Author, 1919.

Buchanan, Milton A. "Some Aspects of Spanish Journalism before 1800," "Revue Hispanique," LXXXI (1933), 29-45.

Buchner, Eberhard. "Aerzte und Kurpfuscher, kulturhistorisch-interessante Dokumente aus alten deutschen Zeitungen (17. und 18. Jahrhundert)." Munich: Albert Langen, 1922.

Buess, Heinrich. "Der Beitrag der Schweizer Aerzte zu den Miscellanea curiosa der Deutschen Akademie der Naturforscher," "Sudhof's Archiv," XXXVII (1953), 1-22.

Butterfield, Herbert. "The Origins of Modern Science, 1300-1800." New York: Macmillan, 1950.

Buttress, F.A. "Agricultural Periodicals of the British Isles, 1681-1900, and Their Location." Cambridge, 1950.

Cabanes, --. "Les premier Journaliste medical et ses multiple Atavars," "Lancette Française," XCVII (1924), 141-145.

Callisen, Adolph C.P. "Medicinisches Schriftsteller-Lexicon

der jetzt lebenden Aerzte, Wundaerzte, Geburtshelfer,
Apotheker und Naturforscher Aller gebildeten Volker."
Copenhagen:  The Author, 1836.

Campbell, Frank.  "The Bibliography of Periodical Literature,"  "The Library," VIII (1896), 49-64.

Camusat, Denis F.  "Histoire Critique des Journaux."
Amsterdam:  J. F. Bernard, 1734.

Candolle, Alphonse L. P. P. de.  "Histoire des Sciences et
des Savants depuis deux Siècles." 2d ed.  Geneva:
H. Georg, 1885.

Chereau, Achille.  "Essai sur les Origines du Journalisme
Medicale Française suive de se Bibliographie."
Paris:  Bureau de l'Union Medicale, 1867.

Charlier, Gustav and Mortier, Roland.  "Le Journal Encyclopédique."  Paris:  Libraire Nizer, 1952.

Choulant, L.  "Ueber medicinische Journalistik,"  "Allgemeine medicinische Annalen," 1821, pp. 11-50.

Clark, G. N.  "Science and Social Welfare in the Age of
Newton."  Oxford:  Clarendon Press, 1937.

Clow, Archibald, and Clow, L.  "The Chemical Revolution,
a Contribution to Social Technology."  London: Batch-
worth, 1952.

Cochrane, J. A.  "Lavoisier."  London:  Constable and Co.,
1931.

Cockrell, T. D. A.  "Should Scientific Publication be Controlled,"  "Nature," CXXXVI (1935), 222-223.

Cole, F. J. and Eales, N. B.  "The History of Comparative
Anatomy; Pt. 1:  A Statistical Analysis of the Literature,"  "Science Progress," XI (1917), 578-596.

Conradi, Edward.  "Learned Societies and Academies in
Early Times,"  "Pedagogical Seminary," XII (1905),
384-426.

Couper, William James.  "Edinburgh Periodical Press; Being a Biographical Account of the Newspapers, Journals and Magazines issued in Edinburgh from the Earliest Times to 1800."  Edinburgh:  Stirling and MacKay,

1908.

Couvreur, Albert. "La Pharmacie et la Therapeutique au
    xviiie Siècle Vues à Travers le Journal Encyclo-
    pédique de Pierre Rousseau à Bouillon." Paris:
    Vigot, 1953.

Crane, R.S. and Kaye, F.B. "A Census of British News-
    papers and Periodicals 1620-1800." Chapel Hill:
    University of North Carolina Press, 1927.

Dekeyser, L. "Le Médecine et l'Origine de la Presse en
    Europe," "Bruxelles Medicale," XXVIII (1948), 43-45.

-----. "Les Origines de la Presse médicale," "Bruxelles
    Médicale," XXIX (1949), 1753-1765.

Delage, Anna. "Histoire de la Thèse de Doctorat en Méde-
    cine d'apres les Thèses Soutenues Devant la Faculté
    de Médecine de Paris." Paris:  Ollier-Henry, 1913.

De la Harpe, Jacqueline. "Le Journal des Savants et l'Angle
    terre 1702-1789," "University of California Publica-
    tion in Modern Philology," XX (1941), 209-520.

Delauney Henri. "Les Sociétés Savantes de la France."
    Paris:  Rousset, 1902.

Delorme, Suzanne. "L'Académie-Royale des Science, ces
    Correspondants en Suisse," "Revue d'Histoire des
    Science," IV (1951), 159-170.

-----. "Une Famille de grand Commis de l'État Amis des
    Sciences aux xviiie Siècle:  Les Trudaines," "Revue
    d'Histoire des Sciences," III (1950), 101-109.

Delprat, C.C. "De Geschiedenis der Nederlandsche genees-
    kundige Tijdschriften van 1680 tot 1857," "Ned.
    Tschr. Geneesk.," LXXI, Eerste Helft A (1927), 3-
    116.

Deniker, J., and Descharmes, R. "Bibliographie des Tra-
    vaux Scientifique Publié par les Sociétés Savantes de
    la France." Paris:  Imprimerie Nationale, 1895-
    1922.

Dobell, Clifford. "Antony van Leeuwenhoek and His 'Little
    Animals.'" London:  John Bale, Sons and Danielson,
    1932.

Dorveaux, Paul. "Notes sur quelques Annuaires médicaux aux xviiie Siècle et leurs Auteurs," "La France Médicale," LIX (1912), 341-344.

Dressler, Adolf. "Geschichte der italienische Presse." 2d ed. Munich: R. Oldenbourg Verlag, 1933.

Dulieu, L. "Charles le Roy," "Revue d'Histoire des Sciences," VI (1953), 50-59.

Duveen, Denis I., and Klickstein, Herbert S. "Bibliography of Works of Antoine Laurent Lavoisier," 1743-1794. London: Dawson, 1954.

-----. "Le Journal Polytype des Sciences et des Arts," "Papers of the Bibliographical Society of America," XLVIII (1954), 402-410.

"Early Medical Journals," "British Medical Journal," II (1920), 907.

"Eighteenth Century British Medical Journals," "British Medical Journal," I (1918), 183.

Falk, F. "Ueber die geschichtliche Entwicklung des medicinischen Journalistik besonders in Deutschland," "Schmidt's Jahrbuch," CLXVI (1876), 195-206.

Fay, Bernard. "Learned Societies in Europe and America in the 18th Century," "American Historical Review," XXXVII (1932), 255-266.

Fernandez del Castillo, F. "Historia de las Revistas medicas en Mexico," "Gaceta Medica de Mexico," LXXXIII (1953), 229-244.

Ferguson, John. "Notes on the Work of Polydore Vergil, 'De Inventores Rerum,'" "Isis," XVII (1932), 71-93.

"First Medical Journal and Some of its Progeny," "Medical Times," N.Y., LXXV (1947), 37-39.

Fischer, I. "Zur Geschichte des Wiener alteren medizinischer Zeitschriftwesens," "Wiener medicinischer Wochenschrift," LXXVI (1926), 34-36.

Fleure, H.J. "The Manchester Literary and Philosophical Society," "Endeavour," VI (1947), 147-159.

Fueter, Eduard. "Geschichte der exakten Wissenschaften in der Schweizerischen Aufklaerung." Aarau: H.F. Sauerland, 1941.

Fulton, John F. "The Impact of Science on American History," "Isis," XLII (1951), 176-191.

-----. "The Warrington Academy (1757-1786) and its Influence upon Medicine and Science," "Bulletin of the History of Medicine," I (1933), 50-80.

Fussell, G.E. "John Houghton, F.R.S.," "Notes and Queries," CXLVIII (1925), 345-346.

Gabler, Anthony J. "Check List of English Newspapers and Periodicals before 1801 in the Huntington Library," "Huntington Library Bulletin," November, 1931, No. 2, pp. 1-66.

Garland, Joseph. "Medicine as a Social Instrumen: Journalism," "New England Journal of Medicine," CCXLIV (1951), 838-844.

Garrison, Fielding H. "The Medical and Scientific Periodicals of the 17th and 18th Centuries, with a Revised Catalogue and Checklist," "Bulletin of the History of Medicine," II (1934), 285-343.

-----. "The Medical Periodical and the Scientific Society," "New Orleans Medical and Surgical Journal," LVII (1914-5), 504-509.

Geiger, K. "J.D. Reuss und seine Bibliothek," "Zentralblatt für Bibliothekswesens," XXII (1905), 465-490.

George, Philip. "The Scientific Movement and the Development of Chemistry in England as Seen in the Papers Published in the 'Philosophical Transactions' from 1664-5 until 1750," "Annals of Science," VIII (1952), 302-322.

Gibbs, F.W. "Robert Dossie (1717-1777) and the Society of Arts," "Annals of Science," VII (1951), 149-172.

Girard, A.A. "Catalogo das Obras a Venda na Typographia da Academia Real das Sciencias (1779-1904)." Lisboa: Typographia da Academia, 1905.

Goldfriedrich, Johann. "Geschichte des deutschen Buch-

handels, 1648-1740." Leipzig: Verlag des Börsen-
vereins der deutschen Buchhandler, 1908.

Graf, Herbert. "Die bienenwirtschaftlichen Zeitschriften in
Deutschland." Leipzig: Bienenzeitung, 1935.

Graham, Walter. Beginnings of English Literary Periodicals,
a Study of Periodical Literature, 1665-1715. London:
Oxford University Press, 1926.

-----. "English Literary Periodicals." New York: Thomas
Nelson and Sons, 1931.

Grand-Carteret, John. "Les Almanacs Français; Biblio-
graphie-Iconographie des Almanachs, Années, Annuaires, Calendriers, Chansonniers, Etrennes, États,
Heures, Listes, Livres d'Adresses, Tableaux, Tab-
lettes et autres Publications Annuelles Editté a Paris,
1600-1895." Paris: J. Alisie, 1896.

Gravit, Francis W. "Notes on the Contents of Freron's Periodicals," "Romanic Review," XXXIV (1943), 116-126.

Gray, James. "History of the Royal Medical Society, 1737-
1937." Edinburgh: University of Edinburgh Press,
1952.

Greco, V. "Origins of Medical Journalism," "New York
Medical Journal," XCVII (1913), 131-136.

Griffin, F.J. "The 'Archiv der Insectengeschichte' of J.C.
Fuessly, Heft 1-8, 1781-1786," "Journal of the Society
for the Bibliography of Natural History," I (1937), 83-
85.

Groth, Otto. "Die Zeitung, eine System der Zeitungskunde."
Mannheim: J. Bensheimer, 1930.

Guerlac, Henry. "Some Aspects of Science During the French
Revolution," "Scientific Monthly," LXXX (1955), 93-
101.

Guiart, J. "Creation du Journalisme medicale," in his:
"Histoire de la Médecine Française." Paris: Nagel,
1947. Pp. 143-147.

Guitard, Eugene. "Deux Siècles de la Presse aux Service de
la Pharmacie." Paris: Pharmacie Central de France,
1913.

Harlow, A. F.  "Old Post Bags."  New York: Appleton and
        Co., 1928.

Hatin, Luis Eugene.  "Bibliographie Historique et Critique
        de la Press Périodique Française."  Paris: Firmin-
        Didot Freres, 1866.

-----.  "Les Gazettes de Hollande et la Presse Clandestine
        au xviie et xviiie Siècles."  Paris: R. Pincebourde,
        1865.

-----.  "Histoire Politique et Littéraire de la Presse en
        France."  Paris:  Poulet-Mallassis et De Broisse,
        1859.

Herd, Harold.  "The March of Journalism."  London: Allen
        and Unwin, 1952.

Houben, Heinrich H.  "Zeitschriften des jungen Deutschlands.
        Berlin:  B. Behr, 1906-1909.

Houghton, W. E., Jr.  "The English Virtuoso in the Seven-
        teenth Century," "Journal of the History of Ideas,"
        III (1943), 51-73, 190-219.

Hunkin, J. W.  "William Curtis, Founder of the Botanical
        Magazine," "Endeavour," V (1946), 13-17.

Jaryc, Marc.  "Studies of 1935-1942 on the History of the
        Periodical Press," "Journal of Modern History," XV
        (1943), 127-141.

Jennsen, Christian.  "Zur Geschichte der landwirthschaft-
        lichen Zeitschriften Deutschlands von der Mitte der
        vorigen Jahrhunderts bis auf die Gegenwart," "Land-
        wirthschaftliche Jahrbucher," XVIII (1889), 589-706.

Jones, William P.  "The Vogue of Natural History in England
        1750-1770," "Annals of Science," II (1937), 345-352.

Katz, J.  "Medical Journals, an Historical Review," "Leech
        IX (1938), 77-82.

Kaufmann, G.  "Zur Geschichte der academischen Grade und
        Disputationen," "Zentralblatt für Bibliothekswesens,"
        XI (1894), 201-225.

Kendall, James.  "The First Chemical Journal," "Nature,"
        CLIX (1947), 867.

-----. "Some Eighteenth-Century Chemical Societies," "Endeavour," I (1942), 106-109.

Kirchner, Joachim. "Die Grundlagen des deutschen Zeitschriftenwesens mit einer gesamtbibliographie der deutschen Zeitschriften bis zur Jahre 1790." Leipzig: Hiersemann, 1928-1931.

-----. "Das deutsche Zeitschriftenwesen, seine Geschichte und seine Probleme. I. Von den Anfangen des Zeitschriftenwesens bis zum Ausbruch der Franzoisischen Revolution." Leipzig: Harrassowitz, 1942.

-----. "Zur Entstehungsgeschichte der Acta Eruditorum," "Archiv für Buchgewerbe und Gebrauchsgraphik," LXV, Sonderheft to Heft 4   (1928), 75-88.

Kirpatrick, T. P. C. "The Periodical Publications of Science in Ireland," "Bibliographical Society of Ireland," II (1921), 33-58.

-----. "The Dublin Medical Journals," "Irish Journal of Medical Sciences," VI (1932), 243-260.

Kohlsdorf, K. "Geschichte der Leipziger Oekonomischen Sozietät." Leipzig: Edelman, 1913.

Krakeur, L.G., and Kreuger, R.L. "The Mathematical Writings of Diderot," "Isis," XXXIII (1941), 219-232.

Kreig, Walter. Materialien zu einer Entwicklungsgeschichte der Bucherpreise und des Autoren-honorars vom 15 bis zum 20 Jahrhundert." Vienna: Stubenrauch, 1953.

Laboulbene, M. "Histoire du Journalisme medical, 1679-1880," "Lancette Française," LIII (1880), 1057-1059, 1065-1066, 1073-1074, 1089-1090.

Lacassagne, J. "A propos de Nicolas de Blegny," "Bulletin de la Société Française d'Histoire de la Médecine," XXVIII (1934), 68-69.

Lacy, Mary G. "An Early Agricultural Periodical," "Annual Report of the American Historical Association," I (1919), 445-454.

Lafont, J. "Les Débuts du Journalisme medical italien," "Progres Medicale," Paris, XLI (1926), 1847.

Landes, Ralph R.  "Tommaso Alghisi, Florentine Lithotomist,
    "Journal of the History of Medicine," VII (1952), 325-
    349.

Lang, Carl L.  "Die Zeitschriften der deutschen Schweiz bis
    zum Ausgang des 18. Jahrhunderts (1694-1798)."
    Leipzig: Harrassowitz, 1939.

Lasteyrie du Saillant, R.C.  "Bibliographie Générale des
    Travaux Historique et Archeologique Publiés par les
    Sociétés Savantes de la France."  Paris: Imprimerie
    Nationale,

Le Fanu, William R.  "British Periodicals of Medicine:  a
    Chronological List,"  "Bulletin of the History of Medi-
    cine," V (1937), 735-761, 827-855, VI (1938), 614-
    648.

Lefevre-Pontalis, Eugene.  "Bibliographie des Sociétés Sa-
    vantes de la France."  Paris:  Imprimerie Nationale,
    1887.

Lehmann, Ernest H.  "Einführung in die Zeitschriftenkunde."
    Leipzig: Hiersemann, 1936.

Lehmann, H.  "Zeitungswissenschaft und Zeitschriftenkunde,"
    "Forschung und Fortschrift," XIV (1938), 89-91.

Lennard, Reginald V.  "English Agriculture under Charles
    II; the Evidences of the Royal Society of Enquiries,"
    "Economic History Review," IV (1932), 23-45.

Levy-Valensi, J.  "Histoire de la Presse medicale française
    au xviie Siècle," "Paris Medicale," CX, Annexe (1938),
    157-164, 195-198, 228-234, 271-273.

------.  "Les Origines de la Presse medicale française,"
    "Presse Medicale," XLIV (1936), 2124-2125.

------.  "Les Publications periodiques de J.B. Denis,"
    "Presse Medicale," XLVI (1938), 381-382.

------., and Tellier, J.  "Nicolas de Blegny, Journaliste,"
    "Aesculape," XXIV (1934), 170-173.

Lilley, S.  "Social Aspects of the History of Science,"  "Ar-
    chives Internationales d'Histoire des Sciences,"
    XXVIII (1948-49), 376-443.

-----. "Nicholson's Journal (1797-1813)," "Annals of
        Science," VI (1948), 78-101.

Lion, Madeleine. "Origines du Journalisme Médicale."
        Paris: Jouve et Cie, 1925.

'Liste Genérale par Ordre Alphabétique des Journaux, An-
        ciens et Modernes, Nationaux et Étrangers." Paris:
        Bureau de Bibliographie Universelle, 1790.

Lockwood, Dean P. "Ugo Benzi, Medieval Philosopher and
        Physician, 1376-1439." Chicago, University of Chi-
        cago Press, 1951.

Lombard, E. "Der medizinische Inhalt der schweizerischen
        Volkskalender in 18. und 19. Jahrhundert." Zurich:
        Fussli, 1925. (Zuricher Medizingeschichtliche Ab-
        handlung, Bd. 2).

Loria, Gino. "Acta Eruditorum durante gli anni 1682-1740
        e la Storia delle Matematiche," "Archeion," XXIII
        (1941), 1-35.

-----. 'Il Giornale de' Letterati d'Italia di Venezia e la
        Raccolta Calogera come Fronti per la Storia delle
        Mathematiche nel Secolo xviii," "Abhandlungen zur
        Geschichte der Mathematik," IX (1899), 243-274.

Lustenberger, Fridolin. "Schweizerische medizinische-
        naturwissenschaftliche Zeitschriften von 1751-1871."
        Zurich: Leemann, 1927.

Lyons, Henry. "The Royal Society, 1660-1940. Cambridge,
        University Press, 1944.

McCutcheon, Roger P. "The Journal des Scavans and the
        Philosophical Transactions of the Royal Society,"
        "Studies in Philology," XXI (1924), 626-628.

McKie, Douglas. "The Scientific Periodical from 1665 to
        1798," "Philosophical Magazine," 1948, 122-132.

Madden, Richard R. "The History of Irish Periodical Litera-
        ture from the End of the 17th to the Middle of the
        19th Century." London: T.C. Newby, 1867.

Marshall, T.H. "Jethro Tull and the New Husbandry,"
        "Economic History Review," II (1929), 41-60.

Martin, Alfred.  "Ernest Gottfried Baldinger (1738-1804), a
    Portrait from the Period of German Rationalism,"
    "Medical Life," XXXI (1924), 97-103.

Menz, Gerhardt.  "Die Zeitschrift, ihre Entwicklung und ihre
    Lebensbedingungen." Stuttgart:  D.E. Poeschel Ver-
    lag, 1928.

Merton, Robert K.  "Science, Technology and Society in
    Seventeenth Century England," "Osiris," IV (1938),
    360-632.

-----.  "Social Theory and Social Structure." Glencoe, Ill.:
    Free Press, 1949.

Mish, Charles C.  "Best Sellers in Seventeenth-Century Fic-
    tion," "Papers of the Bibliographical Society of Amer-
    ica," XLVII (1953), 356-373.

Monro, T.K.  "Some Notes on Medical Journalism," "Glas-
    gow Medical Journal," CIX (1928), 133-137.

More, Louis T.  "Isaac Newton, a Biography." New York:
    Charles Scribner and Sons, 1934.

Morgan, Betty T.  "Histoire du Journal Scavans depuis 1665
    jusqu'en 1701." Paris:  Les Presses Universitaires
    de France, 1929.

Mornet, D.  "Les Sciences de la Nature en France au xviiie
    Siècle." Paris:  Armand Colin, 1911.

Müller-Freienfels, Richard.  "Studies in the Social Psychol-
    ogy of Science," "Journal of Social Psychology," IV
    (1933), 26-41.

-----.  "Psychologie der Wissenschaft." Leipzig:  J.A.
    Barth, 1936.

Neave, E.W.J.  "Chemistry in Rozier's Journal. I. The
    Journal and Its Editors," "Annals of Science," VI
    (1940), 416-421.

Neuberger, Max.  "Die Entwicklung des wissenschaftliche
    Vereinwesens und seine Bedeutung für den medizinische
    Fortschritt," "Weiner medizinischer Wochenschrift,"
    L (1937), 666-674.

Nicholls, A.G.  "Nicolas de Blegny and the First Medical

Periodical," "Canadian Medical Association Journal,"
XXXI (1934), 198-202.

Ornstein, Martha. "The Role of Scientific Societies in the
Seventeenth Century." 2d ed. Chicago: University
of Chicago Press, 1938.

Passy, Louis. "Histoire de la Société Nationale d'Agriculture." Paris: P. Renouard, 1912.

Pelseneer, Jean. Aspects statistique du Progrès des Sciences en Belgique à travers les Siècles, "Isis," XXX
(1941), 237-242.

-----. "L'Origins Protestante de la Science moderne,"
"Lynchnos," 1946-47, pp. 246-248.

"Periodische medicinische ökonomische und physikalische
Schriften," "Berlinische Sammlung zur Beforderung
der Arzneiwissenschaft," I (1768), 207-219, 310-329,
426-439.

Pevsner, Nikolaus. "Academies of Art, Past and Present."
Cambridge: University Press, 1940.

Potter, George R. "The Significance to the History of Eng-
lish Natural Science of John Hill's "Review of the
Works of the Royal Society," University of California
Publications in English," XIV (1943), 157-180.

Poynter, F.N.E. "First English Medical Journal," "British
Medical Journal," II (1948), 307-308.

Prutz, Robert E. "Geschichte des deutschen Journalismus."
Hannover: C.F. Rius, 1845.

Przedak, Hlador G. "Geschichte des deutschen Zeitschriftenwesens in Bohmen." Heidelberg: Carl Winter, 1904.

Rauchfuss, C. "Die medicinische Journalistik Russlands,"
"St. Petersburger medicinische Zeitschrift," I (1861),
26-32.

Richardson, L.M. "The Conferences of T. Renaudot, an
Episode in the Quarrel of the Ancients and Moderns,"
"Modern Language Notes," May, 1932, p. 312.

Rigaud, S.P. "Correspondence of Scientific Men of the 17th
Century." Oxford, 1841.

Rohlfs, Heinrich. "Eine literarische Legende,""Deutsches Archiv Geschichte der Medicin und Medicinische Geographie," III (1880), 270-272.

Roller, Duane. "The Periodical Literature of Physics, Some of Its History, Characteristics and Trends," "American Journal of Physics," XIV (1946), 300.

Roepke, W. "Die Veröffentlichungen der Kaiserlich Leopold-isch-Deutschen Akademie der Naturforscher," "Leopoldina," I (1926), 149-158.

Roshem, Julien. "Un Journal de Médicine au xviie Siècle," "Paris Medicale," X, Supplement (1912-13), 663-669.

Rostenberg, Leona. "John Martyn, Printer to the Royal Society," "Bibliographical Society of America, Papers," XLVI (1952), 1-32.

Roux de Tillets, J.J. le. "Notes historiques sur le Journal de Médecine," "Journal de Médecine, Chirurgie et Pharmacie," LXIX (1786), 385-410.

Rowbottom, M.E. "The Earliest Published Writings of Robert Boyle," "Annals of Science," VI (1950), 376-389.

Rudio, F. "Festschrift der Naturforschenden Gesellschaft in Zurich, 1746-1896." Zurich: Zürcher and Furrer, 1896.

Runge, E. "Aus den Anfangen des deutschen medicinischen Zeitschriftswesens," "Medicinische Welt," XI (1937), 950-952.

Sarton, George. "Vindication of Father Hell," "Isis," XXXV (1944), 97-105.

Scharold, Hans. "Naturwissenschaftliche Anschauungen der sittlich-ökonomischen Gesellschaft zu Burghausen (1765-1802)" "Archiv für Geschichte der Naturwissenschaften und Technik," V (1913), 114-126.

Schonbauer, L. "Zur Geschichte des Wiener medizinischen Zeitschriftwesens," "Klinische Medizin," I (1946), 34-41.

Schottenloher, Karl. "Flugblatt und Zeitung, ein Wegweiser durch das gedruckte Tagesschriftum." Berlin: Schmidt,

1922.

Schwarz, G.T.  "Die systematische Arbeitsweise Albrecht
von Hallers," "Centaurus," II (1953), 314-348.

Scudder, Samuel H.  "Catalogue of Scientific Serials."
Cambridge:  Harvard University Library, 1879.

Seiffert, G.  "Deutschlands erste medizinische Wochenschrift," "Munchner Medizinischer Wochenschrift,"
XCV (1953), 1274-1275.

Sergescu, P.  "Les Mathématiques dans le "Journal des
Scavans:" premiere Periode 1666-1701," "Osiris,"
I (1936), 568-583.

-----.  "Mersenne l'Animateur," "Revue d'Histoire des Sciences," II (1948), 5-12.

Sigerist, Henry E.  "Medical Societies Past and Present,"
"Yale Journal of Biology," VI (1933-34), 351-362.

-----.  "Nationalism and Internationalism in Medicine,"
"Bulletin of the History of Medicine," XXI (1947),
5-16.

Silander, A.  "Le Developpement de la Presse finlandaise,"
"International Committee of Historical Sciences, Bulletin," VI (1934), 78-84.

Silva Carvalho, A. da.  "Histoire de la Presse médicale âu
Portugal," "Medicina contemporanea," LIV (1936),
299-304.

Sklavom, J.H.  "Scientific Life of Thomas Bartholin," "Annals of Medical History," III (1921), 67-81.

Smith, Frederick C.  "The Early History of Veterinary Medicine." London:  Bailliere, Tindall and Cox, 1915-
1923.

Sonnenkalb, Christian A.  Kurze geschichtliche Darstellung
von der Entstehung und Fortdauer des medizinischen
Journalistikum." Leipzig, 1820.

Sparn, Enrique.  "Cronologia, Diferenciacion, Matricula y
Distribucion Geografica de las Sociedades de Ciencias
Medicas." Cordoba, 1938.

Sprugge, Squire. "Medical Journalism," "Glasgow Medical Journal," CIX (1928), 110-119.

Stein, Robert. "Alt französische Zeitschrift für deutsche medizinische und naturwissenschaftliche Literatur," "Archiv fur Geschichte der Mathematik," X (1928), 473-475.

Stevenson, Lloyd G. "The Siege of Warwick Lane: Together with a Brief History of the Society of Collegiate Physicians (1767-1798)," "Journal of the History of Medicine," VII (1952), 105-121.

Stiede, Wilhelm. "Die Universität Wittenberg und die Londoner Philosophical Transactions," "Neues Archiv für Sächsische Geschichte und Altertumskunde," XL (1919), 138-153.

Stimson, Dorothy. "Amateurs of Science in 17th Century England," "Isis," XXXI (1939-40), 32-47.

-----. 'Hartlib, Haak and Oldenbourg: Intelligencers," "Isis," XXXI (1939-40), 309-326.

Storz, Werner. "Die Anfange der Zeitungskunde (die deutsche Literatur des 17. und 18. Jahrhunderts über die gedruckten periodischen Zeitschriften)." Halle: Klinz, 1931.

Stutzki, Heinz. "Die Geschichte und Entwicklung der deutschen tierartzlichen Zeitschriften." Unpublished dissertation, Department of Veterinary Medicine, Univ. of Berlin, 1947, pp. 79.

Sudhoff, Karl F.J. "Das medizinische Zeitschriftenwesen in Deutschland bis zum Mittel des 19. Jahrhunderts," "Münchner medizinische Wochenschrift," L (1903), 455-463.

Syfret, R.H. "The Origins of the Royal Society," "Notes and Records of the Royal Society," V (1948), 85-86.

Taton, Rene. "A propos de l'Oeuvre de Monge en Physique," "Revue d'Histoire des Sciences," III (1950), 174-179.

Taylor, F. Sherwood. "The Chemical Society," "Nature," CLX (1947), 6-7.

Tellier, Piere J. "Un Aventurier Médicale au xviie Siècle."

Paris: Louis Arnette, 1932.

Thornton, John L. "Medical Books, Libraries and Collectors." London: Grafton, 1949.

-----, and Tully, R. I. J. "Scientific Books, Libraries and Collectors." London: The Library Association, 1954.

Thorndike, Lyon. "Glimpses of Seventeenth Century Medicine," "Annals of Medical History," N. S. VI (1934), 219-223.

Vallienieri, Antonio. "Observations on the Fly of Rosebusches and Other Insects of the Same Habitat," "Isis," XVII (1932), 290-324.

Vaultier, Roger. "Vieux Annuaires médicaux," "Presse Medicale," LVIII (1950), 657-658.

Verdoorn, Franz. "The Development of Scientific Publications and Their Importance in the Promotion of International Scientific Relations," "Science," CVII (1948), 492-497.

Wagner, Rudolph. "Zur Erinnerung an Albrecht Haller und zur Geschichte der Societaten der Wissenschaften." K. Gesellschaft der Wissenschaften. Erste Sacularfeir der Gesellschaft. Göttingen: W. F. Kästner, 1852.

Walch, Erich. Albrecht von Haller und die Göttinger Gelehrten Anzeigen," "Zeitungswissenschaft," III (1928), 1-3.

Walker, George. "Haste, Poste, Haste! Postmen and Postroads throughout the Ages." New York: Mead and Co., n. d.

Walther, Johannes. "Die Aufgaben der Akademie in Vergangenheit und Gegenwart," "Leopoldina," I (1926), 1-20.

Weld, Katherine K. and Bond, Richmond. "Studies of British Newspapers and Periodicals from Their Beginnings to 1800, a Bibliography." Studies in Philology, Extra Series No. 2, University of North Carolina Press, Dec., 1946.

Weill, Georg. "Le Journal. Origines, Evolution et Role de la Presse Periodique." Paris: Renaissance du Livre, 1934.

Wilde, W.R. "History of Periodic Medical Literature in Ireland," "Dublin Quarterly Journal of Medical Sciences," N.S. I (1846), i-xlviii, 583.

Williams, D. "Medicina Curiosa, an Early Medical Journal," "Glasgow Medical Journal," CIX (1928), 105-109.

Woke, Paul A. "Considerations on Utilization of Scientific Literature," Science," CXIII (1951), 399-403.

Yates, Frances A. "The French Academies of the 16th Century." London: University of London, Warburg Institute, 1947.

Zilsel, Edgar. "The Sociological Roots of Science," "American Journal of Sociology," XLVII (1942), 544-562.

# INDEX

## Names and Subjects

Titles